QL
703   Davis   66-2370
D3   Principles in mammalogy

JUL   2000

Date Due
JUN   2004

AN 20 67			
			JUL 09
			JUL X X 2015

PRINCIPLES IN MAMMALOGY

Reinhold Books in the Biological Sciences

CONSULTING EDITOR: PROFESSOR PETER GRAY
Department of Biological Sciences
University of Pittsburgh
Pittsburgh, Pennsylvania

The Encyclopedia of the Biological Sciences, edited by Peter Gray

Biophysics: Concepts and Mechanisms, E. J. Casey
Cell Function, L. L. Langley
Chordate Morphology, Malcolm Jollie
Concepts of Forest Entomology, Kenneth Graham
Cytology, G. B. Wilson and John H. Morrison
Ecology of Inland Waters and Estuaries, George K. Reid
Evolution: Process and Product, Revised Edition, Edward O. Dodson
Management of Artificial Lakes and Ponds, George W. Bennett
Manual of Insect Morphology, E. Melville DuPorte
Paramedical Microbiology, Stanley E. Wedberg
The Plant Community, Herbert C. Hanson and Ethan D. Churchill

Consulting Editor's Statement

To all too many students of biology a "mammal" is either a pig embryo or an embalmed cat. The mammal as it exists in nature is unknown to them. It is for these students that this book is intended.

Drs. Davis and Golley have, however, adopted an approach that is more widely useful than the general run of textbooks. A broad explanation of what a mammal is, is followed by a detailed and clearly written account of the process of adaptation, and the role which this process plays in evolution in general. This discussion leads logically to the evolution of mammals and their present distribution. The authors, having now placed mammals in their proper position in the biotic world, discuss the reproductive processes, population dynamics, and behavioral characteristics which lead to the stability, or instability, of the mammalian population of this planet. This excellent addition to REINHOLD BOOKS IN THE BIOLOGICAL SCIENCES is designed as a text for an up-to-date course in mammalogy, but will be found equally useful by the many biologists who seek a comprehensive and clearly written reference work.

PETER GRAY

Pittsburgh, Pennsylvania
March, 1963

Sea Otter Resting with Young on the Coast of Amchitka Island, Alaska. (Photograph by Karl W. Kenyon.)

principles in

MAMMALOGY

DAVID E. DAVIS
Pennsylvania State University
University Park, Pennsylvania

FRANK B. GOLLEY
Laboratory of Radiation Ecology
Aiken, South Carolina
and *Department of Zoology*
University of Georgia
Athens, Georgia

New York

REINHOLD PUBLISHING CORPORATION
Chapman & Hall, Ltd., London

PREFACE

MODERN MAMMALOGY includes a wide variety of topics ranging from population genetics to behavior. In recent years our knowledge of mammals has become so extensive that no person or book can be expected to encompass more than a small part. Texts are available, often in abundance, in such areas as physiology, anatomy, and genetics; and there exist many reviews and monographs on special topics such as hibernation and echolocation. However, these contributions consider the mammal as only one part of some general process. We feel there is also a need for a text on principles that treats the mammal as a whole animal integrated within the community.

The orientation of this book is toward the life of the wild mammal. Since our purpose is to guide the reader to an understanding of how a mammal lives, features such as habits, distribution, reproduction, and behavior are emphasized throughout. Naturally, a certain basic knowledge of classification, anatomy, and physiology is necessary to understand these aspects. However, this basic material is treated lightly or omitted here, since it can be assumed that the reader has this general background or at least can obtain such information from easily available sources.

The knowledge of how mammals live is widely scattered in diverse publications and is often anecdotal in form. Thus, this book brings together information from many fields and, wherever possible, introduces available experimental material. Modern mammalogy has produced by now a very large volume of results based on controlled experiments. Exposition of this record is desirable, both to make the information accessible to students and to encourage further experimentation by showing where valuable results are most likely to be obtained.

Wherever possible, the book covers the mammals of the world. However, since North American and European mammals are better known than any others, a large share of the examples are drawn from these species; also, since it is hoped that the reader will often want to consult the original literature, examples published in readily available journals are given preference. In many cases, where equally good examples were available, the less well-known species were chosen simply to increase the breadth of the treatment. The basic principles should apply to mammals everywhere.

This book is also intended to serve as a conceptual model of the "whole animal" approach. The material is selected to provide an idea of how the mammal lives, not only in its environment, but in association with other mammals as well.

The audience for this book is assumed to include both advanced undergraduate and graduate college students. In addition, the text should be of value to professional biologists in such areas as physiology, anatomy, and general ecology, and to those persons interested in the economic aspects of mammalian biology, such as public health or pest control workers. The chapters on population and on metabolism have been especially designed to serve as background principles for economic mammalogy.

Building on the assumption that the reader is well-grounded in the basic areas of animal biology, the chapters to follow deal directly with the specific aspects of mammalian life. The book stresses principles rather than providing a compendium of information, although in a few cases tabular data are presented. Each chapter and subdivision opens with a general statement, and then proceeds to illustrate it with informative examples given to indicate the range of variation applicable to the general conclusion.

The principles are not necessarily at the same level of magnitude or development. In some cases minor or incomplete principles are stated, often with a remark about opportunities for further research. When conflicting evidence exists, examples of several viewpoints are presented. Sometimes the principle is contrasted with a similar situation in other vertebrates. Where the principle is derived primarily from studies in other disciplines, no specific illustrative examples have been given. No attempt has been made to include encyclopedic information, but many references are provided to permit the reader to examine the record at first hand or to search for additional material applicable to the principles.

By this approach it is hoped that the reader will see mammals in a context of principles and in relation to other taxonomic groups. For some of the relatively well-established disciplines such as taxonomy, a brief summary of current practice is given; for less well-established ones, the trends of research are indicated.

Some chapters have extensive references both to original background material and to recent research papers. The latter have been chosen for timeliness and availability. As a rule, the older literature can be traced through the recent references cited. The references in earlier sections of this book will often be textbooks or review articles; in later sections, citations will be primarily to original sources.

An additional aid to the reader is the outline of classification given in Appendix A. This classification has been taken from standard sources, and is intended to indicate to the reader a general scheme of relations among the species mentioned in the text. Appendix B provides a table of representative dental formulae. In addition, a glossary has been prepared to eliminate frequent definition of terms in the text.

Each author wrote his chapters independently and later integrated them with the others. We hope that this method maintains individuality without losing coherence. D.E.D. wrote Chapters 2, 7, 8, and 10, and F.B.G. wrote Chapters 1, 3, 4, 5, 6, and 9.

Several acknowledgments are important. Dr. Charles Mead and Dr. William Cosgrove read Chapters 3 and 4. Dr. Robert Lechleitner read Chapters 2, 7, 8, and 10. During the preparation of the manuscript, F.B.G. was supported by a contract between the U.S. Atomic Energy Commission and the University of Georgia (AT(07-2)-10).

DAVID E. DAVIS
FRANK B. GOLLEY

University Park, Pennsylvania
Aiken, South Carolina
March, 1963

CONTENTS

PRINCIPLES IN MAMMALOGY

chapter one

INTRODUCTION

THE POSITION OF MAMMALOGY IN SCIENCE

TRADITIONALLY, biology has been organized from a taxonomic point of view, with emphasis placed on distinct groups of organisms. The organization of departments and curricula in many universities reflects this orientation. More recently a functional viewpoint has been emphasized which divides biology into areas such as anatomy, physiology, genetics, and ecology, and these functional categories cut across the earlier taxonomic boundaries. Yet more recently there has been an emphasis on levels of biological organization, such as the molecule, cell, organ, individual, population, and ecosystem.

Mammalogy as a field of scientific inquiry can be considered from each or any of these three viewpoints. The major part of formal mammalogical research has been concentrated on the ecology, life history, and behavior of local populations and on the taxonomy and distribution of species populations. Therefore, formal mammalogy has been mainly concerned with levels of biological organization above that of individual organisms and, from a functional viewpoint, would fall within the category of ecology. In addition, a great deal of research on mammals has been carried out by physiologists, geneticists, and others who have used mammals as experimental materials to study biological processes at the cellular or organ-system levels. Recently in mammalogy there has been a trend toward synthesis from the information derived from all levels toward principles which provide greater understanding of the structure and function of mammals as part of natural systems.

This text, placing its emphasis on the life of the wild mammal, considers mammalogy from an ecological viewpoint. The purpose of the book is to guide the reader to an understanding of how a mammal lives, and hence features such as habits, distribution, reproduction, and behavior are considered. The text is also concerned with mammals as part of physical-chemical-biological systems, i.e., ecosystems. Although we know very little about the role of mammals in ecosystems, some of the available information is brought together in the sections on population dynamics and population metabolism. Since these two viewpoints form the basis of our approach to the subject, they pervade the entire text—forming the underlying idea in all the chapters. However, the chapters themselves are generally oriented toward the traditional areas of mammalogical interest.

A RATIONALE FOR MAMMALOGY

Although a special section on the economic role of mammals has not been prepared, it should be understood that the development of mammalogy into a topic of intense research and into a subject taught widely in the universities in the United States has been correlated with the economic development of the country. The early response of scientific institutions and individuals to the opportunities for exploration and collection of new organisms in the New World is well known. In North America, in addition to transient explorers, the resident settlers evidenced a lively interest in the animal life they encountered, and in many instances their observations and drawings were recorded in personal journals, guidebooks, and other publications. In the 1800's the United States government sent out expeditions into the vast western portion of the continent to survey the plants, animals, and minerals to be found there. Exploration was followed by settlement, and the settlers often faced serious problems concerned with the land and wild organisms. These economic pressures were largely responsible for the establishment of the Bureau of Biological Survey and the initiation of specific research on wild mammals. Much of our basic information on the taxonomy and life history of the native fauna stems from work carried out by the pioneer scientists of the Biological Survey. The intense interest in practical mammalogy, in description of the fauna, and in the fossil faunas of North America was finally focused in the foundation of the American Society of Mammalogists in 1919. Applied mammalogy continues to flourish. In addition to the ever-present concern with wild mammals which destroy crops or attack livestock, are newer interests in the value of mammals in recreation and their role in public health.

There is a further, anthropomorphic reason for our interest in mammals. Man is a mammal, as are most of his domesticated animals. It has often been considered legitimate to extrapolate from the results of experiments on laboratory mammals to man; and similarly, as we gain in understanding of natural population processes, this information may be used to understand human population processes. There is no question that it is important for us to know how mammals function when exposed to the natural stresses and strains of existence, as well as when they live in the highly artificial environment of the laboratory.

ASPECTS OF RESEARCH IN MAMMALOGY

Mammalogy has been concerned largely with descriptive data, but has also produced notable results by employing the experimental method in the field and laboratory. In field biology there has been an increasing tendency toward the development of models based on descriptive and experimental data to aid in understanding natural processes. These models may be verbal, mathematical, or mechanical, and seem to be most useful for simplifying very complex phenomena, for describing natural systems, or to permit discussion between field biologists and scientists in other disciplines through the use of a common language. Simple models have been used in various sections of the text to aid understanding; they do not necessarily indicate unusual insight into the processes involved. On the basis of our present state of knowledge, these models may appear to be gross oversimplifications or abstractions of nature; nevertheless, one of the aims of mammalogy should be to develop sufficiently real models so that, given certain information on environment, species, and population level, the dynamics of the population and its action upon the environment can be predicted with reasonable certainty.

Since the literature is such an important research tool, extensive references to background material and to recent research papers have been included after each chapter. A perusal of these lists of references will indicate the wide variety of publications carrying literature of interest to mammalogists. A number of journals and series of papers are mainly devoted to mammals. These include:

The Journal of Mammalogy—The United States, Canada, and Mexico
Mammalia—France
Säugetierkundliche Mitteilungen—Germany
Zeitschrift für Säugetierkunde—Germany
Acta Theriologica—Poland
Lutra—Benelux Countries

In addition, journals which deal with ecology, natural history, or wildlife management, such as *Ecology, Journal of Animal Ecology, Oikos, The Canadian Field-Naturalist,* and the *Journal of Wildlife Management,* are a common source of mammalogical literature. Further, many taxonomic studies are published separately by museums. The mammalogist will also find much of interest in review publications and those which are primarily oriented toward physiology, medicine, and economic zoology.

SUMMARY

In summary, wild mammals are the focus of intense practical and theoretical interest and, in addition, they provide sport and enjoyment to countless thousands of people. We hope that our organization of the subject matter of mammalogy will provide stimulation and useful information to those individuals seriously interested in mammals from either the applied or theoretical viewpoints. We also hope that the obvious incompleteness of some of the information and the many questions of interpretation will encourage further research in mammalogy.

chapter two

THE KINDS OF MAMMALS

WHILE NEARLY EVERYONE can recognize a mammal, the diversity of characteristics among the many kinds and species is so great that definition becomes difficult. Actually, the only characters common to all mammals are the presence of hair and of milk. Mammals in most cases are readily recognized by such obvious characters as these, and by their four legs, characteristic head, and size—few people would confuse a mammal with any other vertebrate. However, some highly specialized mammals possess unusual characters, such as wings in bats and flippers in whales. More universal characters are the type of reproductive system, the specialization of teeth, and certain anatomical features. The wide variation among mammals and frequent convergence makes classification an exciting challenge.

The approximately 3500 existing species in 1000 living genera are grouped into two subclasses: (1) Prototheria, the egg-laying mammals, and (2) Theria, the mammals which bear their young alive. The subclass Theria is further subdivided into two living infraclasses: (A) Metatheria, the pouched mammals, and (B) Eutheria, the placental mammals. The Prototheria include the spiny anteater and duckbill, which are in one order, Monotremata, and are confined to Australia, Tasmania, and New Guinea. The infraclass Metatheria also includes a single order, Marsupialia. The majority of living mammals belong to the infraclass Eutheria, which is divided into 18 orders. These mammals are viviparous, and their young are nourished before birth through a highly developed placenta connecting the fetus and mother.

5

CLASSIFICATION

Classification is the arrangement of animals according to a meaningful plan. Two aspects must be considered. The general principles need to be stated first, and then the actual classification with descriptions of the kinds of mammals should be given. The principles are the same as those developed for any animal, and are the result of experience for the past two centuries (Simpson, 1961). Animals could be arranged according to any criterion (such as size or color), but the biologically fruitful basis is ancestral relationship. Therefore, mammals are placed in groups according to their supposed ancestry as based on anatomical, physiological, geographical, and ecological information. Often two kinds of mammals superficially resemble each other (e.g., muskrat and nutria) but actually are rather distantly related. Naturally, since knowledge is incomplete, many puzzles remain, and classification may change as knowledge appears or as opinions change. Recently the "new systematics" has replaced the "old." The emphasis of the "new" is upon the population, as represented by many specimens, and its geographic and ecologic variation into subspecies or races. The "old" restricted its interest to one or two "type" specimens that were characterized morphologically (Mayr *et al.,* 1958).

A chronic difficulty in taxonomy arises from the attempt to solve two problems that are incompatible. On the one hand a mammal should have a name that can be recognized throughout the scientific world and be permanent; on the other hand, the name should indicate relationships. When new knowledge or viewpoints arise, a change in name may be suggested, thereby causing confusion. For example, a controversy arose recently when a taxonomist suggested that the genus of the white-tailed deer be called *Dama* instead of *Odocoileus.*

This text relies on the authority of published works (see general references for this chapter) and is not concerned with taxonomic or nomenclatural problems. In the present chapter the descriptions of the larger categories include the morphological and ecological bases of classification that are interpreted to indicate relationship. The principle of evolution, of course, brings all the relationships into focus and permits an orderly arrangement. The arrangement here is slightly modified from Simpson (1945).

The class **Mammalia** is divided into numerous orders such as **Rodentia.** Each order is divided into families, as **Sciuridae.** Families in turn are divided into genera and the genera, into species. Each of the above categories may have additional divisions at the sub- or supra-level. The technical name of a mammal consists of the generic and specific. Thus the species *M. monax* belongs in the genus *Marmota,* and its name is *Marmota monax.* Appendix A lists the vernacular names and arrangement of mammals mentioned in this text and provides a summary of classification. An important technical character in classification is the dental formula. Since these numbers impede reading and may become complicated, they are explained and listed in the Appendix.

MAMMALIAN ORDERS

The plan of the following sections is to mention the important characters of the orders and then to describe appropriate subdivisions. In most cases a division into families or even superfamilies provides manageable groups, but in some orders division into suborders or genera is most useful. In all cases the division attempts to provide groups that can be described in general terms, irrespective of the taxonomic category. Then follows a discussion of distribution, habits, and, finally, a summary of reproduction of the group as a whole. In some cases it is feasible to describe one species as a typical example of the group, but usually the diversity is so great that no "typical" species can be cited.

Monotremes

The most primitive living mammals are several highly specialized forms found in the Australian region. The Monotremes, which are about the size of a rabbit, have become adapted for either an aquatic or a burrowing life. The most striking characteristic is that monotremes lay eggs. All monotremes have hair, but the hairs of one kind, echidna (Figure 2-1), are modified into very sharp spines. The teeth are transitory, consisting, in the duckbill, of thirty-four that are replaced by hard crushing plates while the animal is still young. Even though these mammals lay eggs, they have on their ventral side two glandular areas which secrete milk. Echidna has a small pouch and supporting bones for the pouch, much resembling that found in marsupials. Another primitive character is a common cloacal opening. These mammals have very poor temperature controls, and their body temperatures may vary from 77° to 95°F.

Kinds and Distribution

Several genera may be distinguished. The duckbill probably should be placed in the genus *Ornithorhynchus*. It has brown fur, webbed feet, a flat bill, and very small eyes. It lives in the rivers and lakes of Australia and Tasmania, feeds on aquatic insects and other inverte-

Figure 2-1. The Monotreme Echidna. Note the extreme specialization of spines, claws, and beak. (Smithsonian Institution photograph.)

brates, and burrows in stream banks, where it lays eggs in a modest nest. The spiny forms belong to the genera *Tachyglossus* and *Zaglossus*. The collective name for the group, echidna, comes from the presence of many spines. One spine on the hind leg contains a poison that coagulates the blood. Apparently, this poison is present only during the breeding season and only in the male. The bill is very flexible, and the long tongue permits the animal to extract insects from the ground or from bark or rocks.

Habits and Reproduction

Monotremes are found in Australia, Tasmania, and New Guinea. Echidnas live in dry, brushy areas where they are primarily nocturnal and wander about on the surface. They dig into the ground very rapidly, either for protection or to find adequate food. The duckbill in contrast lives along streams or small lakes and swims easily. It burrows into the bank for protection and nesting. Reproduction occurs in a definite season from July to September. In the duckbill only the left ovary functions, but in the echidnas the ovaries alternate at each ovulation. The duckbill copulates in the water and lays its eggs in a nest within a burrow. The duckbill lays from one to three eggs; echidnas lay only one. A hatching tooth in the embryo permits the young to emerge through the hard shell. The female incubates the eggs for approximately ten days.

Marsupials

In contrast to the monotremes discussed thus far, the marsupials will at once be recognized as conventional mammals in that they bear living young and have teeth throughout their lives. The chief distinguishing characters for classification are the nature of the teeth and the absence of a typical placenta. Anatomically, most marsupials are not specialized. Generally they have a very small brain, short legs, five toes, and a long tail. The reproductive organs consist of the usual pairs of testes and ovaries. The genital and urinary openings of females are separate rather than joined. A few species have anatomical adaptations for a special mode of life.

Kinds

Classification of marsupials presents many problems, since many distinct groups lack connecting links. It seems best to arrange the discussion by superfamilies since many small families have only a few species. The most primitive marsupials, belonging to the superfamily **Didelphoidea,** are represented by the Virginia opossum (*Didelphis marsupialis*) and by many South American genera. The snout and tail are long; the limbs are short and somewhat spread out on the sides of the body. The thumb of the hind foot is opposable. A marsupial pouch is present in some genera but incomplete or absent in others. The superfamily, **Dasyuroidea,** includes a number of diverse Australian forms that superficially resemble mice (Figures 2-2 and 2-3), foxes, minks (Figure 2-4), and even moles. They are placed together because various anatomical details suggest a common ancestor. The dental formulae vary, but they always have four upper and three lower incisors. Generally four or five toes are present. The pouch may be absent. The next superfamily, **Parameloidea,** includes several genera (Figure 2-5) that

Figure 2-2. Marsupial Mouse (*Antechinus flavipes*), Showing Typical Rodent Form but Mammae in a Ring Within Pouch. (From Horner and Taylor, 1959. Amer. Mus. Novitates No. 1972.)

have four or five upper and three lower incisors. They show adaptation for jumping by long legs and loss of toes. Their teeth are small and sharp, suitable for feeding on insects. The pouch opens posteriorly. Another superfamily, **Coenolestoidea,** occurs in the Andean regions of South America. These small, mouse-like forms are poorly known. They have five toes and a very small pouch. The lower incisor is very large and horizontal, and the canine of the male is much larger than that of the female. The last superfamily, **Phalangeroidea,** includes the typical kangaroos as well as some species resembling mice and squirrels (Figure 2-6). Some species are large and others are small. The dental formula varies, but the number of incisors is always small. The pouch is highly developed and opens anteriorly. Generally, considerable reduction of toes occurs as in the kangaroo, where the number is only three. Many kinds are arboreal, and one has developed skin flaps for gliding. A number of large fossil forms have been found.

Distribution

The distribution of marsupials illustrates the common principle that primitive forms occur widely scattered throughout the world, generally at the tips of continents. At present, marsupials occur primarily in South America, Australia, and in the islands near Australia, such as New Guinea and the Celebes. This distribution represents the remainder of a world-wide distribution, including the Northern Hemisphere from which the primitive marsupials spread.

Figure 2-3. Fat-tailed Marsupial Mouse (*Sminthopsis crassicaudata*), Showing Again the Rodent Form. (Photo by Stanley Breeden.)

Habits

The behavior and activities of marsupials are highly diverse. In South America, where various kinds had an opportunity to diverge without great competition from placental mammals, marsupials have entered many different ecological roles. Many of them live an arboreal life, feeding on insects and fruits. Others have become predacious and developed habits similar to those of shrews. These forms live on the ground or tunnel under leaves and capture insects. In Australia and nearby areas marsupials have diversified to a fantastic level, as can be seen from the above descriptions of the different kinds. Almost every conceivable ecological niche has been filled, aquatic to arboreal forms having diets ranging from highly specialized carnivorous to omnivorous.

Reproduction

Marsupials show an apparent retrogression in their breeding. Many authorities believe that the ancestral marsupials had a more effective placenta that has diminished in modern kinds. Another device, the

Figure 2-4. Australian "Cat" (*Dasyurus*). Note the similarity to mink in face and body appearance. In spite of its superficial dissimilarity, this "cat" is related to the "mice" shown in Figure 2-3. (Smithsonian Institution photograph.)

pouch, has developed to protect the young during early life. At birth they crawl from the vagina to the pouch and there attach themselves to the nipples for the suckling period. The female kangaroo assists the young by licking a trail in her fur. Gestation may be short (12 days in the Virginia opossum), but the suckling period may last more than a month (Hartman, 1952). The breeding behavior of marsupials is poorly known. Apparently, copulation occurs after minimal courtship behavior. The male does not stay with the female, but is promiscuous.

Insectivores

Members of the order **Insectivora** are usually small terrestrial forms, very ancient but rarely very abundant. Their appearance and characters are exceedingly primitive and, in general, lack any spectacular specializations except for those concerned with their behavioral patterns. The feet are plantigrade and have five toes. The number of teeth is often 40, and all teeth have roots. A set of milk teeth may persist for a relatively long time in some forms. Other generalized characters are the presence of a clavicle and the fact that the tympanic bone is a mere ring. The eyes are very weak. Many species are highly specialized for some particular habit (e.g. moles) as might be expected in an ancient

Figure 2-5. Short-tailed Bandicoot (*Isoodon macrourus*). Bandicoots, although super-ficially resembling marsupial mice (Figure 2-3), are only distantly related. (Photograph by Stanley Breeden.)

order. The only notable specialization found throughout the order is the presence of many musk glands, found usually at the anus but sometimes along the sides.

Kinds

The classification of the groups presents considerable difficulty because there are a number of distinct families, sometimes separated geographically more than anatomically. The first group is the **Chryso-chloridae** or golden moles of Africa. As the name indicates, these are fossorial insectivores, spending most of their life underground and having the usual fossorial adaptations of a short tail, strong legs, and many vibrissae useful for touch in the burrows. Two families, **Soleno-dontidae** and **Tenrecidae**, are closely related and poorly known. The former consists of a few species found in the Greater Antilles, where these primitive forms live in the cloud- and rain-forests in Haiti and other islands. The latter family occurs in Madagascar and has other forms of doubtful relationship in Africa. These insectivores resemble one another greatly in appearance and anatomy, and are often placed together in the same family. Several of the species have developed spines. A number show unusual resistance to venom from snakes and from insects. The family called **Erinaceidae** contains the familiar hedgehogs of Europe. Hedgehogs have developed spines far more elaborately than have other insectivores. Hedgehogs are found from the Philippine Islands through Asia and Africa into Europe, but are not

Figure 2-6. Squirrel Glider (*Petaurus norfolcensis*). This marsupial, belonging to still another group, has developed the adaptations of flying squirrels. (Photograph by Stanley Breeden.)

found in the Western Hemisphere. Those living in the African deserts estivate, and those in Europe hibernate in the winter. The family **Soricidae** includes perhaps the most abundant and typical insectivores, the shrews, which are divided into many genera. Shrews (Figure 2-7) have a very small body and most species have a long tail. The lower front teeth extend horizontally forward and function as pincers. Presumably this arrangement permits the shrew to pick small insects out of crevices in the bark. This family is exceptional among the in-

Figure 2-7. The Cinereous Shrew (*Sorex cinereous*). A typical insectivore. (Amer. Mus. Nat. Hist.)

sectivores in having a world-wide (except Australian) distribution. Another family, **Talpidae,** includes moles, and is well known since its members inhabit the Northern Hemisphere. The species are fossorial forms that are adapted for living underground. Their snout is blunt and well equipped with tactile hairs, and their front feet and shoulders

Figure 2-8. The Elephant Shrew (*Tupaia montana*) is often considered a primate since its reproductive physiology is similar. (Photograph by Ernest P. Walker.)

are strong for digging. One form has developed aquatic habits. Moles are practically blind, for they have very small eyes and in some species a layer of skin over the eyes. Two other families of insectivores, the **Macroscelididae** and the **Tupaiidae,** are found in the East Indies and, in general, resemble (Figure 2-8) the shrew. They frequent trees, and in some cases have a brushy tail similar to that of a squirrel.

Humans have great interest in these insectivores because they have an estrous cycle very similar to that found in primates. Certain forms have a menstrual period comparable to the physiological cycle in lemurs. The animals are polyestrous and have a short breeding season. These two families present taxonomic problems, since their anatomical resemblance may be mere convergence. Also, the Tupaiidae, due to their menstrual cycle, are considered by some authors to be a very primitive primate (Simpson, 1945).

Distribution

Insectivores illustrate the typical disjunct distribution of an ancient group. A number of distinct families, which according to certain authors may be related, are isolated in widely separated areas. Only one group, the shrews, has an essentially world-wide distribution; moles are found in the Northern Hemisphere; the other families are restricted to islands or to the periphery of the continents.

Habits

The habits and behavior of insectivores are highly specialized, presumably functions developed through their long history. Many are fossorial and have extensive anatomical modifications for tunnelling. Some have developed aquatic modifications, as has the shrew that lives in streams and catches fish. Generally speaking, the forms are terrestrial; but some have become squirrel-like in their habits. All of them are carnivorous, feeding on insects or even mice, and only occasionally eating vegetable matter. A spectacular characteristic is a metabolic rate so high that a shrew must eat every few hours to avoid starving to death. Generally, the individuals are solitary, rarely being found in groups.

Reproduction

The reproductive characteristics of shrews are again a reflection of their primitive state. The testes are connected to the exterior by ducts. A series of glands are attached to the ducts, but these glands do not appear to be homologous with similar glands of rodents. The female reproductive tract consists of two ovaries, each with an oviduct carrying the ova to a horn of the bicornuate uterus. The number of mammary glands varies from 12 in tenrecs to a single pair in *Solenodon*. Shrews usually have six glands. The litter size may be large in some forms such as the tenrec, which may have as many as 20 embryos. The elephant shrew (*Elephantulus*) may ovulate 120 eggs at a time, but relatively few survive to be implanted. Most insectivores have a definite breeding season. Some may have several litters per year; others, such as moles, have only one. Although there is great variation within the order, the gestation period is generally long, sometimes lasting for four to six weeks.

Primates

The primates include a large number of forms readily recognized as monkeys or apes, as well as a number of primitive forms greatly resembling some of the insectivores. Indeed, the separation of primates from insectivores becomes rather difficult. The novel development among the primates is the increase in size of the brain, requiring concurrent increases in the skull. Furthermore, the eyes have enlarged and moved towards the front of the skull, thereby distorting the long shape of the primitive head into a round one. Generally, the species have adapted to an arboreal life and, except for the skull changes, retain a number of primitive characters. The hands have five digits and the clavicle is usually present. Their skeleton and organs generally are similar to the ancestral mammals and even the teeth show little modification, a reflection of the continuation of the omnivorous diet. The great specialization, of course, is the development of the brain, which perhaps began as a result of need, in an arboreal existence, for highly accurate judgment of distance both in the sense of vision and in the sense of muscular movement. The development of a clasping hand, also, further permitted this specialization. Almost the only other specializations are the opposable thumb or big toe used for grasping and the development of nails instead of claws. In some monkeys the tail has become prehensile.

Kinds

Classification of primates provides difficulties in presentation because a large number of primitive groups contain many similar species, and the specialized groups contain a few spectacular (and hence well-known) species. Primates of the most primitive subfamily, **Lemuroidea,** are small, arboreal species, greatly resembling insectivores. Lemurs (Figure 2-9) and their allies generally resemble typical monkeys, but may differ by absence of a tail, stockiness of body, or presence of pads on toes. Some kinds are small; others are as large as a cat. The thumb always has a nail rather than a claw. The eyes face somewhat anteriorly. Usually the distribution is geographically restricted—for example the lemurs in Madagascar.

Several kinds of primates are classified in separate groups but include only a few species, usually severely restricted in distribution. Some very peculiar primates (**Daubentonioidea**) have a dentition analogous to that of a rodent. Members of the loris (**Lorisioidea**) group look like toy bears and live in trees and feed on fruits and leaves. Its

Figure 2-9. A Very Primitive Primate, *Lemur macaco*, Male and Female. (Photograph by Ernest P. Walker.)

relative, the *Galago* of Africa, has long hind legs and a long, nonprehensile tail. The suborder **Tarsioidea** includes one living genus and a number of fossils. These little primates live in trees and jump from branch to branch, feeding on insects. Their immense eyes face forward, their ears are large, and their tails are long. A number of skull characters resemble the next suborder.

The **Anthropoidea** includes the typical monkeys, apes, and man. The original primates were arboreal, but many have developed a secondary adaptation to terrestrial living. The brain case is much larger in Anthropoidea than in the more primitive primates. The feet generally have opposable toes and the thumb is atrophied. This large group is easily divided into two infraorders. (1) The Platyrrhini contain the monkeys of the western hemisphere that are characterized by flat nostrils, a prehensile tail, and three premolars. They lack a typical menstrual cycle. Two families, the marmosets and cebids, occur in South and Central America. (2) The infraorder Catarrhini includes all the other forms. These species have narrow nostrils, often lack a tail, and

Figure 2-10. The Rhesus Monkey (*Macaca mulatta*) is widely used for medical research and now is being used for ecological and behavioral studies. (Photograph by Carl Koford.)

have only two premolars on each side of each jaw. The various families may be divided into four groups. The first includes arboreal and terrestrial monkeys, such as the green monkey, baboons, and macaques (Figure 2-10); the second includes gibbons; the third includes certain apes and gorillas; and the fourth, man.

Distribution

Primates are now found in the tropical regions throughout the world. Presumably they originated in Africa and invaded North America at a time when the northern hemisphere was much warmer. They moved on to South America and developed into the typical monkeys found there. In Asia primates dispersed into many areas, and thus became adapted to various kinds of life.

Habits

Most primates are arboreal, although a number of forms have become terrestrial. Some developed the habit of walking on all fours, but others, such as the apes and man, became bipedal instead. We assume that the most primitive primates were nocturnal, as judged by very large eyes, although diurnal types soon developed. The food of primates includes insects and fruits, and some forms have developed the habit of eating grain. The macaque monkeys of India live in open areas and may cause considerable damage to crops, as do baboons in South Africa. Perhaps the most fascinating feature of primates is their social behavior. Many associate in groups of 10 to 20 or even many more individuals. Each group has a territory it defends against others of the same species, and within each group there is a social rank, usually headed by a dominant male.

Reproduction

The reproduction of primates has, of course, been studied intensively. The macaque has proved an especially fine species for research. The anatomical arrangements are generally similar to those found in humans; however, only the Anthropoidea have the united type of uterus —others have the bicornuate type. Usually only one offspring is born at a time, although in some marmosets twins regularly appear. Presumably most forms have a breeding season in the wild (as do macaques). In captivity, however, young may appear in any season of the year.

Bats

Bats include distinctive mammals easily recognized by the presence of wings formed by membranes of skin between the fingers. Some bats have, in addition, a membrane connecting the hind feet with the tail. The teeth of bats are highly modified and show great changes in numbers as well as in type. Therefore, a generalized dental formula for bats cannot be given. The order **Chiroptera** illustrates a problem of classification—the extent of division of a group. Bats are clearly related and have a common character, wings. But beyond this, they are highly diversified physiologically and anatomically. Indeed there is much more variation among various bats than among mammals of many other orders (e.g., Carnivores). The brief treatment here given is clearly inadequate to show the extent of variation.

Kinds

The classification of bats is difficult because so many diverse forms merit the rank of family. For present purposes it seems satisfactory

Figure 2-11. The Flying Fox (*Pteropus poliocephalus*) belongs to the primitive part of the order Chiroptera. Note the development of the toe on the wing. (Photograph by Stanley Breeden.)

simply to divide the bats into the two big groups, based on the extent of evolution of the wing. The **Megachiroptera** still have considerable independence for the second digit, which always has three phalanges. In contrast, the **Microchiroptera** have the second digit attached to the third. Other anatomical differences occur in the skull. The **Megachiroptera** are contained in one family called "flying foxes" (Figure 2-11). These bats flock in large numbers in many areas of Australia and consume large quantities of food. Although the dental formula varies considerably, there usually are three premolars and two upper and three lower molars. The **Microchiroptera** are highly variable and contain some 15 families and many genera. Their teeth range from types adapted to catching insects to types adapted for eating fruit or slashing a wound for sucking blood. Generally, the earlobes are very large, an aid in their powers of echolocation.

Distribution

The distribution of bats is world-wide. The **Megachiroptera** are found only in the Malaysian region including Australia and New Zealand. Among the **Microchiroptera** some families, such as the Phyllostomatidae, are found only in North America; but others, such as the Vespertilionidae, are found throughout the Northern Hemisphere.

Habits

The habits and behavior of bats differ from species to species. Most bats are nocturnal or at least crepuscular. Even the blood-sucking bats are nocturnal. A few species live solitarily but others are extremely gregarious, living in colonies of literally millions of individuals. For example, free-tailed bats live in caves where as many as five million individuals may roost each night. The flying foxes of Australia roost by thousands in trees, and may descend upon a farming area and inflict great damage on fruits. Another feature of note is the migratory behavior of various bats. Some of the common bats spend the summer in one area living in treeholes or houses, then migrate to areas somewhat distant, where they spend the winter in caves. Other bats spend the summer in northern areas, raising their young in caves, then migrate south for the winter. Some solitary bats that live in the northern areas migrate to tropical areas to spend the winter.

Reproduction

The breeding habits of bats are highly variable, and present several peculiarities (see Chapter 7). The reproductive and associated organs change in size seasonally, but in some species sexual activity occurs in the fall and in others, in the spring. The female organs may be asymmetrical, at least functionally, since in some species embryos occur only in the right horn of the uterus. The male organs include a very large prostate gland. Usually only one offspring is born, but some solitary species have as many as four. Little is known about the breeding behavior of bats; indeed, for some species neither the time nor the place is known.

Specialized Orders

A number of mammals have become so highly specialized that they must be classified in a distinct order. Generally, they show some affinities to the insectivores but otherwise bear little relationship to any group of mammals. One has the choice of putting these groups together for convenience (as below), since few species are involved, or setting them apart as many distinct orders, recognizing that they are probably not phylogenetically closely related.

Flying Lemurs

The first group to be mentioned is the **Dermoptera** of Malaysia and the Philippines. These animals live in the forest and have developed a gliding ability similar to that of the flying squirrel. The limbs and tail are long, and the tail has an extension of the skin for assistance in gliding. The teeth are very peculiar structures, for the incisors have a number of grooves. The stomach is simple, adapted to their vegetarian diet. Although called lemurs, they are not close to primates.

Edentates

Other groups of specialized mammals are the armadillos, sloths, and anteaters. Some authors separate these groups into three distinct orders, believing that they do not have a common ancestry, while others unite them into one order called **Edentata**. These mammals are all highly specialized and have degenerated in several characters.

Armadillos (Figure 2-12) are medium-sized animals that live now in the Western Hemisphere and probably developed in South America. The armadillo is covered with a set of bony plates, highly flexible nevertheless, permitting the animal to curl up in a ball and use the plates for protection. These animals are primarily burrowing forms, digging even into hard soil with their strong front feet. Their food is primarily insects and roots. A peculiarity is their large number of incisor (5 or 6) and of premolar (7) teeth. The teeth presumably were once heterodont but through evolution have become homodont.

The sloths (Figure 2-13), found only in tropical areas, belong to another South American group which has no living representatives in North America. However, at one time a large ground sloth lived in

Figure 2-12. The Armadillo (*Dasypus novemcinctus*) shows extreme specialization for digging and protection. (Photograph by William Jackson.)

what are now the southern states. Sloths have lost their incisors, but retain an upper and lower canine as well as three or four premolars in the upper and lower jaw on each side. However, the interpretation of homologues for teeth is difficult, and specialists disagree about the proper names to be applied to the teeth. Sloths live on a very specialized diet of leaves. Indeed, the two-toed sloth (*Choloepus* sp.) feeds almost exclusively on the leaves of the cecropia tree. Sloths move extremely slowly and hang upside down as they search along the branches for food. However, when chased, an individual moves quickly hand over hand from tree to tree. The sloth defends itself by a quick motion of the arm and can give a terrible wound with its front claws. One peculiarity of the sloth is that it cannot stand on four legs or get up when placed on the ground.

Anteaters (Figure 2-14) are another group of peculiar mammals found only in tropical America. Several forms, including the giant anteater (*Tamandua tetradactyla*), attain the size of a collie dog. The anteaters have no teeth at any time in either jaw. They live in the plains region of South America, where they open up the termite mounds with

Figure 2-13. The Sloth (*Bradypus griseus*) is highly specialized for feeding on leaves of the Cecropia tree. (Photograph by William Jackson.)

their strong forelegs and claws and then collect the termites with their very long extensible tongue.

Reproduction in these forms generally occurs at the time of the rainy season. The surprising similarity of the reproductive organs is a major reason for uniting these bizarre forms into one order. Anatomically, the organs of the female are primitive, since there is a large urogenital sinus and the two horns of the uterus are very short, giving rise to one large cavity for the embryo. Many of the forms appear to have estrous periods. A spectacular feature of the armadillos is that at least some species have a delayed implantation followed by a division of the zygote into four parts, which produces quadruplets, all of the same sex.

Pholidota

Another highly aberrant kind of mammal, the pangolin (*Manis* sp.), is placed in the order **Pholidota**. This animal is often called an anteater, since it feeds on ants and lacks teeth. Its body is covered with very large scales, and the scaly tail is about three times the length of the body About four species live in Africa, and others live in Malaysia and

Figure 2-14. The Anteater (*Tamandua tetradoctyla*) has adaptations for digging out termites for food. (Photograph by William Jackson.)

southern China. The pangolin is separated from the other peculiar orders by a number of detailed differences in the skeleton, the structure of the skull, the limb bones, and the digestive system. No fossil form that could be ancestral to the pangolin is available, and thus it must be left in its isolated order.

Rodents

Most of the mammals in the world are rodents. In numbers of species and in numbers of individuals, the most abundant forms belong to the order Rodentia. Naturally there is a wide variety of sizes and adaptations within this immense group. Some rodents, such as mice, are very small; and others, such as beaver and capybara, are large. The outstanding characteristic is the presence and adaptation of the incisor teeth for gnawing. The first incisor on each side of the upper and of the lower jaw has become tremendously enlarged to produce a very effective cutting instrument. The other incisors, as well as the canines, have disappeared. The molar and premolar teeth vary in numbers in different families. The rest of the rodents' anatomy is relatively generalized.

In a few cases, one or two toes have become lost or the legs elongated. A few forms have become specialized for digging or for aquatic existence. In general, their high reproductive potential has permitted them to survive in spite of a high mortality rate, and thus these animals maintain themselves as species.

Kinds

For many years the classification has been based primarily on the musculature of the jaws. It is not surprising that a gnawing mammal has very strong muscles with extensive attachments on the jaws ·for chewing. Tullberg long ago noticed that these muscles could be classified into four general types that seem logically to divide the kinds of rodents. The main muscle under consideration is the masseter, which has a superficial and a profound part. In the most primitive forms (Aplodontia), the superficial part extends from the zygomatic arch almost horizontally back to the lower part of the mandible. The profound part lies under this and runs almost perpendicular to it from the internal base of the zygomatic arch to the anterior part of the mandible. In the second, more advanced type of muscle (found in squirrels), the superficial part extends up ahead of the zygomatic arch forming a groove in the upper jaw bone. The profound part lies underneath and runs perpendicular to the superficial. In the third category (mice and rats), the superficial part extends somewhat up in front of the zygomatic arch, but the profound part has extended upwards and then forwards, through a canal in the front of the orbit. In the fourth type (porcupines), the superficial part is small, but the profound part extends through a canal in front of the zygomatic arch and orbit and makes a deep groove in the facial bones similar to that formed in squirrels by the superficial muscle. Using this basic muscular organization, the rodents have been classed into a number of suborders containing superfamilies.

A more recent suggestion for a basis of classification is the work of Shaub in 1953, who divided the whole rodent group into three big categories on the basis of the teeth. The basic anatomical situation is the development of ridges in the teeth. Certain groups of rodents develop five clear transverse ridges and are thus classified together. Next, a group of rodents has a very typical tooth containing a number of cusps lacking ridges, except secondarily. The third group, the most primitive, lacks any specialization in reference to ridges. In the following description of suborders the families will be mentioned first according to the classification by the masseter muscle, and then changes to fit the classification by ridges will be noted.

Sciuromorpha: The first suborder includes four superfamilies. The most primitive superfamily contains an aberrant form called the mountain beaver (Aplodontia), a small mountain rodent of western North America. It is a stocky form about 30 cm. long, with strong legs, very

Figure 2-15. The Woodchuck (*Marmota monax*) spends much of its time watching for its most frequent enemy, another woodchuck. (Photograph from Fish and Wildlife Service.)

short tail, and five toes on each foot. Another superfamily, Sciuroidea, includes tree squirrels and ground squirrels. This abundant group has a world-wide distribution (except Australia) and contains a large number of genera. The tree squirrels are well known in size and shape. They generally have a large tail used both for balancing and for protection. The ground squirrels have developed the habit of living underground, but otherwise greatly resemble tree squirrels. The woodchuck

(Figure 2-15) is simply a specialized ground squirrel with a very short tail. Within the squirrel group at least two different animals have developed the mechanism for gliding; the North American flying squirrels have a wide membrane of skin stretching between the legs; and several African forms have an even more highly specialized development of a membrane connecting the tail to the legs. Another superfamily within the Sciuromorphs is the Geomyoidea, containing the gophers. These are burrowing forms which have extreme fossorial adaptations. A last group is the Castoroidea, containing the beavers. These large rodents occur in the northern areas, where they live in lodges and construct dams to provide deep water.

Myomorpha: The next big group of rodents contains several superfamilies. The first to be mentioned is the Muroidea. This immense superfamily includes animals known as mice and rats, and has a number of diverse forms with world-wide distribution. These mammals are relatively well known and require no general description. Suffice it to say that the many genera (about 190 living) are surprisingly uniform in size and appearance as well as habits. Some odd members occur, such as the African "mole" rat, that lacks hair on the body. Some have minor specializations, such as the "comb" on the toes of lemmings, the spines on spiny mice, the predatory habit of the grasshopper mouse (*Onycomys* sp.), or the equipment of gophers (Figure 2-16). It may be that specialization for survival was relatively unnecessary in these forms, thanks to their remarkable reproductive rate.

A second group is the Dipodoidea and contains a number of jumping mice (Figure 2-17) that have developed the long legs and long tail resembling the adaptations of the kangaroo. These forms are found in America and in Asia. Many of them live underground. At least one of them has developed very large ears similar to a rabbit's. Still another group, Gliroidea, includes the dormice, found only in Europe and eastern and western Asia. Although these rodents are generally small, they greatly resemble a squirrel in appearance.

Hystricomorpha: The last group of rodents includes a large number of South American forms, but one superfamily, the Hystricoidea, includes spiny forms found in Africa and the Malaysian region. These have essentially the adaptations of a porcupine. Another subfamily is the Erythrizontoidea and includes the porcupines of South and of North America. It seems likely that this group developed in South America and spread northward. Another large associated group is the Cavioidea, including the guinea pig (*Cavia* sp.) of South America. Also associated are a number of large forms such as the capybara (*Hydrochoerus capybara*) which is the size of a pig and lives in the marshes of Argentina. A number of Andean forms developed a general similarity to rabbits. In still another group, Chinchilloidea, are chinchillas, pacas, and several other forms of South America. The last group, the Octodontoidea, contains a number of mouse-like South American forms. Many of these are the size of rats. Some are burrowing types. There exist still other

Figure 2-16. *Cryptomys lugardi* is a peculiar rodent from southern Africa, highly specialized for living underground. (Photograph by Ernest P. Walker.)

groups that cannot very well be placed in any particular group of Hystricomorpha. Several very peculiar South African rodents of quite isolated families seem to belong in this big group.

The above summary of the superfamilies simply lists them according to the classification based on the muscles. Based on teeth, the classification would be slightly different since the dormice (Gliroidea) would be put with the squirrels into the group called Non-pentalophodonta. Then the beavers (Castoroidea) would be taken out of the squirrel group and placed in the big South American category called Pentalophodonta. While these changes do not seem to be great, the arrangement seems far more logical since the beavers appear to have originated in the Western Hemisphere.

Figure 2-17. Banner-tail Kangaroo Rat (*Dipodomys spectabilis*) shows the strong hind legs for jumping and the long tail for balancing. (Photograph from Fish and Wildlife Service.)

Distribution

Rodents have dispersed throughout the world and, with the help of man, invaded most of the isolated islands in the Pacific. However, a number of families or groups are restricted to large or small areas, and illustrate a number of zoogeographical principles. For example, the Muridae are found naturally in the Eastern Hemisphere, especially in the northern part, but are not found naturally in the Western Hemisphere although commensal rats and mice have traveled with man throughout the world. In contrast, the Cricetidae are found throughout both the Eastern and Western Hemispheres and have developed several different species even in South America. Presumably, the Cricetidae spread as a wave of immigrants from Northern Europe into North America, but the Muridae have not yet naturally invaded the Western Hemisphere. An example of highly restricted distribution is illustrated by the Geomyidae that occur in the southern and western United States. One species, the plains pocket gopher (*Geomys bursarius*), is found in the western states down into Mexico, while another species, the southeastern pocket gopher (*G. pinetus*), occurs in three states. Apparently the ancestral species lived in North America but was pushed south by the glaciers and became divided into two parts over a period of several thousand years. Since the glaciers have retreated, these forms have moved north to regain the area of former distribution, but have become sufficiently distinct that they cannot interbreed and hence are called separate species. In addition, the gophers illustrate a very local distribution in relation to the type of soil. Gophers can burrow only in relatively soft soils, and in Florida are found only in sandy areas. Their distribution can be very clearly seen along highways by the presence or absence of the characteristic mounds of sand thrown up at the burrow.

The distribution of the Octodontoidea in South America illustrates in a modest way the radiating evolution that often occurs when a group is isolated for a long period of time without much competition. Presumably, the ancestral Octodonts entered South America long ago in Eocene times when a bridge from North America through Panama existed. After this bridge was broken, the primitive rodents had a chance to diverge while exploiting the whole South American continent. The result is a great diversity of rodents, some large and some small, living in open plains, in forests, and at high or low altitudes. An extreme form is the nutria (*Myocastor coypu*), an animal twice the size of a muskrat, that has developed the same type of life. Other forms, such as the Argentine tuco-tuco (*Ctenomys* sp.) have developed extreme fossorial habits. Others are arboreal and have a peculiar protective device. A special vertebra in the tail breaks easily, so that when grabbed, the tail breaks off letting the rat free. The bamboo rat (*Kannebateomys* sp.) has suckers on its toes to hold the smooth stalks. This extreme radiation results from the conditions of an isolated distribution.

Still another kind of distribution occurs. Highly specialized families exist at the tips of continents, such as the southern part of the African continent. For example, *Heterophalus* is a small, burrowing rodent that has lost most of its hair and reduced the number of molar teeth simply to three molars. This form is relatively rare and belongs to a highly specialized family with no close relatives. Another rodent, *Spalax*, has developed the mole type of existence, lives underground, and has the usual adaptations of small eyes, short tail, short fur, and strong feet. Still other highly specialized families having no close relatives occur in southern Africa.

Habits

The habits and behavior of rodents are highly diversified, as might be expected from the large number of species. A number of rodents are fossorial and spend a large part of their time underground. Voles tunnel in the upper layers of the soil or underneath the snow, emerging only for short periods of time. Other rodents, such as ground squirrels, dig extensive burrow systems used for resting and caring for their young. Squirrels and many rats and mice have developed arboreal habits. These forms usually develop great agility of the feet and a long bushy tail for balancing. An extreme of this adaptation is the development of a gliding habit permitted by a wide layer of skin stretching between the front and hind legs. These flying squirrels glide from the top of one tree down to the base of another, climb up again and start a new glide. Still another type of adaptation is the saltatory mode often found in mice. Jumping mice, kangaroo rats, and many forms in various continents have developed long hind legs and a long tail which usually has a bunch of hairs at the tip to serve as a balancing organ. These forms generally develop in open or desert areas where there is little interference with long jumps. Rodents have not developed extensive adaptations for an aquatic life. Many forms, however, live in the water along the banks or in swamps and have some minor adaptations, such as a flattened tail and somewhat webbed feet. However, no rodent has evolved the extensive physiological or anatomical changes found in marine mammals.

The food of rodents is generally some kind of plant. Certain forms are relatively omnivorous and eat fruits, leaves, and insects of many varieties. Other forms, however, are rather restricted to a diet of grain seeds, or specialize in opening nuts like acorns or walnuts. Stems and roots of grasses are almost the sole diet of many species, such as the voles. Often a seasonal change in diet occurs, and a form that feeds on green vegetation during the summer will feed on bark during the winter. An example of extreme specialization of diet occurs in that of the woodchuck, which eats only green leafy vegetation and almost never touches seeds or dried grass. Perhaps the most aberrant item is the food of a piscivorous mouse in Panama that swims in streams and catches small minnows.

The homes of rodents are almost always a type of den in a burrow in the ground or in a cavity among rocks or in trees. Generally, the den is lined with leaves or grass. Sometimes a rather extensive system of tunnels is connected to the burrow. In beaver and muskrats, a rather elaborate structure is built to contain the burrow system. One mouse (*Micromys* sp.) lives in a small ball of grass built about two feet above the ground in marshy vegetation.

Reproduction

The breeding by rodents is surprisingly uniform. In addition to the laboratory rat, which is the best known, many species have been examined. Minor differences occur in number of young, gestation period, and other details. Since the information in Chapter 7 relies so heavily on rodents, no further comments will be included here.

Carnivores

The order Carnivora includes a number of very diverse kinds that form a natural group based on common ancestry. The main similarity is the structure and arrangement of the teeth. The incisors and canines are always prominent, and the molars tend to decrease in number. Several other characters prevail in the group. The temporal and orbital fossae are broadly connected. Four or five toes are present on each foot, although in many species the first toe is greatly reduced. The habits are very diverse, and many forms distantly related within the order have developed similar habits. Parenthetically, two confusing words need explanation. A carnivore is a meat-eater (is carnivorous) and is not necessarily a Carnivore (a member of the order Carnivora).

Kinds

Classification presents a number of problems. Formerly, the Pinnipedia (seals) were included in the order, but now they are often separated as a distinct order although the relation is close. True Carnivores descended from the Miacidae family in the fossil order called Creodonta. Living Carnivores may be divided into seven distinct families, which can be divided into two separate lines of specialization. Both lines begin with the raccoon type of Carnivore. One line (Canoid) includes bears and weasels, and terminates with dogs; the other (Feloid) ends with cats.

The family Canidae includes dogs and foxes, which occur throughout the world. The cranium is large, and the tympanic bulla is well developed. The legs are long and usually have five toes possessing nonretractile claws. The teeth are relatively unspecialized, although the lower first molar is arranged to promote a shearing action with the upper fourth premolar. Dogs are running animals that capture their prey by chasing and dispatch it by slashing with the canines.

The Ursidae (bears) are characterized by large size, short tail, nonretractile claws, and plantigrade gait. The dental formula is the same as that of the Canidae, but the premolars rather than the molars have become reduced in size. Furthermore, the teeth are flat and blunt, adapted for crushing.

The family Mustelidae contains weasels, skunks, badgers (Figure 2-18), and many other flesh-eating mammals. Characteristically, the body is long, and the animal has an agile form. Most species have a very powerful scent in special glands near the anus. In contrast to primitive Carnivores, most Mustelids walk on the tips of their toes. The

Figure 2-18. The Badger (*Taxidea taxus*), a member of the weasel family, has developed the ability to dig out its prey. (Photograph from Fish and Wildlife Service.)

teeth are very sharp and used for capturing and killing prey. Mustelids have a very short muzzle. This family includes a number of ecologically diverse species ranging from the fisher (*Martes pennanti*), which is usually arboreal, through the terrestrial weasels to the semi-aquatic minks and the aquatic and even oceanic otters. The relationship of the Mustelids to other Carnivores is problematical.

The Procyonidae (raccoons) contains a homogeneous group of mammals that are probably the most primitive living Carnivores. They lack distinctive major characters but are plantigrade, and have a long tail and several anatomical distinctions in the bones of the skull. Pandas resemble both raccoons and bears, and are often placed in a distinct family rather than in the Procyonidae.

The Viverridae greatly resemble Mustelids but have several different characters. In contrast to the Mustelids, the Viverrids have weak shearing molar and premolar teeth. In appearance the Viverrids are agile mammals, greatly resembling weasels, although some resemble cats.

Although the Hyaenidae greatly resemble dogs in appearance, they differ in many characters. They have a large body and head, very long legs, and the very heavy teeth specialized for crushing rather than shearing. Their neck and front legs tend to be very strong. They capture their prey by chasing, but eat large quantities of carrion also.

The Felidae (cats) have a very short face. The clavicle is always present and often large. The incisor teeth are generally quite small. Cats stalk their prey, capture it by a quick leap, and break the neck or penetrate the skull with their sharp teeth. Cats walk on the tips of their toes, which have retractile claws.

Distribution

The distribution of the Carnivores is world-wide except for Australia and, of course, for many of the oceanic islands. The Australian wild dog, the dingo, is presumably descended from domesticated dogs brought to Australia centuries ago by the natives. The Canidae are widely distributed throughout all of the continents, but the bears are limited somewhat to the mountainous areas. The Mustelidae occur throughout the world (except Australia), as do the Felidae. However, the Viverridae are restricted to Africa and Asia, and the Hyaenidae are found only in Africa and adjacent Asia.

Habits

The habits and behavior of the Carnivores present few complexities; generally the animals are predators and thus tend to be solitary. However, some species (many of the dogs) associate in groups that hunt in an organized manner. The coatis (*Nasua* sp.), a kind of raccoon living in tropical America, forage through the forest in large herds of some 50 to 100, picking up any available food. Carnivores generally rest in some sort of a burrow or at least in a shelter among rocks or under thick bushes.

Reproduction

Reproduction among Carnivores is varied in detail. Most species have distinct and short breeding seasons in spring and bear only one litter. The number varies but is usually near four. Several physiological phenomena exist among Carnivores. Bears give birth during the prolonged winter sleep. The infant is relatively very small, and the mother stays in its warm den for several weeks. Some Canids bleed during the estrous cycle, but at the time of heat rather than at the midpoint as in primates. The bleeding is connected with ovulation. Many Mustelids have a very peculiar physiological process called delayed implantation (see Chapter 7). The ovum in various species is shed from the ovary weeks or even months before it implants in the uterine wall. Some behavior peculiarities exist. Most Carnivores have a prolonged copulation, lasting one to two hours in many species. The penis usually has some locking device to prevent separation.

Seals

A group of Carnivores called Pinnipedia has successfully invaded the ocean and become highly adapted for aquatic existence. However, the individuals must come out onto the land to breed. Seals, walrus, and sea lions have developed a number of very highly specialized adaptations. The limbs have become shortened and so completely webbed as to be transformed into broad flippers. In general, there is a tendency for the skull to be flat and heavy and for external structures such as ears and scrotum to be reduced. The teeth are simple and unspecialized, and the molars and premolars are similar in shape.

Kinds

The Otariidae include the sea lions and fur seals (Figure 2-19), and may be collectively called "eared seals." These are the least specialized of the group but are highly adapted to living in the water. However, an external ear is present and the hind limbs can rotate forward. The digits are still visible and nails are present. The teeth are small and adapted for holding the prey briefly. The Odobenidae are a highly specialized family which includes the walrus. The body is extremely large, and the head is short. The external ear is lost. The foot has five toes with a nail present. A spectacular specialization of the walrus are its canines, which have developed into long tusks used to dig up clams and

Figure 2-19. A Rookery of Fur Seals (*Callorhinus ursinus*). Note the large bulls surrounded by cows and pups. (Photograph from Fish and Wildlife Service.)

other food from the bottom. The Phocidae include the well-known typical seals (Figure 2-20). The skeleton is highly modified for aquatic life, although the digits are still visible. The hind limbs are perpetually directed towards the rear, serving as a sculling device.

This group illustrates some of the problems of phylogeny. Seals arose apparently from Carnivores, but which ones? McLaren (1960) suggests that the Otariidae and Odobenidae arose from a primitive bear and the Phocidae arose from an otter. If this ancestry is correct then the fur seals and walrus should be classified close to bears, and seals close to weasels.

Distribution and Habits

Members of this order are found in oceans throughout the world, but are most abundant in the cold regions in response to the ample supply of marine food. The habits, generally poorly known, are diversi-

Figure 2-20. The Elephant Seal (*Mirounga angustirostris*) belongs to a different family but also hauls out on land. However, it lacks the social organization of fur seals. (Photograph by G. A. Bartholomew.)

fied. Usually the individuals are gregarious, at least on land, and breed in colonies of thousands. The female gives birth on land without any special nest or any characteristic behavior.

Whales

The largest mammals, whales, belonging to the order Cetacea, are characterized by the most complete adaptation to aquatic life. They lack skin glands, clavicle, and even the external part of the ear. Hair is restricted to certain parts. The hind limbs have disappeared externally, but the pectoral girdle is strong, and the forelimbs are modified into flippers that still contain a number of bones. A striking development is the presence under the skin of a layer of fat called "blubber," that serves the function of hair in temperature regulation. The teeth of whales have become highly modified. In some forms the teeth have

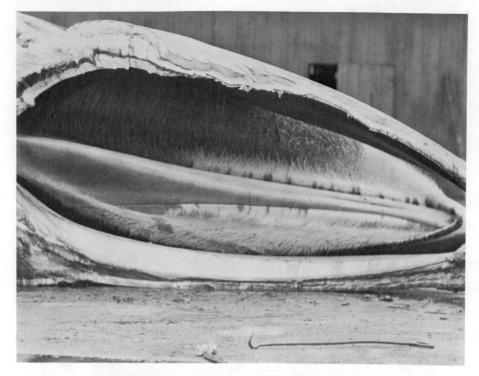

Figure 2-21. The "Whale-bone" Plates of the Finback Whale (*Balaenoptera physalis*) Shown on the Roof of the Mouth. (Photograph from Fish and Wildlife Service.)

completely disappeared, but in others the numbers have increased. Some primitive extinct whales had a conventional number, similar to those of a primitive carnivore. However, in living forms all teeth in each jaw are identical and may number as many as 50 on each side. The toothless whales have a special development of the mucous membrane of the roof of the mouth (Figure 2-21), providing horizontal plates that serve as a sieve to collect small marine food. The stomach, especially in the vegetarian whales, is huge and may have several separate pouches.

Kinds

The classification of whales into two large groups is based on presence or absence of teeth. The suborder **Odontoceti** contains many forms belonging to about six different families, including the beach whales, sperm whales, and dolphins. Members of the other suborder, **Mysticeti**, lack teeth in the adult but show rudiments of teeth in the embryo.

Three families, including gray whales and whalebone whales, are present in this suborder.

Distribution and Habits

Though whales occur throughout the oceans, they are generally found in the colder areas, presumably because of the greater food supply. In recent years the whaling industry has reduced numbers to such low levels that many species are now rare. Relatively little is known about the habits and behavior of whales apart from the observations of whaling crews. Such forms as the killer whale are actively predacious and pursue and capture fish or seals. Others, like the whalebone whales, travel in large groups, feeding on minute forms of aquatic organisms. Many of the species associate in large groups containing several hundred; other species live singly. Generally the breeding occurs within a short period during the year. The reproductive organs are abdominal in the male at all times. The female has one pair of mammae, and the ovary and uterus resemble the basic mammalian type. Gestation lasts 9 to 12 months, and lactation persists for several months. The single young is born in the water and feeds from the mammary gland of its parent while swimming.

Associated Mammals

Several peculiar orders of mammals are associated with the whales since they seem to have derived from the same basic stock. Unfortunately, the extent of relationship cannot at present be determined. One order, **Tubulidentata,** includes the aardvarks of South Africa. Because these mammals have such a highly modified skull, their ancestry is a complete enigma. They are approximately the size of a pig and feed almost exclusively on ants and termites. Their biology is poorly known.

Manatees

Another order, **Sirenia,** includes the manatees or sea cows. These aquatic mammals have large lips and on the roof of the mouth a horny structure that replaces the teeth in function. Manatees have milk teeth, but as adults they possess some 10 to 15 molars gradually superseding one another. The manatees are herbivores, feeding on vegetation in the rivers. Their stomachs have a number of very large pouches. The aquatic adaptations are quite complete since the pelvic girdle has disappeared, but the front flippers and pectoral girdle are still well formed.

The Sirenia may be classified into three families: one found in both Africa and South America, another around the Indian Ocean and Southwest Pacific, and the third found on the coasts of southern Siberia and adjacent to Japan.

Hyrax

Still another order of mammals, **Hyracoidea,** is found in southern Africa and up into Arabia. They include a peculiar form resembling rabbits in some characters. The toes are reduced in number. The teeth, somewhat resembling those of a horse, are clearly bunodont for a vegetarian or omnivorous diet. The testes are intra-abdominal.

Elephants

Another group of mammals is associated with these orders. The elephants, **Proboscidia,** are well known by their enormous size. The skeleton is extremely heavy to support the immense body on land. The skull is especially large but contains a relatively small brain. The two tusks are the upper incisor teeth of the adult. The second incisor on each side is present only in the young animal and soon disappears. The molar teeth show a peculiar development consisting of a successive breaking down of the front side with advancement of the tooth towards the front. Each tooth has a number of horizontal plates that are gradually broken off. Thus, an elephant's age can be roughly estimated by the extent of wear and disappearance first of the premolars and then of the molars. The classification of the living members groups all the forms into one family, Elephantidae. Some fossil forms belong to other groups. The habits and behavior of elephants are known in a general way. They feed on herbaceous material, either browse or herbs. The individuals live in herds containing members of both sexes and all ages. Reproduction presents no unusual features. The testes remain within the abdomen at all times. The penis is located relatively far forward in the body. The uterus has two horns, but the embryo implants at their junction. The elephants have no distinct breeding season.

Odd-toed Ungulates

A large order of mammals, **Perissodactyla,** contains the tapirs, rhinocerotes, and horses. This group in ancient times was far more abundant than at present. The outstanding characteristic is that the animals have become specialized for running, and the horse has all of the toes except the middle one reduced. This terminates in a hoof. The loss of toes was progressive, and presents an excellent example of stages in evolution. The bones of the feet and girdles have been highly modified in relation to running. The stomach is simple, even though the animals are primarily vegetarian.

Kinds

The classification separates the more primitive forms from the advanced. The suborder **Ceratomorpha** includes the tapirs and rhinocerotes. An example of primitive character is the presence in tapirs of four toes on the front feet and three on the hind feet. Tapirs are large forms living in tropical areas of America and of Malaya. They have a short proboscis on the nose. Their teeth are adapted for a diet of vegetation. They are primarily browsers. Other members of this suborder are the four genera of rhinoceros that differ from tapirs in having only three toes on each front foot. The very heavy body is similar to an elephant's in its structure. The teeth have developed grinding surfaces, and the number of incisor teeth vary with the different genera, some of which lack the uppers entirely. The horn of the rhinoceros is an elaboration into a solid structure of the bone on the top of the head.

The advanced group, **Hippomorpha,** in the order includes horses, asses, and zebras. These animals have carried the adaptation for running to the ultimate, and have very long legs and only one toe on each foot. Although at one time there were many different species of horses, at the present time there is even doubt that any of the so-called wild horses are really a wild species, but are thoroughly mixed perhaps with liberated domesticated horses. There are, however, a number of genera of wild asses in Asia and of zebras in Africa.

Habits

This order contains animals with rather diverse habits, especially when one considers the extinct forms that are well known. However, they all are large in size and all are herbivorous. Members of the horse suborder, especially, tend to travel in herds. The reproduction of the wild forms is poorly known, but no striking anatomical peculiarities occur. Generally only one offspring is born.

Rabbits

A relatively small but important order of mammals, **Lagomorpha,** includes rabbits and hares. Although these forms superficially resemble rodents, they have two pairs of upper incisors. An important distinction is that the jaw movements while chewing are transverse rather than rotary, as in the case of the rodents. The Lagomorphs are all short-tailed forms that have long hind legs. A striking character in the skull is the large size of the orbitosphenoid bone. The rabbits can be divided into two groups: a large family, **Leporidae,** includes typical rabbits and hares; the other family, **Ochotonidae,** includes a relict form called pika (*Ochotona princeps*). This primitive form is found in western North America, in Siberia, and in the Himalayan region. Typical rabbits are found throughout the Northern Hemisphere and South America. The European rabbit (*Oryctolagus cuniculus*) has been domesticated for food and is widely used for biological research. It has been liberated in many such areas as Australia, and causes extensive damage. Rabbits are exclusively herbivores, feeding on bark, buds, and grasses. Most forms feed principally at night and spend the day in burrows or hidden under heavy vegetation. Some forms are solitary, but others live in colonies consisting of 10 to 20 individuals. Reproduction of rabbits has been studied rather extensively both in the laboratory and in nature.

Even-toed Ungulates

Many of our best-known mammals—cattle, deer, sheep, pigs, and goats—belong to a large group, **Artiodactyla,** or even-toed mammals. The distinguishing feature is the development of a third and fourth toe into a distinct structure adapted for running. In addition, many detailed characters in the arrangement of the supporting bones for these toes separate the Artiodactyla from other mammals. Another feature is the frequent presence of glands on the legs or about the eyes. Generally, Artiodactyls are long-legged mammals, although the more primitive forms such as pigs have not progressed very far in this direction. Several groups of Artiodactyls have developed horns or antlers varying considerably in detail. Pigs lack horns. Deer have developed a special type of antler generally shed each year. The cattle group and sheep have horns that are not shed. Still a third type occurs in the prong-horned antelope whose horns consist of a bony core and an outer layer shed each year. These mammals are herbivores, and consequently have large intestines and stomachs to accommodate the great quantities of food material they ingest. In the most evolved forms, the ruminants, the stomach may be subdivided into various parts, each having a specific function for digestion. The most highly developed stomach has four parts and occurs in cattle, deer, camels, and others (see Chapter 4). In contrast, the more primitive Artiodactyls have a stomach with only a rudimentary indication of division in two parts. The teeth of Artiodactyls vary considerably in number, but generally there is a reduction of the front teeth. In some cases the canine is very large, but in others it is completely lost. The evolution of the molar teeth follows a definite sequence in the various forms. Presumably, the most primitive tooth was rather square with four cusps at the corners. In the hippopotamus, these cusps have become flattened, and in pigs the teeth retain their primitive cusps but add cusps in the center. In the most evolved kinds, the surface of the cusps becomes elongate fore and aft, providing an excellent grinding surface when the jaws move laterally.

Kinds

The classification of this large group presents a number of difficulties simply because there are so many species. The most primitive suborder, the **Suiformes,** is composed of two families. The Hippopotamidae includes the large, primitive, well-known hippopotamus. Only two species exist and are characterized by huge lungs and by eyes on top of the head adapted for seeing when the animal is largely submerged. A primitive character is the presence of four toes on each foot. The stomach is enormous and divided into poorly defined sections. The incisors are almost horizontal, permitting the animal to root out aquatic vegetation. The other family, the Suidae, includes eight genera of wild pigs, two of them living in the New World. They are characterized by a long snout; and, although there are four toes, only two of them are functional on each forefoot. Pigs are omnivores, but have a very large stomach. The canine teeth, especially the uppers, may be greatly enlarged. In some forms the upper canines curve upward and may be a formidable defense weapon, six to ten inches long.

The other big division of the Artiodactyla includes the ruminants. The most primitive family, Camelidae, is characterized by high separations of the bones of the two toes. Camels have a special stomach able to conserve water in the rumen. In some camels the canines are sharp. The camels of Africa and Asia are widely used for domestic purposes.

In addition, a less-well-known group of camels lives in the Andes. The guanaco (*Lama guanaco*) and the vicuña (*Vicugna vicugna*) (Figure 2-22) are primitive forms that presumably entered South America when the bridge at Panama was open in Eocene times. Two additional species of camels present interesting examples of domestication: the llama (*L. glama*) has been specialized as a beast of burden, and the alpaca (*L. pacos*) provides wool. Camels are often placed in a separate suborder called Tylopoda.

The largest group of ruminants in number of species, the Cervidae, includes many different kinds of deer. The toes are small and delicate,

Figure 2-22. Vicuña (*Vicugna vicugna*) Grazing in Natural Habitat. (Photograph by Carl Koford.)

and the limbs excellently adapted for running. A spectacular development is the pair of antlers usually found in the male. These bony structures grow out from the top of the head annually, and are covered during growth by a layer of skin called the "velvet." At maturity the velvet dries and peels off, and eventually after the breeding season the entire antler falls off. In most deer the canine resembles an incisor, but in some forms an upper canine becomes a tusk. Some 20 genera are found throughout the world.

Another group of ruminants includes the prong-horned antelopes (Antilocapridae) found only in the western plains of North America. The horns are peculiar in that they consist of a bony core with a covering that is lost each year. Pronghorns are eminently adapted for high speed on the plains.

The most abundant group of Artiodactyla are the Bovidae, containing cattle, goats, and many African and Asian antelopes. This immense group includes some 52 genera and perhaps 100 species. Their abundance on the plains of the world was spectacular. The bison, of course, roamed the western area in herds numbering many millions; and the antelope and gazelles of the African plains still number hundreds of thousands.

The final family, the Giraffidae, includes two remnant forms in Africa. The family is technically separated from other Artiodactyla by a number of skull characters. The long neck is particularly spectacular. As in deer, the lower canine resembles an incisor. A small type of giraffe, the okapi, was found recently in the dense jungles of the Congo. It has a long and prehensile tongue. The horns of the giraffes are only small bumps on the head.

Distribution

The distribution of this large order is nearly world-wide, although many forms are restricted to limited areas. The cattle tribes found primarily at the extremities of the continents are one of several examples of peripheral distribution. The camels occurring in Africa and South America are examples of disjunct distribution. Generally, the more primitive forms live in the forests, and the more advanced forms live in large groups on the open plains.

Habits

The habits and behavior of this large assemblage are surprisingly uniform. Almost all are herbivores, though some (such as pigs), eat a wide variety of foods. To obtain their food they must go out into the open where there is danger of attack by carnivores. Presumably the habit of bolting a large quantity of herbivorous food and retiring to shelter for chewing the cud has developed in part as a protective device against predators and in part as a protection against the sun. Artiodactyls are eminently social and found generally in small or large groups. Even the primitive forms like pigs go in herds of from 10 to 200, depending on the species. The social organization of the immense herds of buffalo and of South African ruminants has hardly been examined. It is, however, clear that a social rank exists. Perhaps, also in connection with the herbivorous diet, is the development of migratory habits. Bison, a number of Old World antelope, and many other forms travel great distances from season to season following the rains and the green vegetation.

Reproduction

The reproductive organs present no spectacular developments. The testes are scrotal, but in many forms regress into the abdomen in the nonbreeding season. The female has one or two pairs of mammae. The breeding season is generally in the fall. A gestation period of approximately six to ten months allows the calf to be born at the time of maximum green feed. Some forms (pigs) have several breeding periods during the year, although apparently there is a maximum production in the spring. Wild pigs may produce as many as eight to ten young, deer often produce twins, but bison and most other forms have only one offspring at a time.

REFERENCES ON KINDS OF MAMMALS

General

Allen, Glover M. 1942. Extinct and vanishing mammals of the Western Hemisphere. Amer. Comm. Intern. Wildl. Prot. Spec. Pub. 11: 1-620.

Baumann, F. 1949. Die freilebenden Säugetiere der Schweiz. Hans Huber (Bern). 492 pp.

Bourliere, D. F. 1951. Vie et moeurs des mammifères. Payot (Paris). 250 pp.

Burt, W. H. 1952. A Field Guide to the Mammals. New York, Houghton Mifflin Co. 200 pp.

Burt, W. H. 1957. The Mammals of the Great Lakes Region. Univ. Mich. Press. 246 pp.

Carter, T. D., J. E. Hill, and G. H. H. Tate. 1945. Mammals of the Pacific World. New York, The Macmillan Co. 227 pp.

Eadie, W. Robert. 1954. Animal Control in Field, Farm and Forest. New York, The Macmillan Co. 257 pp.

Flerov, K. K. 1952. Fauna of USSR—Mammals. Acad. Sci. USSR (Translation 1960 by Nat. Sci. Found.). 257 pp.

Grassé, Pierre-P. 1955. Mammifères. In: Traite de Zool. 17(1): 1-1170, 17(2): 1171-2300.

Hall, Raymond, and Keith R. Kelson. 1959. The Mammals of North America. New York, Ronald Press Co. 2 vols. 1083 pp.

Hamilton, W. J., Jr. 1939. American Mammals. New York, McGraw-Hill Book Co. 434 pp.

Hamilton, W. J., Jr. 1955. Mammalogy in North America. In: A Century of Progress in the Natural Sciences. 1853-1953. Calif. Acad. Sci.: 661-688.

Harper, Francis. 1945. Extinct and vanishing mammals of the old world. Amer. Comm. Internat. Wildl. Protection 12: 1-850.

Ingles, Lloyd Glenn. 1947. Mammals of California. Stanford Univ. Press. 258 pp.

Jackson, H. H. T. 1961. Mammals of Wisconsin. Univ. Wisc. Press. 504 pp.

Mathews, L. Harrison. 1960. British Mammals. Collins (London). 410 pp.

Mayr, Ernest, E. Gordon Linsley, and Robert L. Usinger. 1953. Methods and Principles of Systematic Zoology. New York, McGraw-Hill Book Co. 328 pp.

Miller, Gerrit S., and Remington Kellogg. 1955. List of North American Recent Mammals. Bull. U. S. Nat. Mus. 205: 1-954.

Moore, Clifford B. 1953. Ways of Mammals in Fact and Fancy. New York, Ronald Press Co. 273 pp.

Ognew, Sergej I. 1959. Säugetiere und ihre Welt. Akademie-Verlag (Berlin). 362 pp.

Palmer, Ralph S. 1954. The Mammal Guide. New York, Doubleday and Co., Inc. 384 pp.

Roberts, Austin. 1951. The Mammals of South Africa. Central News Agency. 701 pp.

Seton, Ernest Thompson. 1937. Lives of Game Animals. Vol. I. Cats, Wolves, and Foxes. 640 pp. Vol. II. Bears, Coons, Badgers, Skunks and Weasels. 746 pp. Vol. III. Hoofed Animals. 780 pp. Vol. IV. Rodents, etc. 949 pp. Lit. Guild America (New York).

Simpson, G. G. 1945. The principles of classification and a classification of mammals. Bull. Amer. Mus. Nat. Hist. 85: 1-350.

Simpson, G. G. 1961. Principles of Animal Taxonomy. Columbia Univ. Press. 247 pp.

Tate, G. H. H. 1947. Mammals of Eastern Asia. New York, The Macmillan Co. 366 pp.

Troughton, Ellis. 1941. Furred Animals of Australia. Angus and Robertson. 374 pp.

Weber, Max. 1927-28. Die Säugetiere (Zweite Auflage). I. Anatomischer Teil 1-444. II. Systematischer Teil 1-898. Gustav Fischer (Jena).

Wender, Leo. 1949. Animals Encyclopaedia. Mammals. New York, Oxford Univ. Press: 1-266.

Wodzicki, K. A. 1949. Introduced mammals of New Zealand. Bull. Dept. Sci. and Indust. Res. 98: 1-255.

Young, J. Z. 1957. The Life of Mammals. Oxford Univ. Press. 820 pp.

Rodents

Allen, Durward. 1943. Michigan fox squirrel management. Michigan, Dept. Conserv. Pub. 100: 1-404.

Ellerman, J. R. 1940-41, 49. The families and genera of living rodents. I. Rodents other than Muridae. 689 pp. II. Family Muridae. 690 pp. III. Additions and corrections. 210 pp. The British Museum.

Linsdale, Jean M. 1946. The California Ground Squirrel. Univ. Calif. Press. 457 pp.

Linsdale, Jean M., and L. P. Tevis. 1951. The Dusky-footed Wood Rat. Univ. Calif. Press. 664 pp.

O'Neil, Ted. 1949. The muskrat in the Louisiana Coastal Marshes. New Orleans, Louisiana Dept. Wildl. and Fish. 152 pp.

Schaub, S. 1953. La trigonodontie des Rongeurs simplicidentes. Ann. Paleont. 39: 29-57.

Carnivores

Braestrup, F. W. 1941. A study of the arctic fox in Greenland. Meddelelser Om Gronland. 131(4): 1-101.

Grinnell, Joseph, J. S. Dixon, and Jean M. Linsdale. 1937. Fur-bearing Mammals of California. Univ. Calif. Press. 777 pp. (2 vols).

Neal, Ernest. 1948. The Badger. New Naturalist Series. 176 pp.

Scheffer, Victor B. 1958. Seals, Sea Lions, and Walruses. Stanford Univ. Press. 179 pp.

Storer, Tracy I., and Lloyd P. Tevis, Jr. 1955. California Grizzley. Univ. Calif. Press. 335 pp.

Whitney, Leon F., and Acil B. Underwood. 1952. The Raccoon. Orange, Conn., Prac. Sci. Pub. Co. 177 pp.

Young, Stanley P. 1958. The Bobcat of North America. Wildl. Manag. Inst. 193 pp.

Young, Stanley P., and E. S. Goldman. 1944. The Wolves in North America. American Wildlife Institute. 636 pp.

Young, S. P., and H. H. T. Jackson. 1951. The Clever Coyote. Wildl. Manag. Inst. 411 pp.

Ungulates

Buechner, Helmut K. 1950. Life history, ecology, and range use of the pronghorn antelope in Trans-Pecos Texas. Am. Midl. Nat. 43(2): 257-354.

Darling, F. F. 1937. A Herd of Red Deer. Oxford Univ. Press. 215 pp.

Einarsen, Arthur S. 1948. The Pronghorn Antelope and its Management. Wildl. Manag. Inst. 238 pp.

Linsdale, Jean M., and P. Q. Tomich. 1953. A Herd of Mule Deer. Univ. Calif. Press. 567 pp.

Peterson, Randolph L. 1955. The North American Moose. Univ. Toronto Press. 280 pp.

Roe, Frank Gilbert. 1951. The North American Buffalo. Univ. Toronto Press. 957 pp.

Taylor, Walter P. (editor). 1956. The Deer in North America. Wildl. Manag. Inst. 668 pp.

Other Orders

Allen, Glover M. 1939. Bats. Harvard Univ. Press. 368 pp.

Griffin, Donald R. 1958. Listening in the Dark. Yale Univ. Press. 413 pp.

Hartman, Carl G. 1952. Possums. Univ. Texas Press. 174 pp.

Hill, W. C. Osman. 1953. Primates—Comparative Anatomy and Taxonomy. I. Strepsirhini. 798 pp. II. Haplorhini (Tarsioidea). 347 pp. III. Pithecoidae (Platyrhini). 354 pp. IV. Cebidae (Part A). 523 pp. Interscience Pub., Inc. (New York).

McLaren, I. 1960. Are the Pinnipedia biphyletic? Syst. Zool. 9(1): 18-28.

Thompson, Harry V. 1956. The Rabbit. Collins (London). 240 pp.

chapter three

THE NATURE OF ADAPTATION
AND EVOLUTION

THE PHYSIOLOGICAL PROCESSES of the mammal function within a relatively narrow range of internal environmental conditions. Homeostasis or constancy of the internal environment is maintained by physiological adjustments on the part of the individual. Those adjustments which occur within a period of one life cycle are called physiological or behavioral adaptations, while those which require several generations to develop are termed evolution. Through adaptation, the individual, population, or species continues to survive and reproduce while being a part of a fluctuating physical and biological system.

Adaptation implies a positive or useful response permitting greater survival in a changing environment. Environmental variation appears to be ordered in a continuum. Thus there are minute or hourly changes, daily variations (as in light, temperature, and moisture), and annual variations of regular and irregular periodicity, as well as regular large-scale changes (such as the advance and retreat of the Pleistocene ice sheets) and irregular catastrophes (such as volcanic eruptions). Since the time required by mammals to respond parallels this continuum, we can categorize adaptation according to a time scale (Table 3-1).

Not all types of environmental variation are equally significant to mammals. Among the variables which have been shown to be most important are food, temperature, water, defense, and social interactions. Adaptation to each of these variables can be studied directly in living mammals. However, for fossil forms we must use the opposite approach. For these, only the morphological result of the adaptations persists in

TABLE 3-1.   Time of Response to Environmental Variation *

Reaction	Time
Immediate Response	minutes
Sense organ stimulation	
Shock-type reaction	
Stabilized-state Response	hours
Fluctuations with environment	
Rate regulation	
Regulation of nonspecific disturbance	
Acclimation	days to weeks
Morphological Adaptation	days to weeks
Behavioral Transmission	few generations
Evolutionary Adaptation	many generations
Selection of mutants	
Formation of races and ecotypes	
Reproductive isolation	
Species formation	

* Adapted from Prosser, 1958.

the skeletal remains, and we are required to speculate about the environmental conditions responsible for the adaptations. To do this, we assume that the physiology and ecology of fossil mammals were closely similar to those of their living relatives.

In this chapter we will be concerned with the underlying basis for adaptation at the various levels of the time continuum. In the following several chapters specific mechanisms, examples, and principles of adaptation will be presented.

GENERAL PRINCIPLES OF ADJUSTMENT

In the individual, the neural and endocrine systems control the internal environment. An external disturbance to the body is met by adjustments which act to maintain internal homeostasis. These adjustments are generally of two forms, open control and closed-sequence control.

Open Control

Open control acts in the following manner (Ashby, 1956): a disturbance, D, acts through some dynamic system, P, on a process, organism, or species, A. A has other dynamic systems, R, acting as regulators which can be coupled to P and limit the variability from D, as shown in the diagram below:

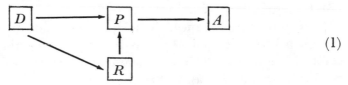

$$(1)$$

Another form that this type of control may take is for P to be responsive to some outside regulator, R, so that the direct action of D on A is reduced:

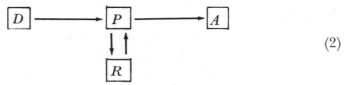

$$(2)$$

In this type of control system the defense against disturbance is that of a gambler playing the odds. That is, a regulator of limited capacity is used to handle variety within a certain fixed range of D. If D exceeds this range, A, or a certain number of A's, die.

Examples: Control of Coat Color and Breeding Cycle

Many different biological phenomena are regulated by the open-control type system. One process which has been studied in considerable detail and which provides an example of this system is the control of coat color in the varying or snowshoe hare (*Lepus americanus*). In this mammal the coat is brown during the late spring, summer, and early fall, but changes to a pure white in winter. Presumably this adaptation protects the hare against predation, although there may be other adaptive values for the color change. Through a series of experiments, Lyman (1943) showed that the change of color through molting and replacement of hair is controlled by the amount of light received by these mammals. The decreasing length of day in the fall triggers the molt cycle, and the brown coat is quickly replaced by the winter coat. In the spring, increasing daylight stimulates the molt from white to brown. Lyman also showed that the eyes were the main receptors of the stimulus. Length of day has also been shown to regulate the molt cycle in the ferret (*Putorius vulgaris*), mink (*Mustela vison*), and other weasels (Bissonnette and Wilson, 1939; Bissonnette and Bailey, 1944).

In addition, illumination regulates the breeding cycle in the field mouse (*Microtus agrestis*) (Baker and Ransom, 1932) and the ferret (Bissonnette, 1932).

In each of these instances the adaptation is not to the light *per se* as the disturbance. That is, light is not *directly* significant to the coat-color or breeding cycle. The fundamental disturbance here is probably predation and, in the case of breeding, adverse climatic conditions. One might expect that the species would respond to the presence of snow or green food and warm weather directly. However, the processes of coat-color change and breeding are expensive in terms of time and energy—they cannot be immediate responses—and it is necessary for the species to "anticipate" the change in the environment. The changing length of day is quite regular and has been employed as the regulator in these instances. Therefore, the control of coat color described here follows the form of the open-control system shown in diagram (2). Control is geared to average conditions, and if the snowfall is earlier than normal the brown-colored hare may be susceptible to predation. Similarly, if the snowfall is late the white-colored hare may also be subject to predation. Nevertheless, on the average, the control is sufficiently precise for the species to survive.

In summary, the open system of control is sufficiently effective for survival in many circumstances, but it has several obvious shortcomings. First, it can only deal with standard conditions, and second, the regulation requires careful calibration. In the case of the control of coat color, length of day provides such conditions; however, in many other processes another type of control may be more effective.

Closed-sequence Control

Closed-sequence regulation avoids the shortcomings of the open system, is more sophisticated, and seemingly more effective. Other names given to this type of control—error control or feedback regulation—indicate the method by which adjustment is achieved. When D produces through P a fluctuation in A, A transmits information to R which acts on P to control the error in A, as below:

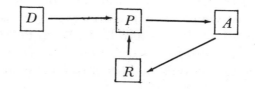

(3)

Control cannot be perfect in this system, since error is used to bring about the regulation; the objective is to make the error as small as possible.

In addition, there is a time lag in sending information from A through R to P. Therefore, if P—affected by D— oscillates, then A will

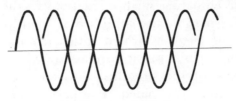

1. Continuous oscillation

2. Damped oscillation

3. Amplified oscillation

Figure 3-1. Types of Oscillation in Three Feedback Systems. First, continuous oscillation when feedback is equal and opposed to its error. Second, damped oscillation when feedback is less than, and opposed to, the error. Third, amplified oscillation when feedback is greater than, and opposed to, the error.

also oscillate, but not simultaneously or necessarily in the same way. The oscillation will have the same frequency, however. Time lag usually increases with frequency; the faster D varies, the farther A falls behind. In a simple linear system, if the feedback is equal in strength to the original oscillation and the frequency of the time lag is one-half a period of oscillation, there will be a continuous, steady oscillation which maintains itself (Figure 3-1). However, if the feedback is smaller and opposed to the oscillation, the disturbance in the system will be reduced or damped. Conversely, if the feedback is greater and opposed to the oscillation, the disturbance will be amplified (Figure 3-1).

For accurate control the feedback must be increased—but without simultaneously accentuating small oscillations in the system. One way that this objective may be accomplished is to introduce a time-lead mechanism into the feedback which anticipates the time lag. In this system, maximum response of the regulation occurs slightly before the maximum response of the stimulus; thus an overshoot in response or excessive oscillation is avoided. The pattern of nerve response to stimulation of a sense organ operates in this anticipatory manner.

This discussion of regulation of a disturbance through a feedback process applies mainly to linear systems in which effects are directly proportional to causes. Many systems in nature are not linear, and in these, control is a more complex process than that described above. Nevertheless, unless departure from linearity is very large or of some special kind, the general principle of feedback control applies.

An Example: The Anterior Pituitary-Adrenal Cortex System

The anterior pituitary-adrenal cortex feedback system is of basic importance in the ability of the individual mammal to adapt to disturbance. Both specific disturbance (such as injury to a limb) and non-specific disturbance (excessive social interaction) appear to operate in part through this system of control. It has also been used in an explanation of the control of mammal populations (see Christian, 1959, and others). Although the system is not yet completely understood, the main outlines seem clear and may be summarized as follows: A disturbance penetrates the normal defenses of the organism to reach the specific or nonspecific targets. Damage to the target may produce local inflammation, and a stimulus is then sent directly to the anterior pituitary (Figure 3-2). The route which the stimulus follows is not completely understood; it may be through a discharge of a biochemical material into the blood stream, or through a neural stimulus, or both. In addition, the disturbance may act directly upon the anterior pituitary (Figure 3-2). The stimulation of the anterior pituitary results in the release of adrenocorticotrophic hormone (ACTH). The ACTH acts on the adrenal cortex, stimulating it to release two types of hormones. The first are glucocorticoid hormones, such as hydrocortisone and cortisone, which

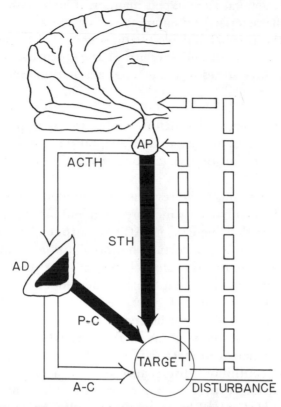

Figure 3-2. Diagram of the Anterior Pituitary-Adrenal Cortex Feedback System. A disturbance acts on the anterior pituitary either directly or through the target; the anterior pituitary, in turn, reacts on the target directly or through the adrenal gland. AP indicates anterior pituitary, AD indicates adrenal gland. For other abbreviations see text. (Redrawn from Munday, 1961, after Rosch, 1958.)

have an anti-inflammation action (A-C, Figure 3-2). The second are mineralocorticoid hormones which have an inflammatory action (P-C, Figure 3-2). The influence of conditioning in this system by such factors as age, nutrition, and so forth, may be extremely important but is poorly understood at present.

From this discussion it is clear that the anterior pituitary-adrenal cortex feedback system permits a graded response to a variety of disturbances. Indeed, it was this nature of the mechanism which led Selye (1950) to formulate his concept of the adaptation syndrome. Selye found that mammals responded to such stimuli as infection, cold, fatigue, etc., in a specific and a general stereotyped manner. The general, nonspecific response was characterized by enlargement of the adrenal cortex and involution of the thymus and lymphatic organs. Selye suggested that, depending on the length and severity of the disturbance, an animal passed through three stages in the general adaptation syndrome. These stages were:

(1) The alarm stage before adaptation is acquired.
(2) The resistance stage when adaptation is maximal.
(3) The exhaustion stage when adaptation is lost.

First, in the alarm stage, the response to a sudden, temporary period of stress results in a temporarily increased demand for cortical hormones which causes a sudden increase in ACTH output. This is associated with a rapid decrease in the cortical hormone and a slight increase in adrenal size. Response to a very slow change in the environment results in a gradual increase in demand for cortical hormones. There is a gradually increased output of ACTH, associated with a gradual increase in the size of the adrenal. Cortical hormones remain at a constant level, indicating that new secretory units in the adrenal cortex can be produced at a rate sufficient to meet the demands.

With intense, continuous disturbance there is a very great and continuous demand for cortical hormones, resulting in a maximum production of ACTH. Cortical hormones are rapidly depleted and do not recover normal levels, even though the adrenal increases in size. If these mechanisms are sufficient to permit adaptation, as in the resistance phase, the demand for cortical hormone is reduced and a quantity is accumulated in the overexpanded gland. Eventually there is a return to the condition existing before the disturbance.

When the pituitary is in maximum production it may be incapable of increasing production to meet added disturbance, and thus death may occur. In this type of death, the animal characteristically shows extreme extension of the neck and limbs, low liver glycogen, gastric ulcers, and lesions.

The pituitary also produces other hormones, including lactogenic and gonadotrophic hormones. When an animal is subjected to intense stress resulting in maximum production of ACTH, the pituitary may not be able to continue normal production of the other hormones. Thus reproduction, lactation, and growth may be adversely affected. Generally the effect of one stress is to reduce the resistance of the organism to additional stress.

The adaptation to nonspecific disturbances, and the suggested explanation of the side effects on reproduction and growth, have made the general adaptation syndrome attractive to population ecologists. This summary cannot discuss the problems of application of the theory to natural populations. Suffice it to say that this application has a number of critics (see Munday, 1961).

The open-control and the closed-sequence control systems underlie the process of adaptation. We will now consider them in relation to the time sequence of adaptational response.

TIME SCALE OF ADAPTATION

Physiological and Behavioral Adaptations

Immediate Response

Immediate response (Table 3-1) may be a simple reflex process in which the animal withdraws instantaneously from a toxic or unfavorable material or situation. Where a rapid response is required, the nervous system is employed as the control mechanism, since nerve impulses can move with a speed of several hundred feet per second. In processes regulated by hormones, the response cannot begin until the hormones reach the target via the blood stream, requiring at least a fraction of a minute.

Probably the simplest example of immediate response is the spinal reflex. A stimulus is sent from the receptors through the sensory nerves toward the spinal cord, and then through the dorsal root ganglion to the cord where it connects with other neurons. These send impulses through the ventral root, containing the motor fibers, and then out through the motor nerve to the end organ.

Behavioral responses such as occur when individuals meet one another in the social group or when an individual or a herd meets a predator, may also be of this immediate-response type.

The shock reaction is another form in which we often observe a momentary oscillation or overshoot before adaptation is achieved. For example, when a mammal is quickly moved from a cold to a hot environment, for a short period oxygen consumption often increases to a level higher than that at the adaptation level. This overshoot in oxygen consumption is due to a time-lag in the system of feedback regulation. Depending on the process, the immediate response may be either open- or closed-sequence control.

Stabilized-State Response

Following the immediate response in the time continuum is the stabilized-state response, which takes place in several hours. There are two patterns of the stabilized adjustment. First, adjustments may conform to fluctuations in the environment. Temperature regulation in poikilotherms and, among the mammals, in Monotremes, as well as in the young of many species, follows this pattern. Adaptations to food and social conditions are also often of this type. Second, a regulatory process may change with, but does not conform to, environmental fluctuation. Stabilization of the internal environment may be achieved through feedback control—regulation of body temperature in most adult mammals is of this nature.

Acclimation

The process of acclimation is a further step in the adaptation time sequence. Acclimation refers to acquired changes in an animal produced by the alteration of an environmental factor, and resulting in a shift of the tolerance limits to variations in the internal environment or in the critical limits in the external environment where regulation fails. Mammals may become acclimated to a single environmental factor or to a complex of factors.

One example of this type of adaptation is the influence of acclimation on the survival of mammals in relation to change of temperature. Hart (1953) subjected groups of four separate species of rodents to a series of different temperatures, ranging from $-10°$ to $30°$C, for a minimum of seven weeks. Subsamples were then subjected to low temperatures which killed the animals in times ranging from 20 to 5000 minutes. The influence of prior exposure to a certain temperature on the average time for all the animals to die was then determined (Figure 3-3). Hart found that the increase in resistance temperature (the lethal temperature corresponding to the average time for the group to die) for the same decrease in acclimation temperature was not uniform. The response to acclimation was greatest at the highest acclimation temperature and decreased progressively until a lower limit to acclimation was reached at 0 to $-10°$C.

Morphological adaptations are in the same time sequence as accli-

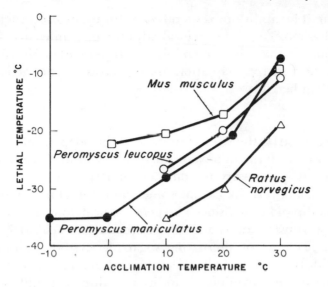

Figure 3-3. Response of Four Groups of Rodents to Low Temperature. The rodents were held at the acclimation temperature for seven or more weeks, then were subjected to low temperatures. That temperature at which all the experimental group died in 200 minutes, is called the lethal temperature. Note that the response to acclimation is greatest at the higher temperatures. (Redrawn from Hart, 1953.)

mation. While the ability to respond to disturbance morphologically is inherited, the morphological adaptation is induced by the environment. An example of this type of adjustment is the change in coat color or the thickness of the coat with season discussed earlier.

Behavioral Transmission

Through longer periods of time—several generations—adaptive trends may be maintained and transmitted by nongenetic means. In many cases behavioral adaptation appears to follow this pattern. Some behavior is innate or genetically determined; other behavior is learned, and may be transmitted from one generation to another. It may be extremely difficult to determine if a certain type of behavior is innate or learned; however, in any case, the underlying ability to *respond* to a specific learning experience is inherited.

Evolutionary Adaptations

Adaptation through spans of time longer than a few generations takes place at the level of the population, and is called evolutionary adaptation. The ability to respond to a disturbance through morphological, physiological, or behavioral adjustment is inherited. There are genetic limits to the ability of an individual to regulate the disturbance, and thus the basis of adaptation and evolution is the gene, the unit of Mendelian heredity.

The Gene

The genes carry the information used in adaptation at this time level. In order to form an idea of the quantity of information available for control, it is necessary to consider the structure of the gene. The genes are contained in chromosomes and therefore exist in pairs (alleles) in diploid organisms. The genes appear to consist of a double helix of polynucleotide chains—deoxyribonucleic acid (DNA). These chains are made up of alternating sugar (deoxyribose) and phosphate groups with two purine bases, adenine and guanine, and two pyrimidines, cytosine and thymine. In addition, a third pyrimidine, 5-methyl cytosine, may sometimes be present. The two chains of the helix are held together between their purine and pyrimidine bases by hydrogen bonds, and the bases are paired off with each other according to a definite rule: adenine in one chain is always connected by a hydrogen bond to thymine in the other, and guanine to cytosine or 5-methyl cytosine. Therefore the helix, when separated into two chains and placed in an environment containing purine or pyrimidine bases, acts as a template for the formation of identical chains.

Since the gene is the informational unit of the DNA molecule, the genetic information is coded in a language of four letters—the four nucleotide bases. A gene may contain hundreds or thousands of linearly arranged nucleotides, and the variety of the genetic information can be enormous. For instance, if the gene covered a section of the polynucleotide with only ten nucleotide pairs, the possible variations of four letters in a ten-letter word 4^{10} or 1,048,576 (Dobzhansky, 1959).

Segregation and Recombination

In mammals, the genetic information is transferred to the new generation through the processes of segregation and recombination. When the gametes are formed, the two genes of a chromosome pair segregate into sister gametes, and therefore each gamete contains only one gene for each character. Of course, there are many genes on each chromosome. The genes are then recombined through fertilization. When the egg is fertilized one set of genes comes from each parent. If two genes at a particular location on the chromosome are identical (homozygous) the original character will reappear in the offspring. However, if the gene pair is unlike (heterozygous), one gene may be dominant and be expressed to the exclusion of the other; the two genes may together produce a trait intermediate to the two pure types; or, finally, they may produce a trait unlike the homozygous or parental types. However, the genes are not in any way diluted in the heterozygous condition, since if they later become recombined in a homozygous condition the original character will reappear.

Since theoretically any individual sperm has an equal chance of fertilizing an egg (except in certain cases of interbreeding hybrids), the expected ratio of traits in a sample of offspring can be calculated. Thus, the offspring of two hybrids (Aa) would include 25 per cent homozygous dominant (AA), 25 per cent homozygous recessive (aa), and 50 per cent heterozygous (Aa). Each gene segregates independently of the others, and the number of phenotypes obtained when A is completely dominant to a is 2^n, where n is the number of gene pairs on different chromosomes being considered. However, if the cross involves gene pairs located on the same chromosome, the genes may be linked together so that the number of recombinations would be like a monohybrid cross. In other instances, blocks of genes may be exchanged between homologous chromosomes (crossing over) so that recombination of the gene pairs would arise. Through these processes the frequency of gene distribution in a random-mating population of diploid individuals would be expected eventually to come to equilibrium. Let us now consider some of the factors which act to change gene frequencies and lead to evolution.

Mutation

Mutation, or change of the gene to a permanently inheritable allele, is the ultimate source of evolution. In most instances chance appears to determine whether or not an individual gene will mutate within its particular physical and chemical capabilities. However, in certain cases, environmental factors such as high temperature and ionizing radiation appear to induce mutation. In addition to individual gene mutation, the chromosomes themselves may be rearranged in various ways, resulting in an alteration in the expression of the genes as a result of a phenomenon called a "position effect." In general, five different types of chromosomal rearrangements are recognized. First, a segment of a chromosome may be lost. Second, a segment of a chromosome may be repeated, possibly by unequal crossing-over. Third, a segment of the chromosome may be inverted or reversed. An inversion can occur if a chromosome is broken, as in a radiation experiment, and reheals in a reversed fashion. Fourth, a broken segment could be transferred within the chromosome; this is called transposition. Finally, in translocation, a segment of a chromosome may be transferred to a nonhomologous chromosome.

The rate at which mutation occurs is usually quite low. Lush (1945) states that in general mutation rates observed in the laboratory under otherwise natural conditions fall between one mutation of each gene in 100,000, to one in 1,000,000 generations. However, higher mutation rates are not rare. For instance, the mutation from the horned to the polled (hornless) condition in cattle occurs with a frequency of about 1/20,000; the mutation for albinism in man at 1/20,000; and that for dwarfism in man at 1/40,000. While many mutations and position effects are deleterious to the organism (especially where the mutation results in a large visible effect), in other instances they may be beneficial. In still other cases they may be beneficial or neutral in the heterozygous condition, but disadvantageous in the homozygous. Assuming a constant mutation rate, the incidence of the mutated gene eventually comes into equilibrium in the population. All individuals carry a certain complement of new mutations which may or may not endow them with advantage in the face of new disturbance.

Selection of Mutants

The variety of genetic information due to mutation and sexual recombination permits each individual in the population to respond to and regulate environmental disturbances in slightly different ways. If the genetic complement does not permit positive regulation, the organism does not survive. If the regulation is sufficient to permit survival to reproductive age, the organism can pass its traits on to the next generation. Since many mutations are very minor and not even visible, and the equilibrium rate is low, a disadvantageous mutation often confers only a slight disadvantage to the organism. In natural populations, the result of this would be a slightly higher death rate for those having the mutation and possibly a slightly lower natality. In this case, there would be a very gradual change in the proportion of each variant in the population, and only seldom an all-or-none change in survival.

The rate at which a gene is selected depends in part upon its frequency in the population. If a gene occurs at very low or very high frequencies, the selection pressure on that gene will be very low. However, if the frequency is moderate, the rate of selection might be quite high. For instance, Dodson (1960), citing Haldane, states that the following generation times would be required to increase the frequency of a dominant gene, assuming that 1000 of the dominant survive to 999 of the recessive:

Frequency Change	Number of Generations Required
0.000,001 to 0.000,002	11,739
0.000,01 to 0.01	6,920
0.01 to 0.50	4,819
0.99 to 0.999,99	309,780

This shows that it is very difficult for mild selection pressure alone to establish a new dominant in a species or to fix a dominant at 100 per cent incidence. In nature, selection works against mutation because most mutations are disadvantageous. However, if the mutation rate was appreciable and the mutation was favored by selection, a new character could be spread rapidly and become apparent in the population.

Influence of Population Size

In addition to mutation and selection upsetting the equilibrium of gene frequency, another factor must be considered. *Genetic drift* is the accidental increase or decrease of genetic information due to the fact that independent assortment and sexual recombination are random processes. In large populations the random deviations in frequency of genes tend to cancel out in time, since an accidental increase in A in one part of the population is usually cancelled out by an increase in a in another part or at another time. However, in small populations, an accident might remove a gene from the population or increase the frequency manifold. Genetic drift may work against selection, since by mere chance it preserves or destroys favorable and unfavorable genes without distinction.

In nature the size of the population is thus extremely important. Many natural mammal populations are small and the individual animal relatively sedentary. In these small populations genetic drift may result in a higher degree of homozygosity, with a lower degree of adaptibility. This effect of size of population could be extremely important in those species which fluctuate widely in density, since in these instances the smallest population limits the genetic material available to the larger populations which develop later. An accidental change in the genetic constitution might be nonadaptive. Acting against this conservative tendency is migration. Mayr (1959) suggests that as many as 40 per cent of the members of the effective local breeding population may be immigrants. Migration would introduce that all-important variability into the small population. Actually there may be a positive value for the wandering animals found in any field population study. If the combination of mutation rate, selection pressure, and population size is favorable, it is conceivable that rapid evolution may occur.

Ecotypes and Species

As selection and mutation occur, the separate populations which comprise the species make adjustments to local conditions. These adaptations are sufficiently frequent to be noticeable, and the populations may be recognized as ecotypes. Particularly in species with wide geographical distribution, the populations at the extremes of the range may show differences due to different selection pressure and genetic drift. Nevertheless, in these gene flow continues or is at least theoretically possible through migration of individuals between the separate populations. If some barrier to random mating between populations develops, further genetic variations may result in the formation of organisms sufficiently different to be recognized as a new species. These barriers may be geographical, ecological, behavioral, or morphological. If at a later time the barriers are removed, usually a reduction in fertility (a nonproductive F_1) maintains the separation.

Species may be arranged in groups according to their mode of adaptation. First is the narrow specialist which becomes extremely well adapted to a narrow ecological niche. The advantage here is that the species is very well equipped to exploit the resources of the niche; yet the disadvantage is that the fate of the species is totally tied to it. Mayr (1959) points out that the advantage of specialization is so tempting that a high percentage of species falls into this category. Second is the successful universalist. These species can cope with a variety of climates, be successful in a number of niches, but lack conspicuous specialization. Probably these species are highly heterozygous and rich in genetic variability. Third is the opportunist, a type of species with considerable geographical variability. Usually a species of this type has a collection of central populations and an ability to form peripheral geographical populations. These peripheral populations are able to become specially adapted to local environments and may eventually form new species.

REFERENCES

Ashby, W. R. 1956. An Introduction to Cybernetics. New York, John Wiley & Sons. 295 pp.

Baker, J. R., and R. M. Ransom. 1932. Factors affecting the breeding of the field mouse (*Microtus agrestis*). Part 1. Light. Proc. Royal Soc. London, B 110: 313-322.

Bissonnette, T. H. 1932. Modification of mammalian sexual cycles; reactions of ferrets (*Putorius vulgaris*) of both sexes to electric light added after dark in November and December. Proc. Royal Soc. London, B 110: 322-336.

Bissonnette, T. H., and E. Wilson. 1939. Shortening daylight periods between May 15 and September 12 and the pelt cycle of the mink. Science 89: 418-419.

Bissonnette, T. H., and E. E. Bailey. 1944. Experimental modification and control of molts and changes in coat-color in weasels by controlled lighting. Ann. N. Y. Acad. Sci. 45: 221-260.

Christian, J. J. 1959. The roles of endocrine and behavioral factors in the growth of mammal population. In: Comparative Endocrinology, A. Gorbman, Ed. New York, John Wiley & Sons, Inc.: pp. 71-97.

Dobzhansky, T. 1959. Evolution of genes and genes in evolution. Cold Springs Harbor Symp. Quant. Biol. 24: 15-30.

Dodson, E. O. 1960. Evolution: Process and Product (revised ed.). New York, Reinhold Pub. Corp. 352 pp.

Hart, J. S. 1953. The relation between thermal history and cold resistance in certain species of rodents. Canad. J. Zool. 31: 80-98.

Lush, J. L. 1945. Animal Breeding Plans. Iowa State Col. Press. 443 pp.

Lyman, C. P. 1943. Control of coat color in the varying hare, *Lepus americanus* Erxleben. Bull. Mus. Comp. Zool. 93: 393-461.

Mayr, E. 1959. Where are we? Cold Spring Harbor Symp. Quant. Biol. 24: 1-14.

Munday, K. A. 1961. Aspects of stress phenomena. In, Mechanisms in biological competition. Symp. Soc. Exp. Biol. No. 15: 168-189.

Prosser, C. L. 1958. General summary: the nature of physiological adaptation. In: Physiological adaptation, C. L. Prosser, Ed. Washington, Amer. Physiol. Soc.: pp. 167-180.

Selye, H. 1950. The Physiology and Pathology of Exposure to Stress. Montreal, Acta, Inc. 822 pp.

chapter four

ADAPTATION

ADAPTATION has been defined as the ability of a living system to regulate disturbance to the system and maintain homeostasis. It is exceedingly difficult to erect a priority list of disturbances which must be regulated by individual mammals. In the preceding section we mentioned several, such as food, defense, temperature, water, and social interactions, which are among the more significant to consider. In this chapter we will discuss the first four of these and reserve discussion of social adaptation for a later chapter on behavior.

NUTRITIONAL ADAPTATIONS

The procurement and utilization of food is an important aspect in the life of all mammals. Primitive mammals were probably omnivores, with a strong tendency toward insectivory. From these have developed a variety of specialists capable of utilizing special types of food. We can classify mammals on the basis of their food habits into:

Omnivorous
  Omnivores   Consuming both plant and animal foods
Herbivorous
  Grazing Herbivores   Consuming green plant food
  Fructivores   Consuming fruit
  Granivores   Consuming seeds

Carnivorous

Carnivores	Consuming flesh of vertebrates and invertebrates
Insectivores	Consuming insects
Scavengers	Consuming dead animals

Only a few mammals are so specialized that they are unable to eat more than one type of food.

Methods of Determining Food Habits

A great deal of mammalogical research has been concerned with determining what mammals eat. Since most mammals are secretive or are active at night, study of food habits can be exceptionally difficult. Usually the investigator studies the food remains in the stomach or intestines of slain animals, or in the feces, or in den and nest debris. Seldom can feeding be observed directly. Often the remains of food in the stomach or feces are examined under low magnification using a dissecting microscope; however, for small mammals and for detailed analysis certain investigators (Dusi, 1949; Golley, 1960) have resorted to histological examination of the materials, using differential staining for specific identification. The feces or "scats" of mammals are often used in food-habit analysis, since the bones, hair, seeds, and vegetable matter which are not digested can often be identified.

There are various problems of interpreting the results of indirect measurement of food habits. First, the identifiable material remaining in the stomach, intestine, or feces of a mammal often represents the least digestible food material. In any analysis a great deal of the material consists of unidentifiable matter, which may represent the most digestible and palatable food items. Thus, the results of the analysis may furnish misleading and erroneous data.

Second, obtaining a sufficient number of samples to represent the food habits of the species in a specific locality may be a problem. Most mammals are flexible in their ability to consume various kinds of food, and probably a mammal leaving its place of refuge to eat will sample almost every type of food encountered in the particular stratum of the community in which it hunts. Of course, mammals learn which foods are palatable, have definite preferences, and are limited in what foods they can collect, yet this curiosity about food seems to be an important part of the makeup of most species. If this is true, availability strongly influences food habits and the investigator must collect samples from sufficient individuals, over enough seasons, in each locality to obtain a real representation of the food habits of the species.

Third, different methods of determining food habits for the same species in the same area may give varied results. For example, in studies of the black-tailed deer (*Odocoileus hemionus columbianus*) Brent (in Brown, 1961) counted and identified the individual bites of food made by several semiwild, free-living deer throughout one day, each week, for one year. These direct observations were compared with analyses of stomachs from deer living in the same region (Table 4-1). The major

TABLE 4-1.   Comparison of the Twenty Most Important Deer Foods as Determined by Each Method *

Observation of Semitame Deer		Stomach Sample Analysis	
Rating	Species	Rating	Species
1	Trailing Blackberry	1	Trailing Blackberry
2	Grasses	2	Salal
3	Plantain	3	Grasses
4	Vine Maple	4	Red Alder
5	Annual Agoseris	5	Vine Maple
6	Salal	6	Western Hemlock
7	Red Alder	7	Douglas Fir
8	Huckleberry	8	Huckleberry
9	Salmonberry	9	Fireweed
10	Clover	10	Western Red Cedar
11	Common Pearly Everlasting	11	Annual Agoseris
		12	Deerfern
12	Scotch Broom	13	Horsetail
13	Western Red Cedar	14	Plantain
14	Western Thimbleberry	15	Common Pearly Everlasting
15	Bitter Cherry		
16	Western Yarrow	16	Apple
17	Blueberry Elder	17	Oxalis
18	Peavine	18	Clover
19	Rose	19	Willow
20	Willow	20	Salmonberry

* From Brown, 1961.

food items appeared in both analyses, although their rank of importance differed. The greatest variation was seen in the numerically minor items which were not found equally by both methods. Although the general character of the food habits of the deer is clear, the lack of correspondence for the less abundant food items is of concern, since these may be extremely important from a nutritional point of view.

Collection of Food

The problems of collecting food have been solved differently by herbivorous and carnivorous mammals.

Herbivores

Adaptations for collecting plant food have been mainly confined to the teeth and the jaw musculature. The incisors have often been modified or lost. Rodents and lagomorphs have developed a pair (the small peg-like second pair of incisors in the rabbit is hardly important in this connection) of upper and lower incisors which grow persistently from the roots as the tips are worn away. Since these teeth are used to cut down coarse plant material, cut bark, or break nuts, they would be worn down rapidly if continued replacement did not occur. In the ruminant herbivores, cattle, deer, and sheep, the upper incisors have been lost and replaced by a heavy pad of skin. These animals collect food by holding the plant material between the lower teeth and the pad, then tearing it off with a jerk of the head. In elephants the upper incisors are greatly elongated tusks.

The canines in herbivores are usually insignificant or absent. Adaptation to diet has been especially apparent in the cheek teeth, which in most herbivores have become elongated into efficient grinding structures. In general the premolars are more simple than the molars, although in the horse they have assumed a molar-like cusp pattern. The molar teeth are usually of a rectangular shape, formed by the addition of a cusp on the back, inner corner of the original triangular tooth form. Further, in grazing herbivores the cusps have grown tremendously in height (Figure 4-1) and the peaks are fused together by a growth of cement over the entire tooth surface. As wear occurs it must grind down through the resistant complex of enamel, dentine, and cement.

Although there appears to be considerable variation among the teeth of herbivores, the principle here is that plant foods, especially grasses, wear the teeth down rapidly. Therefore, the teeth have developed a larger surface, have become high-crowned—with a complex pattern of cusps and ridges, and may grow persistently throughout life. Conversely, in omnivores which eat a mixed diet, the cusps of the cheek teeth have become low and rounded.

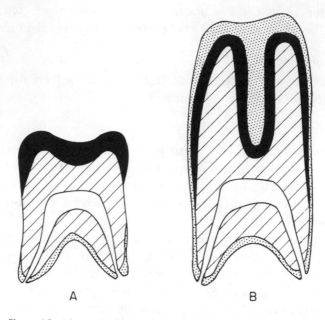

Figure 4-1. Diagram to Show Development of High-crowned Tooth of Grazing Herbivore. A, normal, low-crowned tooth of an omnivore; B, high-crowned tooth, with elevated cusps and the entire tooth covered with cement.

Terrestrial Carnivores

Adaptation toward terrestrial carnivory has involved the teeth and the muscular and skeletal systems. The incisor teeth are retained and the canines, which are prominent biting and piercing weapons, are well developed. These teeth reached an extreme in the extinct saber-tooth tiger. Since many meateaters do little or no chewing of food, the cheek teeth are often reduced in number. Usually the premolars and molars retain their simple and primitive triangular pattern; however, in many carnivores a pair of sharp-crested, shearing carnassial teeth have developed to deal with tendons and bones. In these carnassial teeth the last upper premolar shears against the first lower molar. Insectivorous carnivores retain the premolars and molars, and these are serrated, permitting the insectivores to crush the cuticle of their prey.

The rapid movement and agility of the carnivores permit them to travel long distances to find and to overtake their prey. For instance, the mountain lion (*Felis concolor*) may hunt over a circuit of more than 100 miles. The weasels are superb predators. Their long, thin bodies allow them to pursue their prey into holes or burrows and to grab and wrap themselves around the animal while it is being dispatched by a bite at the base of the skull. The least weasel (*Mustela rixosa*) can in this way successfully attack and kill a rat its own size.

Social behavior may also be well developed in carnivores. Murie (1944), studying the wolf (*Canis lupus*) in Alaska, reported that members of the wolf pack cooperate in capturing caribou (*Rangifer arcticus*) and mountain sheep (*Ovis dalli*). The Canidae best illustrate carnivorous social behavior. Other groups, such as the Felidae and Mustelidae, are usually solitary hunters.

Aquatic Carnivores

The whalebone whales or Mysticeti have developed an unusual means of capturing their small prey of crustaceans and fish. In these large mammals the mouth does not contain teeth, but instead holds a large number of fibrous plates. There may be 400 plates on either side of the mouth. These plates are triangular in shape, with the broad base of attachment on the roof of the mouth. Each plate in the series is arranged in a direction transverse to the long axis of the mouth. The outside of the plates, toward the lips, is straight and hard, while the inner surface is frayed into many hair-like fibers. These form an effective apparatus to strain the sea water entering the mouth. The tongue may be large and muscular, as in the gray or balaenid whales, or very small and weak. In the first type water is forced from the mouth by raising the tongue; in the latter type specialized muscles in the grooved throat region raise the floor of the mouth.

While the animals are swimming through a school of small crustacea or fish the mouth is opened. The inrush of water carries the food into the mouth where it is caught among the balaen plates. When the whale wants to swallow what has been captured, the tongue or floor of the mouth is raised and the water expelled. The food then passes into a remarkably small esophagus on the way to the stomach. Howell (1930) states that a finback whale (*Balaenoptera physalus*) 70 ft. long has an esophagus not larger than 5 in. in diameter.

Aerial Carnivores

Many of the bats are also carnivorous, and these have solved the problems of collecting food in a way different from other mammals. The insect-eating bats of the families Vespertilionidae and Molossidae use their echo-location system to find and capture small insects. The precision of this technique was illustrated in laboratory feeding experiments reported by Griffin (1959). A *Myotis* weighing 3.5 g was fed mosquitoes weighing 0.002 g, by releasing live mosquitoes in the room with the flying bat. The food consumption of the bat was determined by weighing the bat before and after feeding. In 15 min the bat's weight increased 10 per cent to 3.85 g. This indicated that the *Myotis* was able to capture approximately 175 mosquitoes in 15 min, a truly amazing feat! Some bats may also utilize the interfemoral membrane as a bag or "catchers mitt" to catch insects.

Food Utilization

Let us now consider the adaptations associated with the utilization of food. All mammals require protein, fats, carbohydrates, vitamins, and minerals for growth, reproduction, and maintenance of their bodies. For animals of a comparable age and functional state the nutrient and energy requirements per unit of metabolic body size are remarkably similar. Since each general type of food contains different proportions of the necessary constituents (Table 4-2), mammals with specialized

TABLE 4-2. Approximate Chemical Composition of Mammalian Food

	Mature, dry grass	Young green grass	Fruit (plum)	Seeds (legume)	Vertebrate Animals	Insects (larvae)	Crustacea * (crab)
Protein, %	5.7	5.1	.7	23.4	16	1.3	16.1
Fat, %	2.3	1.5	.2	1.2	19	7.8	1.6
Carbohydrate							
N.F.E.**, %	44.9	13.8	12.4	57.0	1	1	.6
Crude fiber, %	30.4	6.8	.5	6.1	–	–	–
Minerals, %	7.4	3.0	.51	3.0	4	14.9	1.7
Water, %	9.3	70.3	85.7	9.3	60	75	80
Energy value, Cal/gm live weight	4.1	1.26	0.56	4.61	1.37	1.34	0.81

* Crustacea without shell—the shell is approximately 50 per cent of the dry weight.
** Nitrogen-free extract.

food habits have tended to develop special anatomical and physiological mechanisms which enable them to utilize their food efficiently. In general, animal foods have a more constant composition than foods of plant origin, and because they contain large proportions of proteins and fats, are more highly digestible. Plant foods, with the exception of fruit and seeds, are high in cellulose and lignin and are not easily digested.

Functions of the Digestive Tract

One function of the digestive tract is to reduce the food to small particles so that the digestive juices can break down the nutrients into a form that can be absorbed. Since foods vary in the ease with which they can be reduced, the digestive tract has undergone considerable modification. We will compare the generalized digestive tracts of omnivores, herbivores, and carnivores. Of course, the actual form of the digestive tract is not totally dependent upon the type of food the animal consumes, since the digestive tract of each species is conditioned by the types of tracts common to the family or order. Thus, the omnivorous raccoon (*Procyon lotor*) has a digestive tract more closely similar to its carnivorous relatives than to other omnivores such as the opossum (*Didelphis marsupialis*). Nevertheless, there are broad similarities between mammals with the same food habits and these are the phenomena which we will consider below.

Esophagus: The esophagus is a straight tube extending from the mouth and pharynx to the stomach. Its muscles push the food along by an involuntary movement of peristalsis. The epithelium is generally a tough, stratified type which can withstand coarse food particles such as grass, and there are also folds which render the esophagus distensible. In ruminant and some nonruminant herbivores the distal end of the esophagus has been elaborated into a large storage organ closely associated with the stomach. In the meadow mouse (*Microtus pennsylvanicus*) the esophageal stomach is a thin-walled and high, distensible storage area. In ruminants the first three parts of the stomach (rumen, reticulum, and omasum) are of esophageal origin. In carnivores the esophagus has not been greatly modified.

Stomach: The stomach of mammals is highly variable in external shape. In many omnivores and carnivores the organ is a simple J-shaped sac (Figure 4-2). In this type, at the esophageal end, a cardiac region is usually recognized, followed by fundic and pyloric regions. These regions are difficult to distinguish externally since they are identified on the basis of their epithelial tissue. The cardiac region is transitional between the stratified epithelium of the esophagus and the important glandular region of the fundus. The cardiac region may contain mucus-

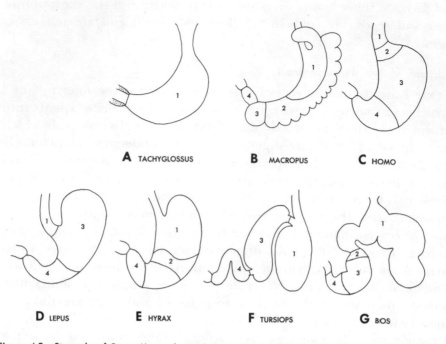

Figure 4-2. Stomachs of Seven Mammals. Epithelium types are: 1, esophageal; 2, cardiac; 3, fundus; 4, pyloric. (From Jollie, Malcolm, 1962. Chordate Morphology. New York, Reinhold Pub. Corp.)

secreting glands. In the fundic region digestive enzymes are produced. Here in tubular glands are two types of cells, chief cells and parietal cells. The chief cells secrete pepsin and the parietal cells hydrochloric acid. In the acid media pepsin breaks down proteins into peptones and proteoses. These molecules are not absorbed until they are further acted upon in the small intestine. In the pyloric region the gastric glands have no parietal cells, and mainly secrete mucus.

In the ruminant the true stomach, containing all three types of epithelium, is the abomasum (Figure 4-2). When food is eaten it descends to the reticulum and rumen, where it is reduced to a more workable pulp by the addition of water, is kneaded by muscular action, and is subjected to bacterial fermentation. At leisure the animals regurgitate the food for further chewing. When swallowed the second time, the food bypasses the reticulum and rumen by way of a deep fold in the wall of the reticulum and enters the omasum for further physical working. Finally it enters the abomasum.

In the reticulum, rumen, and omasum microflora attack the cellulose and hemicellulose, producing acetic, proprionic and butyric acids. These fatty acids are absorbed at their site of fermentation. By breaking down the cellulose walls of the plant food, the bacteria also release the cell contents containing fats, starch, and proteins for digestive action in the abomasum and intestines. In addition, the microflora synthesize all necessary B-complex vitamins and all of the essential amino acids.

In nonruminant herbivores the cardiac portion of the stomach is often absent and the fundic stomach may be enlarged for storage (Figure 4-2). In some of these animals bacterial fermentation may take place in the esophageal or fundic sac. This is not always true, however, since in the meadow mouse the contents from the esophageal stomach are usually fresh and do not give any evidence that digestion or fermentation has taken place.

The stomach of whales is also very complicated and has many divisions (Figure 4-2). Most forms have four, but the ziphoid whales may have as many as 9 to 14 divisions (Beddard, 1900). Since these animals are carnivorous, it is not clear what role these successive regions play in the digestive process. Possibly food intake in these forms is irregular and a large quantity taken at one time is held until the intestine can take care of it.

Small Intestine: Both the small and large intestines, with the exception of the ceacum, are similar in function in most mammalian herbivores and carnivores. The most noticeable variation is in the relative length of the various sections (Table 4-3). Within families where genera with different food habits do not display structural differences of the digestive tract, the influence of food habits is often evident as a difference in the length of the intestine.

In the small intestine, chemical digestion and absorption of the food take place. The first part of this intestine is the duodenum, which receives secretions from the liver and pancreas. When the liquefied food, the chyme, first enters, it is mixed with bile from the liver, enzymes, and secretions from Brunners glands of the duodenum. The mechanical action of the wall of the small intestine, aided by the bile salts, emulsifies the fats. Bile may be stored in the gall bladder, but this organ is absent in some herbivorous mammals such as the horse, deer, elephant, tapir, and rhinoceros. The chyme then comes into contact with the enzymes from the pancreas. Pancreatic protein-digesting enzymes (trypsinogen, chymotrypsinogen, and elastose) are activated in the intestine and split proteins and polypeptides into fractions contain-

TABLE 4-3. Percentage Length of the Major Divisions of the Intestine in Mammals *

Species	Per Cent of Total Length		
	Small	Large	Caecum
Herbivores:			
Microtus montebelli	45	38	17
Microtus pennsylvanicus	58	24	18
Clethrionomys andersoni	54	31	15
Apodemus speciosus	68	25	7
Apodemus argenteus	73	20	6
Sigmodon hispidus	66	24	10
Anteliomys smithii	54	30	16
Ondatra zibethica	23	25	52
Cavia porcellus	56	36	8
Neotoma sp.	46	47	7
Sylvilagus floridanus	45	18	37
Rhinoceros indicus	72	28	
Elephas maximus	66	34	
Omnivores:			
Mus musculus	80	18	3
Oryzomys palustris	82	15	3
Rattus norvegicus	84	13	3
Rattus rattus	78	18	4
Procyon lotor	90	10	
Carnivores:			
Lynx rufus	86	12	2
Otaria jubata	93	7	
Callorhinus alascanus	94	6	
Eumetopias jubata	96	4	
Balaenoptera rostratus	91	9	

* Partly from Miyao, *et al.* (1960).

ing several amino acids. These are then acted on by a mixture of peptidases formerly called erepsin, produced by the intestinal mucosa and forming single amino acids which are absorbed into the cells of the intestinal wall. The digestion of starch and other carbohydrates (with the exception of cellulose) is completed by enzymes from the intestinal glands such as maltase, sucrase, and lactase to form monosaccharides, such as glucose, which can be absorbed. Pancreatic lipase acts on fats, splitting them into glycerol and fatty acids which are absorbed. Thus, the secretions of the duodenal wall, liver, and pancreas provide a number of enzymes able to split many types of ingested food into products useful to the body.

Most absorption of metabolites takes place in the second part of the small intestine, the ileum. In some mammals two sections can be recognized, the jejunum, with thicker more vascular walls, and the ileum. The mucosa of the entire small intestine is thrown into finger-like villi which, together with folds in the mucous and submucous layers, greatly increase the surface area for absorption. Protein products are probably taken in as single amino acids, and may be acted upon by enzymes in the intestinal cells so that they appear in the blood as amino acids and di- or tri-peptides. Glucose and other products of carbohydrate metabolism pass directly through the intestinal wall into the blood stream. Fatty acids usually do not reach the blood stream but enter the lymph spaces. Here the fats are resynthesized and collected by special lymphatic vessels (lacteals), ultimately discharging into the thoracic duct.

The Large Intestine: The large intestine often can be separated into an ascending, transverse, and descending colon. Here is where the water secreted earlier to make the chyme is reabsorbed. In the last portion of the descending colon, the rectum, the pellets or feces are formed and held between periods of defecation.

Between the small intestine and the colon in most mammals a caecum is present. In carnivores and omnivores this organ is small or absent and relatively unimportant in digestion. But in many herbivores it is extremely large and functions in a fashion similar to the rumen. In the caecum the cellulose and other resistant materials in the food are acted on by bacteria. And, since the caecum is a thin-walled, sacculated structure, some of the materials liberated by the bacteria are absorbed into the blood stream through the caecal walls.

Not all of the products of bacterial fermentation in the caecum can be absorbed. In some mammals vitamin B_{12} is produced in the caecum but cannot be taken through the caecal walls. These species, many rodents and lagomorphs, consume their own feces (coprophagy). Eden (1940), Harder (1949), and Ingeburg, *et al.* (1951) have shown that at definite periods during the day the rabbit excretes caecal feces, which have a different composition and consistency than normal feces, and the animals eat these as they pass from the anus. These caecal feces contain large amounts of vitamin B_{12}, and if the animals are deprived of them, stunting of growth ensues as a result of a vitamin deficiency.

Summary

In summary, adaptations to carnivory have largely been concerned with food collecting. The carnivore must track, capture and kill a moving "food item" which may be able to defend itself. Once the job of killing is accomplished, the food is bolted down and easily digested, with bones, hair, and other undigestible materials passing through the short digestive tract.

Herbivores have much less of a problem collecting food, but once the food is consumed, it is difficult to digest and assimilate. The complicated stomach, long intestines, and well-developed caecum are adaptations which have permitted herbivores, with their symbiotic flora and fauna, to utilize food high in cellulose.

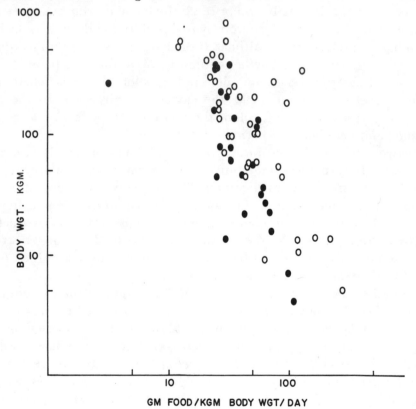

Figure 4-3. Food Consumption of Herbivores (open circles) and Carnivores (closed circles) as a Function of Body Weight. Taken from standard zoo diets. Body weight represents typical weights for adult animals. (Data obtained from Albritton, E. E., Ed., 1953. Standard Values in Nutrition and Metabolism, A.I.B.S. and Nat. Res. Council.)

Food Consumption and the Efficiency of Digestion

The intake of food is partly regulated by the hypothalamus. Two areas in this part of the brain are antagonistic: the medial area inhibits food

TABLE 4-4. Food Consumption and Efficiency of Assimilation in Mammals *

Species	Body Wt, grams	Daily Food Intake		Feces		Authority
		Grams	Grams/g	Grams	Assim. Eff.,** per cent	
Grazing Herbivores:						
Microtus pennsylvanicus	46	28.1	.61	2.8	.90	Golley, 1960
Sigmodon hispidus	100	31.2	.31	0.7	.88	Golley, 1961
Sylvilagus floridanus	312	224	.72	89.6	.60	Golley and Amerson (unpubl.)
Sylvilagus aquaticus	1,518	641	.43			Svihla (1929)
Lepus sp.	2,043	80	.04			Forbes, et al. (1941)
Castor canadensis	12,998	393	.03		.69	Cowan, et al. (1957)
Odocoileus sp.	24,970	606	.02	111	.83	Bissell et al. (1955)
Bos taurus (domestic cattle)	181,600	4,994	.03		.70	Brody (1945)
Elephas maximum	3,672,000	49,900	.01	97,992	.40	Benedict(1936)
Granivores:						
Peromyscus polionotus	13	2.1	.16	.3	.86	Connell (1959
Tamiasciurus hudsonicus	190	13.4	.07			Layne (1954)
Sciurus niger	1,000	38	.04	8.5		Baumgartner (1939)
Omnivores:						
Mus musculus	19	7.6	.40	1.7	.78	Willard (unpubl.)
Peromyscus maniculatus bairdii	18.4	3.6	.20			Sealander (1952)
P. leucopus noveboracensis	26.1	4.3	.16			Sealander (1952)
Oryzomys palustris	37	1.7	.04	1.0	.93	Sharp (1961)
Procyon lotor	18,160	385	.02	18.6	.96	Golley (unpubl.)
Euarctos americanus	59,020	1,180	.02			Cowan et al. (1957)
Insectivores:						
Sorex cinereus	3.4		2.80			Morrison et al. (1957)
Cryptotis parva floridana	5.0	5.5	1.1			Springer (1937)
Sorex palustris	10.0	10.3	1.0			Conaway (1952)
Sorex araneus	11.0	6.8	.62			Rorig (1905)
Blarina brevicauda	24.0		.53			Morrison et al. (1957)
Scalopus aquaticus	46.5	28.7	.62			Christian (1950)
Carnivores:						
Mustela rixosa	60	15.0	.25		.90	Golley (1960)
Mustela frenata	230	49.0	.21			Howard (1957)
Lynx rufus	10,090	1,000	.10	57	.91	Golley (unpubl.)

* Estimates calculated from experimental data, using most natural food items and food intake between 25 and 30°C., where possible.
** Assimilation efficiency calculated from caloric intake and feces output.

intake, while the lateral area facilitates it. How these centers are regulated is not exactly known. In a review of this subject, Grossman (1955) reported that contractions and distension of the stomach and duodenum were highly effective in influencing the quantity of food consumed. Stimulation in the oro-pharangeal region (by sense of taste, smell, etc.) was of less importance. It is not clear if circulation of large quantities of nutrients in the blood, such as glucose, reduces the food intake.

The regulation of the quality of food eaten is also an unsolved problem. Most mammals display "nutritional wisdom" and will choose a

TABLE 4-5.   Differential Digestibility of Foods by Deer *

Diet	Total Daily Caloric Intake	Digestibility, per cent
Alfalfa and barley	3652	86
Alfalfa and oats	2921	82
Alfalfa	2905	70
Live oak and chamise	1097	55
Bitter brush	3765	52
Sagebrush	641	49

* From Bissell, Harris, Strong, and James, 1955.

diet that will satisfy their requirements. How they distinguish the required food items is unknown.

The quantity of food consumed varies with the body weight of the mammal (Table 4-4). Small mammals have a larger surface area and higher metabolic rate per unit body weight than large mammals, and therefore need more food to satisfy their metabolic requirements. Table 4-4 and Figure 4-3 also suggest that food consumption of herbivores may be higher than that of carnivores. This difference is a reflection of the nature of the food which is eaten (see also Morrison *et al*, 1957). Food consumption is also influenced by temperature (Sealander, 1952), and other factors.

The efficiency of assimilation (calculated as the quantity: energy in the food consumed minus energy in the feces/energy consumed) is remarkably high for the mammals on laboratory diets (Table 4-4). Mammals fed poor diets (Table 4-5) or those in poor condition may have a much lower efficiency. The assimilative efficiency of mammals living unrestrained on their natural diets is unknown.

ADAPTATIONS FOR MOVEMENT AND DEFENSE

Movement

Animals move to obtain food and shelter, to escape from predators, and to satisfy their curiosity. These movements are usually confined to a definite area called the "home range" and the mammal leaves the area only under extreme pressure (see Chapter 10)! Other mammals regularly move long distances during the year in search of proper conditions. If these latter movements consist of a regular move from one home site to another and a return, they are called "migrations."

Finally, in many populations there are also wanderers or vagabonds which move continually.

Movement on Land

In many primitive reptiles a sprawling posture with the limbs extending out to the side of the body made land movement laborious. This position was slow and inefficient since it was difficult to lift the body off the ground surface. The therapsid reptiles and early mammals showed an improvement over this posture by a shift of the knee forward, the elbow backward, and by bringing the limbs under the body. These changes allowed greater fore and aft swing of the limbs and made possible greater speed. Muscular efficiency was also increased, since most of the body weight was carried by the bones of the limbs.

The primitive mammals of Triassic time, and many modern small mammals which live hidden among the vegetation at the ground surface, have not progressed far beyond this stage of development. However, large mammals have new problems of support and movement. These animals, especially those living in non-forested areas, are easily seen and must develop rapid movement to escape from predators, or to capture prey. These must also support their greater body weight on their limbs.

There is a limit to how large a land mammal can grow, since the growth-rate of the supporting limbs increases more slowly than the body weight. When the volume of the body doubles, the weight triples; thus an animal ten times as high, wide, and thick an another will weigh a thousand times more! However, the cross-sectional area of the limb bones which must support this weight only doubles as the weight triples. Mammals have adapted in several ways to this problem of supporting increasing weight. Some, such as the rhinoceros and elephant, have developed very short, thick legs with a large cross-section so that every pound of weight still has about the same area of bone to support it. Others, such as the giraffe (*Giraffa camelopardis*), have reduced weight by compressing the body and stretching out the legs obliquely to gain stability.

Speed in Terrestrial Mammals: The development of speed is a complex problem of changing the length of the limbs, the rate at which the limbs move, and the "gear ratio" of the limbs. A full cycle of motion is called a "stride," and speed is the product of length of stride times the rate of stride. High speed requires long strides taken at a high rate. Hildebrand (1959 and 1960) has studied how animals achieve a high rate of speed, by relating comparative anatomy to an analysis of motion pictures of running animals—and much of our discussion is taken from his reports.

In running (cursorial) mammals, the length of stride has been increased by the development of long legs in relation to the other parts of the body. This increase in length has taken place in the parts of the limb away from the body—the forearm, foreleg, wrist, shank, and foot. Most mammals, including man, are plantigrade and walk on the carpals or tarsals, metacarpals or tarsals, and phalanges. In the digitigrade mammals, such as the cats, the limb is lengthened by supporting the body on the phalanges. In the ungulates increase in limb length has reached the limit, since these mammals walk on the tips of the phalanges. Associated with this trend has been a reduction in the number of functional digits. In the most advanced Perissodactyla the weight of the body is supported entirely on the third digits.

The shoulder of running mammals has also been modified. The collarbone (clavicle) is reduced in carnivores and absent in ungulates, allowing greater freedom of movement of the shoulder. In both carnivores and ungulates the shoulder blade (scapula) lies against a high narrow chest and pivots near the center of its length, thus adding length to the limb.

The supple back of the dog and cat also aid in increasing the length of stride. In these running animals the back is extended its full length when the hind limbs are pushing against the ground. In the cheetah (*Acinonyx jubatus*), this results in a 23-ft stride.

The *rate* of stride is partly dependent on the speed of contraction of the muscles and the gear-ratio of the muscles and bones. Although cursorial mammals can contract their muscles faster than other mammals, this ability is limited. The rate of muscle contraction varies inversely with the linear dimensions of a muscle, assuming a constant load on the muscle fibers. Thus, the larger muscle contracts more slowly. The gear-ratio is equal to the distance between the pivot of motion (the shoulder joint, for example) and the point where the motion is applied (the hand or foot), divided by the perpendicular distance between the pivot and the point at which the muscles are attached to the bone. In running mammals the activating muscles are attached close to the pivot of motion, which, with the long legs, gives a high gear-ratio— enabling the animal to reach higher rates of speed. By combining the velocities of each segment of the cursorial limb and body moving in the same direction at the same time, a high total velocity is obtained.

The larger running mammals must have great endurance, since the locomotor muscles also raise the heavy body which falls during the unsupported period of the stride. In these mammals weight is reduced by reducing the mass of the limbs and the muscles which draw the limbs toward or away from the midline, or rotate and move the digits and arm. The fibula and ulna are also reduced in size. These changes combine to make the lower segment of the leg light in weight. Since the kinetic energy that is developed and must be overcome in moving the limb is equal to half the mass times the square of its velocity, the load on the muscles can be also reduced by reducing the velocity of the more massive parts of the limb. These are close to the body where they do not move as far or as fast as the distal, lighter segments.

TABLE 4-6. Maximum Speeds in Miles per Hour of Mammals *

Mammal	Max. Speed	Mammal	Max. Speed
Short-tailed shrew	2.2	Black rhinoceros	28
Red-backed vole	4.2	Wolf	28
Pine vole	4.2	Wart hog	30
Opossum	4.4	Giraffe	28 to 32
Deer mouse	4.5	Indian Wildass	30 to 32
Woodland jumping mouse	5.3	Jackal	35
Meadow jumping mouse	5.5	Cape buffalo	35
Meadow mouse	6.6	Roan antelope	30 to 35
White-footed mouse	6.8	Hare	35 to 45
House mouse	8.1	Springbok	35 to 60
Red squirrel	9.0	Jackrabbit	40
Camel	9 to 10	Cape hartebeast	40
California sea lion	10.6	Mountain zebra	40
Eastern chipmunk	10.6	Spotted hyena	40
Domestic sheep	11	Coyote	40
Big brown bat	15	Red fox	45
Domestic horse	15	Grant's gazelle	40 to 50
Kouprey	15 to 18	Thomson's gazelle	50
Grey squirrel	17	Wildebeast	50
Northern fur seal	17	Lion	50
Wild rabbit	20 to 25	Cheetah	65 to 70
African elephant	15 to 25		

* After Bourliere (1956), Howell (1944), and Layne and Benton (1954).

Other terrestrial mammals, such as rabbits, kangaroos, and jumping mice, have developed the ability to move rapidly by leaping. In these mammals the femur, tibia, and fibula have increased in length, with associated changes in musculature. In some forms the tail is also greatly elongated and serves as a further support in the leaping gait. By powerful extension of the hind feet these mammals may move very rapidly.

Some kangaroos, for instance, may reach speeds of 30 miles per hour and cover almost 40 ft in a single leap.

The maximum speed attained by mammals may be considerable (Table 4-6). Most of the speeds of large mammals shown in the Table, were measured by keeping an automobile abreast of the animal running on a course parallel with the road. The speed of the small mammals was measured by releasing them in the center of a chalk circle and recording the time they took to cross the line when frightened by shouting, clapping, or chasing. The fastest mammal is a predator, the cheetah, which at full gallop can reach 45 miles per hour two seconds after starting.

Arboreal Movement

A number of species of mammals spend almost their entire lives in trees. Arboreal movement requires several adaptations. First, the weight of the body is limited by the strength of the limbs and branches of the trees. Thus most arboreal mammals are relatively small. Second, there must be some effective means of holding onto branches and bark. Many species, such as the squirrels, have well developed claws which allow them to freely run up and down the trunks. The claws of the tree sloths are curved and serve as hooks to support these animals from tree branches. In some marsupials, rodents, and carnivores, and in the primates, the hands and feet are flexible and the fingers and toes long, permitting an effective grasp of the branch. In addition, the tail of the new-world monkey is prehensile and can, alone, support the swinging monkey. Most arboreal mammals scamper along the tree branches in a running fashion, but some primates, such as the lar gibbon (*Hylobates lar*), can move along tree branches by swinging with the arms—a type of movement called brachiation. This is an effective type of locomotion, since the gibbon can move 10 ft in a single swing.

Movement Within the Soil

A number of mammal species have the ability to dig burrows for their shelter or to utilize the underground openings dug by other animals, but only a few, such as the moles and pocket gophers, are able to spend almost their entire lives beneath the soil surface. Profound changes have occurred in the structure of these fossorial mammals.

The forelimbs, which are employed in digging and tearing roots and soil, are much shortened and thickened. The pectoral girdle is moved forward and is greatly enlarged for attachment of the digging muscles. In moles the forefeet are palmate and serve as shovels; in gophers the strong, curved claws function in a similar manner. The hind limbs are used to push the body forward and to move accumulated dirt backward and are, therefore, firmly attached to the pelvic girdle. The small and narrow pelvic girdle together with the more or less pointed rostrum give the body a torpedo-shape. Finally, the ears and eyes are greatly reduced and the pelage is short, dense, and capable of lying forward or backward. All of these modifications aid the animal to move through the soil by offering little resistance against the walls of the tunnel.

Movement in the Water

Many terrestrial mammals can swim or float if the need arises but are seldom observed in water. Others, such as the mink and otter, are amphibious and appear to be equally at home in water or on land. Yet others (the pinnipeds) spend most of their life in water but can move with difficulty on land at certain periods of their life history. Finally, the cetaceans and sirenians are totally restricted to an aquatic existence. Typical characteristics of amphibious mammals are short, dense fur, webbed feet, and a flattened tail. In this discussion we will be concerned only with the more truly aquatic Pinnipedia and Cetacea.

Structural Adaptations for Swimming: The average body size of the pinnipeds is larger than other Carnivora and has probably evolved in response to a cold environment and to the aquatic medium. Aquatic mammals do not have the problem of supporting body weight in response to a pull of gravity. The largest pinniped reported by Scheffer (1958) is the southern elephant seal (*Mirounga leonina*)—full-grown males may weigh 8000 pounds. The skull of pinnipeds is somewhat telescoped and flattened—an advantage in diving. The tail is short and rudimentary, the external ears are reduced or absent, the external genitalia and teats nearly withdrawn beneath the smooth surface of the body, and the base of the limbs to or beyond the elbows and knees is deeply embedded within the body.

Among the mammals, the whales are the most highly developed for an aquatic life. Telescoping of the skull and the reduction of surface structures which could offer resistance to the water are maximum. The body is almost totally unhaired and is covered by a thick layer of blubber which is extremely strong and aids in the conservation of body heat. Even in the tropics whales require this protection since their body temperatures are higher than that of the surrounding water. According to Kellog (1928) the body temperature of the Sei whale (*Balaenoptera borealis*) is between 95 and 97°F and that of the common porpoise (*Phocoena phocoena*) is 96°F. Further, Kanwisher and Senft (1960) reported that the rectal temperature of a beached finback whale was 33°C (91.5°F).

The first requirement for aquatic locomotion is a streamlined or fusiform shape which offers a minimum of resistance to the water during movement. The second requirement is some means of propulsion. The principle of movement in certain sea lions is similar to that of a rowboat. The body form is long, and tapers from the middle to both ends. The forelimbs are located near the center of the body and the flippers are moved obliquely, pushing the water from the ulnar border of the manus which is held in a transverse plane. The effectiveness of this mode of swimming can be seen by comparing the speeds of the sea lion and seal with those of other mammals as shown in Table 4-6.

The walruses use both fore and rear limbs in swimming. The hind feet are moved from side to side, while the forefeet are moved alternately. On the other hand, some seals never use the front limbs for propulsion; in these, movement is effected entirely by the hind feet.

Whales have lost the hind limbs, although bony remnants of these are present internally. The forelimbs have been converted into flippers which serve as rudders. Although there is little resemblance between the flippers of whales and the forelimbs of land mammals, both are constructed of similar bones, muscles, blood vessels, and nerves. The hand has been modified by a change in the shape of the wrist bones, and a reduplication of the bones of the fingers. The margins of the flippers are hardened with fibrocartilage.

In the whale, the tail has been expanded laterally to form flukes. The flukes are constructed of an extremely strong fibrous tissue without any bony elements. Parry (1949a, 1949b) has studied the use of the tail and flukes in propulsion of whales by careful analysis of both muscular and skeletal anatomy, and by a series of motion pictures of whales swimming at the Florida Marine Studios. The tail moves up and down in a vertical plane about a center of rotation posterior to the dorsal fin, through an angle of about 70°. The flukes also move up and down in a vertical plane about a center of rotation at the level of their insertion in the tail. As the tail is at the top of the stroke the flukes are horizontal; as the tail moves downward the flukes bend upward reaching a maxi-

mum angle from the horizontal at the middle of the stroke (Figure 4-4).
This angle is reduced until the flukes are again horizontal at the end
of the tail stroke. On the upward swing the movement is reversed. These
movements of the fluke are necessary, since to get forward movement
or positive thrust on the downstroke, the water must be incident on
the underside of the fluke, and to achieve this on the upstroke, the
water must be incident on the upper side of the fluke.

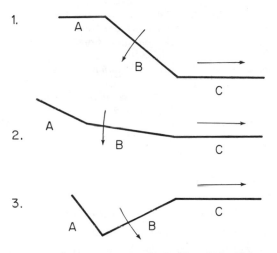

Figure 4-4. Diagram Showing the Position of the Flukes
and Tail of the Whale, at Three Consecutive Periods During One Oscillation While Swimming. A, position of the
flukes; B, position of the tail; and C, position of the body.
(After Parry, 1949b.)

Physiological Considerations of Aquatic Living: It is also appropriate
here to consider some of the peculiar problems of living in water. All
mammals obtain the oxygen required for metabolism from the air. The
problems of obtaining sufficient oxygen while at the surface, of storing
oxygen and resisting the effects of accumulating carbon dioxide (CO_2)
while under water, and of resisting the pressure at extreme depths must
be solved by the aquatic mammals. Some whales may stay under water
as long as two hours (Table 4-7). The maximum depth of the dive is
also of interest. According to Scheffer (1958) the steller sea lion (*Eu-
metopias jubata*) may reach a depth of 110 to 146 m (363 to 482 ft), the
gray seal (*Halichoerus grypus*) between 128 to 146 m (422 to 482 ft) and
the harp seal (*Phoca groenlandica*) possibly 183 m (595 ft). The fin

TABLE 4-7.   Duration of Dives of Some Aquatic Mammals *

Aquatic Mammal		Duration of Dive
Sea elephant	*Mirounga angustirostris*	6 min, 48 sec
Muskrat	*Ondatra zibethica*	12 min
Harbor seal	*Phoca vitulina*	15 min
Gray seal	*Halichoerus grypus*	15 min
Beaver	*Castor canadensis*	15 min
Florida manatee	*Trichechus manatus latirostris*	16 min, 20 sec
Fin whale	*Balaenoptera plupalus*	20 min
Finback whale	*Balaenoptera physalus*	30 min
Common rorqual	*Balaenoptera borealis*	49 min
Blue whale	*Sibbaldus musculus*	50 min
New Zealand humpbacked whale	*Megaptera nodosa*	60 min
Sperm whale	*Physeter catadon*	60 to 75 min
Bowhead whale	*Balaena mysticetus*	80 min
Bottle-nosed whale	*Hyperoodon ampullatus*	120 min

* After Irving, 1939.

whale (*Balaenoptera plupalus*) may dive to 76 to 348 m (250 to 1150 ft), while the sperm whale (*Physeter catadon*) may reach 909 m (3000 ft) (Bourliere, 1954). Man can descend to about 165 m (540 ft) in a flexible diving suit with a special breathing mixture.

The ability to remain submerged for relatively long periods is due in part to a more complete renewal of the oxygen in the lungs at each inhalation and to an insensitivity to an increase in the amount of CO_2 in the blood (Figure 4-5). Large whales may renew 90 per cent of the air contained in the lungs, as contrasted with 15 to 20 per cent in man. These adaptations increase the amount of oxygen available at the beginning of the dive and reduce the stimulating effect of CO_2 on the respiratory center of the brain. In addition, the stored oxygen is used economically during the dive. The muscles of locomotion essentially function anaerobically during submergence; lactic acid increases in the blood immediately following the dive (Figure 4-5). Further, Irving, Scholander and Grinnell (1942a and b) have shown that in the seal (*Phoca vitulina*) the heart rate decreases about 90 per cent during the dive (Figure 4-5). A 50 per cent reduction in heart rate has also been observed by these workers in the porpoise and the manatee (*Trichechus manatus*). These authors have shown that the blood pressure falls rapidly in the small arteries while circulation in the large arteries and brain

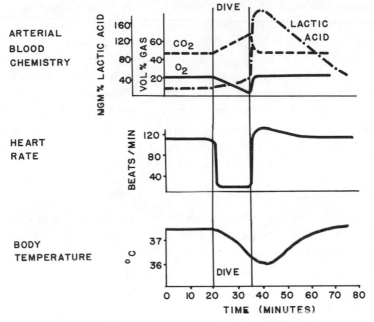

Figure 4-5. Summary of Several Aspects of the Physiology of Diving in Aquatic Mammals. Note the drop in O_2 content of the blood, heart rate, and body temperature during the dive. (Compiled by W. Cosgrove, Univ. Georgia, from data of Irving, Scholander, and Grinnell, 1942a; and others.)

remains normal. This makes the oxygen available to vital activities, while circulation to the rest of the body is reduced. Body temperature is also lowered.

Human divers who descend to great depths and rise to the surface quickly may be subject to the "bends," or caisson disease. This is due to the dissolved nitrogen in the blood, which increased during descent, separating out of the blood in the form of bubbles. These bubbles of nitrogen may lodge in vital arteries and veins and cause paralysis or death. Very slow ascent permits the dissolved nitrogen to separate out at the lungs. Scholander (1940) has shown that similar problems may occur in Pinnipeds and Cetaceans which dive to great depths, but the danger is reduced for the following reasons: First, the high heart rate as the animal rises to the surface aids in the elimination of dissolved nitrogen. Second, the pressure of the water on the body compresses the alveoli of the lungs and forces air into the bronchi and trachea, thus reducing the entry of nitrogen into the blood.

We might expect that the great pressure during deep dives would force water into the nostrils of whales. This is prevented by a special closing apparatus. In the toothed whales the narial cavity is divided into a series of pockets into which the narial passages open. Between these pockets are a series of plugs controlled by muscles, which apparently contract when pressure is exerted on the external flap of cartilage which covers the single external nostril. In the whalebone whales, the narial passages are equipped with spiral folds which fit into one another when pressure is applied. In whales the narial passages do not communicate with the throat as in land mammals. Instead a continuous tube between the nares and trachea exists.

Movement in the Air

Bats are the only mammals which have achieved true flight. The flying squirrels, flying lemurs, and several marsupials of the genera *Petaurus, Acrobates,* and *Schoinobates* have developed the ability to glide through the air from tree to tree or ground, but these latter forms bear the same relation to bats and birds as gliders bear to powered airplanes.

The wings of bats consist of a thin layer of skin stretched between the bones of the arm, hand, and leg to form the wing membrane. The finger bones, except the thumb, support the wing from the front edge to the back. In addition there is also a fold of skin, the interfemoral membrane, between the legs and including all or part of the tail. The large sail-like wing increases the surface area of the bat to about ten times that of the head and body (Griffin, 1958). The wings are operated by massive muscles attached to the humerus and scapula; these form the thick breast muscles similar to those observed in birds.

The manner of bat flight varies widely with different species. The flying foxes (*Pteropus*) are the largest bats, with wingspans of about 4 ft, and may glide for long distances (Allen, 1939). The freetailed bats of the tropics are extremely rapid flyers, with long, narrow wings and swift wing beats. Some of the large fruit bats of the tropics fly by vigorous sweeps of the wings and appear to the observer as steady flyers. However, the common bats of North America and Europe, of the family Vespertillionidae, exhibit an extremely erratic or fluttering flight. The small *Myotis* characteristically dive, turn, flutter, and dodge about in the air hunting for their insect prey. In this irregular flight the two wings may move in completely different directions. One wing may be fully extended, while the other is sharply bent and folded. This ability permits extremely agile flight, and is one of the advantages of having flexible-skin wings rather than the stiff feather wings of birds.

Eisentraut (1936) studied the flight of bats by means of the motion picture camera. He found that in general the wing movements of bats are the same as in birds, that is, there is first a stroke downward and forward, then the recovery upward and backward on a slightly different course. Progress in direct flight is slightly wavy because there is a slight lift on the downstroke and drop on the upstroke. Steering is done by the wings. The tail does not appear to be used in controlling the direction of flight, although it may serve as a brake when landing. The long-eared and horseshoe bats are also capable of hovering. In this case the body is held perpendicular while the same stroke is used but with just enough exertion to overcome the pull of gravity.

Very little information is available on the speed of flight by bats. Eisentraut reported the large mouse-eared bat *(Myotis myotis)* typically flew at 4.3 m per sec (8.4 mph), making about 11 to 12 wing-beats per second. Griffin (1958) reported the little brown bat *(Myotis lucifugus)* flying between 2.4 and 6.3 m per sec, and suggested that the red and hoary bats *(Lasiurus borealis* and *cinereus)* may fly twice as fast as *Myotis.* The lesser horseshoe bat may make slightly more wing strokes than *Myotis,* about 16 to 18 per second. Layne and Benton (1954) measured the big brown bat *(Eptesicus fuscus)* flying at 15 miles per hour (Table 4-6).

Griffin (1958) has suggested that a bat in flight may consume 200 cal per g per hr while on the wing, and that as much as 78 per cent of the annual metabolism of the bat is required for the two hours of active flight at night during the warmer half of the year. As yet no one has directly measured the energy consumption of a bat in flight—Griffin's calculations were based on information on resting metabolism of bats and metabolism of bats crawling on their cages, plus knowledge that in the humming bird there is a five-fold increase in the metabolic rate while hovering over that during perching. Nevertheless these calculations roughly indicate the expense of this type of movement to the flying mammal.

Flight Navigation in Bats: While in flight bats make a variety of sounds. Some of these sounds are audible to the human ear as low ticks, but most of the sound energy lies at frequencies out of the range of human hearing. These high-frequency sounds are used in flight to generate echoes that tell the bat where distant objects are located. Bats, therefore, navigate in flight by echo-location—a type of animal radar!

The common insectivorous bats of North America and Europe have a characteristic sound which lasts for only a few milliseconds. These orientation sounds start at a very high frequency and drop rapidly, to end about an octave below the beginning frequency. *Myotis lucifugus* begin at about 90 kc and end at 45 kc; each sound lasts 2 msec (Griffin, 1959). Actually this is a sweep through double the whole range of the human ear, in 2 msec. Not all bats make this type of sound. The horse-shoe bats, for instance, make a much longer, sharply beamed tone of nearly constant frequency.

When the little brown bat is flying straight, it emits its orientation sounds at rates of 10 to 20 per sec. But when it comes close to an obstacle or an insect, the sound rate increases to as high as 250 per sec. At this rate the duration of the sound decreases to about 1 msec, thus allowing for intervals of silence between sounds to enable the bat to hear the echo. Griffin states that the cruising bat emits a lazy "putt-putt," but the sound increases to a buzzing when it closes in on an insect. Of course, these sounds are detectable only with special instruments.

The precision of the bat's echo-location system is amazing, and indicates how bats so effectively avoid obstacles in the dark. When wires are strung from floor to ceiling across a room, each wire spaced 30 cm apart (the wing span of *Myotis*), it is necessary to reduce the diameter of the wires to 0.07 mm before the bats hit them at random. A bat in good condition can regularly miss wires as small as 0.12 mm in diameter, and can detect them at a considerable distance (Table 4-8).

TABLE 4-8.   Range of Detection of Wires by Bats *

Diameter of Wire, mm	Average Repetition Rate before Approaching Wire, pulse/sec	Average Maximum Repetition Rate, pulses/sec	Average Distance at which Repetition Rate First Increased, cm
3.0	12	50	215
1.07	12	40	185
0.65	13	30	150
0.46	13	40	120
0.28	12	27	105
0.18	12	22	90

* After Griffin, 1959.

Special Adaptations for Defense

In addition to moving away from a disturbance, many species exhibit special defense mechanisms. Certain individuals of some species will actively defend themselves and are especially equipped morphologically and behaviorally for this purpose, while others passively defend themselves by remaining quiet.

Active Defense

Many mammals, when cornered by an attacker, will defend themselves with teeth and feet. In others, particularly the Artiodactyla, horns and antlers are used against an attacking predator and also to defend a breeding territory or harem of females against other males of the same species. Certain species actively band together to defend the females or young. An example of this form of behavior is found in musk oxen (*Ovibos moschatus*), which form themselves defensively into a tight band, body against body, with their heavy horns pointing outward toward the disturbance. In certain primates the males will scout the disturbance and may actually attack by throwing various objects. Active defense seems to be especially characteristic of the larger mammals which inhabit open terrain and are active during the daylight hours.

Passive Defense

The defense of many mammals in forested regions, as well as of mammals which nest during the day and are active at night, is often simply to remain quiet until the disturbance is past. The coat color of many of these animals blends into the normal background of the habitat and makes the animal exceedingly difficult to see. The grizzled appearance of forms in temperate grassland and forest, the spotted appearance of tropical forms living in deep rain-forest, the white color of the arctic hare and northern weasel during the winter, the pale hues of desert mammals, and the dark color of mammals living on desert lava beds, all suggest that color plays an important protective role.

Certain mammals have morphological adaptations which permit passive defense. The spines of the porcupine and the dermal armor of the armadillo (*Dasypus novemcinctus*) act in this way. Of course, these mechanisms do not provide total protection, since certain predators do prey on these species. For instance, the fisher (*Martes pennanti*) successfully attacks porcupines by flipping the animal over on its back and ripping open the unprotected belly. Bobcats (*Lynx rufus*) and other predators may also learn to prey on porcupines.

ADAPTATIONS TO CHANGE IN ENVIRONMENT

Even though most mammals can move away from locally unfavorable conditions, they must adapt to broad environmental variations. Much of the attention of investigators has been focused on adaptations to temperature and water, and these will be briefly considered below.

Temperature

Temperatures on the earth vary widely, ranging from −70°C in the Siberian Arctic to +58°C in Death Valley and the northern Sahara desert. Mammals and other animals are found living successfully at these extremes. Adjustment to heat and cold is dependent upon the ability to regulate the gradient between the body and the air by changing the body temperature, by the production of heat, or by insulation.

Since the loss or gain of heat to the body is related to the gradient of temperature between the body and environment, animals might be expected to resist extremes by directly varying the body temperature, but this method of adapting to temperature does not appear to have been commonly employed, since body temperature is about the same for all species in all climates (Morrison and Ryser, 1952; Irving and Krogh, 1954).

Insulation

Adaptation to heat and cold is mainly through change in the insulation of the body. The degree of insulation can be varied by changing the thickness and type of fur, the degree of vascularization of the skin and limbs, or the abundance of sweat glands; and by posture and behavior. Scholander, Walters, Hock, and Irving (1950), in their studies of the insulation value of the fur of some arctic and tropical mammals, found that insulation value was correlated with thickness of the fur (Figure 4-6). In small mammals fur thickness and size are correlated, while for mammals the size of a fox or larger there is no clear correlation between fur thickness and body size. Apparently in these larger mammals insulation has reached a useful maximum, while in the small forms the fur must be short and light or the animals could not move easily.

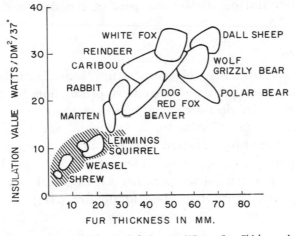

Figure 4-6. Insulation in Relation to Winter Fur Thickness in Arctic Mammals. The insulation of tropical mammals is shown by the shaded area. (Redrawn from Scholander, Walters, Hock, and Irving, 1950.)

Scholander (1955) has summarized the important aspects of vascularization as a device for conserving or getting rid of heat. Many animals, including the seal, whale, and tree sloth, have extensive *retia* or anastomoses of veins and arteries in the extremities. These *retia* serve as heat-conserving organs, since the arteries carrying warm blood can effectively transfer the heat back to the returning venous blood in the veins lying adjacent to them and thus cool the extremities.

Posture and other behavioral mechanisms are exceedingly important in controlling insulation. In cold climates many animals curl up, holding their poorly insulated extremities close to the body and covering these with their tail. Alternately, in hot climates these animals will expose the thinly haired belly and legs to reduce the heat load. Molting or shedding of the thick winter fur also aids in reducing the insulation in warm weather. Small mammals, such as mice, cannot vary their own insulation effectively, and may huddle or nest together to conserve heat (Pearson, 1947). In this case the group would be roughly similar to one larger individual, and the surface area and heat loss would be reduced. The construction of shelters and nests also aids the small mammals exposed to excessive heat or cold to maintain their normal body temperatures. Finally, the period of activity is often timed to coincide with favorable temperatures. For instance, tropical mammals which cannot stand extremes of either heat or cold may move into dense shade or water during the hottest part of the day, and seek shelter at night.

Heat Production

Within a certain range of temperature (the thermoneutral zone) mammals can maintain their basal heat production by changing the body insulation. In declining temperatures there is a point where insulation is no longer effective for any mammal, and body temperature must be maintained by increased heat production. This point is called the critical temperature by Scholander, Hock, Walters, Johnson, and Irving (1950). The critical temperature varies greatly for tropical and arctic mammals (Figure 4-7). The arctic fox (*Alopex lagopus*) and

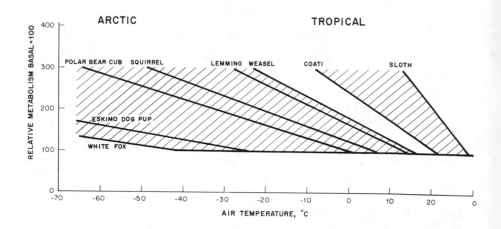

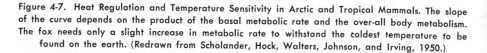

Figure 4-7. Heat Regulation and Temperature Sensitivity in Arctic and Tropical Mammals. The slope of the curve depends on the product of the basal metabolic rate and the over-all body metabolism. The fox needs only a slight increase in metabolic rate to withstand the coldest temperature to be found on the earth. (Redrawn from Scholander, Hock, Walters, Johnson, and Irving, 1950.)

Eskimo dog can maintain basal conditions down to about $-40°C$, and these animals sleep outside at this temperature without distress. In contrast, many tropical mammals reach the critical temperature at about $26°C$. These species differences are not due to a higher metabolic rate in arctic mammals, but to differences in effective insulation. The ability of tropical forms to insulate the body is much less effective than arctic forms, even though the thickness of fur may be about the same (Figure 4-6).

The increase in heat production as a response to cold is more rapid in tropical mammals than in arctic forms. For this reason, tropical mammals can endure only a narrow range of temperature even when they increase their heat production, while the arctic fox can tolerate the coldest temperatures on earth merely by increasing its metabolism 30 to 40 per cent. The critical temperature of a naked white man is between 27 and 29°C, placing him among the tropical mammals; however, he can change his insulation by adding clothing, and therefore can span the entire range from tropical to arctic conditions. Further, some types of man—for example, the Australian aborigines and the Indians of Tierra del Fuego—are cold-adapted, and maintain their internal temperature by high metabolism and transfer of heat from arteries to veins before it is radiated from the extremities.

Individual Adjustment to Temperature

We have been considering adaptation to temperature from the point of view of species populations. Individuals may also adjust to temperature changes by becoming acclimated to higher or lower temperatures. At high temperatures the lethal limit is not raised in acclimation but rather the animal develops improved efficiency in holding body temperatures below the lethal limit (Fisher, 1958). For instance, in humans, and probably in other species as well, the basal metabolism is reduced at high temperatures. In addition, radiation of heat from the environment to the body may be reduced by change in insulation. Thick clothing is used for this purpose in hot regions; and in certain species, such as the camel, thick wool insulates the body. Heat is transferred to the periphery of the body by increased blood flow to the skin and superficial tissues. Finally, evaporative cooling is increased by panting (shallow, high-frequency respiration), by increased sweating, or in some forms such as small rodents, by wetting the fur.

Cold acclimation by individuals is somewhat different from cold adaptation by species. The low-temperature survival limit is reduced (as much as 10°C in mice, Hart, 1957) through an ability to produce more heat for a longer period of time. In warm-acclimated animals which have been moved to low temperatures, heat production is increased by physical means such as shivering, while in cold-acclimated forms heat is produced by chemical thermogenesis. Individuals adapted to cold have a higher metabolic rate at thermoneutrality than animals not exposed to cold, which is probably partly due to increased activity of the thyroid (Fisher, 1958). Cold-acclimation does not usually result in an increase of the maximum insulation, although the quantity of insulation may vary seasonally.

For many years it has been suggested that adaptation to temperature is brought about by change in surface area of the body and in the length and width of the extremities. These conceptions have been used to explain Bergman's Law and Allen's Rule, which state that the larger races are found in the coldest part of the species range, and that members of a species in the coldest parts of the range possess relatively shorter protruding body parts. The larger races, with shorter extremities, would have a smaller surface area and therefore, a lower heat loss. Bergman's Law and Allen's Rule may or may not describe the facts of intraspecies size relationships—only exhaustive analyses of individual species can answer this question. Nevertheless, adaptation to cold or hot climates seems to take place through processes which regulate insulation rather than surface area.

Water and Humidity

In the arctic and tropics, mammals are confronted with the problems of maintaining body temperatures in extreme cold and heat. Deserts represent yet another extreme situation. In deserts, mammals must contend with the problems of maintaining water balance and body temperatures in a climate with extreme range in temperature, low humidity, high evaporation, and low precipitation. Although arctic regions may also be considered as deserts since water is tied up in ice and snow and is generally unavailable to mammals, here we are concerned with adaptations in deserts characterized by high temperatures and low precipitation.

In the desert, the high temperatures often necessitate the use of water for heat regulation. As a rule, small mammals do not need to utilize water in this way because they escape the main heat stress by remaining in their underground burrows during the day. Large mammals, however, which cannot escape in this manner, may prevent a critical increase in body temperature by evaporation of water.

To maintain the water balance, intake must equal output. Water may be obtained from food, by drinking, or by combination of oxygen with hydrogen in the body (metabolic H_2O). Water may be lost through the urine, feces, and by evaporation from the skin and lungs.

Adaptation to Desert Environments by Small Mammals

Some small desert rodents, such as the kangaroo rat (*Dipodomys*) live and thrive on dry plant material and seem not to require green plant food or access to drinking water. Water loss in these mammals is prevented by several mechanisms: First, they are able to excrete a very concentrated urine. Urea concentrations are quite high in the kangaroo rat (up to 3.8 M/l (22.8 per cent)) and in the jerboa (3.9 M/l), as compared to the white rat (2.5 M/l) and man (1.0 M/l) (Schmidt-Nielsen and Schmidt-Nielsen, 1952). In *Dipodomys* the reabsorption of water from the renal tubules of the kidneys is very high, and there is, in addition, excretion of urea by the tubules. The ability to concentrate urine permits these animals to excrete waste products with a low expenditure of water. Second, the feces of these small desert rodents are quite dry. And, third, there is a relatively low rate of evaporation of water from the moist surface of the lungs. Evaporation may also occur through sweat glands (which are absent in many mammals), and from the surface of the skin. In the kangaroo rat, the major portion of the evaporation probably takes place through the lungs.

In the kangaroo rat the water requirement is largely met by oxidation water resulting from the metabolism of food materials to H_2O and carbon dioxide (CO_2). In protein metabolism, there is also excretion of nitrogen as urea ($CO(NH_2)_2$). Since urea requires two atoms of hydrogen for each atom of nitrogen, there is a lower yield of oxidation water from protein than from carbohydrates and fats.

The kangaroo rat escapes heat stress in intense solar radiation and high air temperatures above 40°C by staying in its burrow where the temperature is seldom more than 30°C and where the humidity is higher than in the air outside. Since this animal can maintain water balance when the absolute humidity is about 2 to 3 mg H_2O/l of air, the evaporative water loss in the burrow is so low that oxidation water formation represents a definite gain in water balance (Schmidt-Nielsen and Schmidt-Nielsen, 1952).

Other small desert mammals do not use water for heat regulation but still cannot survive on dry food. These include ground squirrels (*Citellus*), packrats (*Neotoma*), and grasshopper mice (*Onychomys*). Herbivores, such as the woodrat, obtain their water from succulent green foods. The grasshopper mouse is partly carnivorous, so that fairly large amounts of water are also taken in with the food (insects may contain 60 to 85 per cent). These mammals are adapted to desert life by their food habits and not by any special ability to conserve water.

Adaptation to Desert Environments by Large Mammals

The large mammals use water effectively for cooling by evaporation of water from the skin or respiratory tract. These animals can depend upon water for cooling, since their large bulk and lower internal heat production results in a slower over-all heat gain than in small mammals.

The camel and donkey, representing two large mammals adapted to desert life, have been studied by Schmidt-Nielsen (1959). The camel can go for long periods without water, and can function effectively in a climate where summer temperatures may reach 120°F or more. The camel has adapted to these conditions in several ways. First, like the kangaroo rat, the camel excretes a concentrated urine, high in urea and low in water. Second, the camel can stand dehydration up to 25 per cent of the body weight without being seriously weakened. Man will usually die when his water loss reaches 12 per cent, because during high water loss the blood loses water and becomes thickened, taxing the heart; eventually circulation is reduced to the point where heat cannot be carried to the body surface, resulting in death. The camel tolerates dehydration because the blood volume stays relatively constant. Water is drawn from the body tissues and other body fluids rather than from the blood. Third, the camel loses water slowly. Water loss is reduced in several ways. The gradient between body temperature and air temperature is lowered, since the camel's body temperature is labile. At dawn it may drop to 93°F, and during the hottest period of the day may increase to 105°.F. The camel does not begin to sweat until the body temperature reaches the higher levels. Fourth, the thick wool of this animal provides excellent insulation and reduces the flow of heat inward to the body. And lastly, since the fat is concentrated in the hump rather than being distributed under the skin, the absence of fat insulation between the body and skin aids in heat flow away from the body.

In the winter when succulent plants are available, camels can obtain sufficient water in their food. During the summer, or when they are on dry food and have become dehydrated, they can rapidly drink back their water loss. Schmidt-Nielsen reports that one of his camels drank 27 gallons of water in ten minutes! The combination of a concentrated urine, ability to withstand dehydration, reduced water loss, proper insulation, and the ability to take in water rapidly permit the camel to survive in extreme desert conditions.

The donkey is native to arid climates and can tolerate the same degree of water loss (25 per cent) as the camel. However, the donkey loses water much more rapidly because the body temperature is more stable, the coat thinner, and sweating begins when the temperature rises only slightly. Thus, the donkey cannot go without water for long periods of time. The donkey has a truly amazing ability to drink back its water loss, however. A donkey can recover a 25 per cent loss of water in less than two minutes. This may be an advantage to wild donkeys, since an animal that could drink quickly from a water hole would be less likely to be killed by waiting predators.

Adaptation to Snow

Pruitt (1960) has emphasized the importance of snow in the life of many mammals. In many parts of the earth the repeated winter snowfall results in a deep but light and fluffy snow which covers the ground surface making movement difficult and covering the food supply. Because of these conditions, mammals such as the elk (*Cervus canadensis*) and caribou migrate to areas where the snow is absent or thin enough to allow them to dig down to the food plants. Small mammals, such as lemmings and mice, burrow beneath the snow where the temperatures are more moderate and where they have access to plant foods. In the taiga the temperature of the forest floor under the winter snow seldom drops below 20°F, even though the air above may fall to −50°F. One of the most difficult periods in the lives of these small mammals is during the season between the onset of freezing temperatures and the development of the proper depth of snow, about 6 in., according to Pruitt.

The large animals which are able to live in the snowy regions during the winter have the problem of moving about when snow is soft and reaches considerable depths. The long stilt-like legs of the moose (*Alces americana*) and the enlarged feet of the snowshoe hare aid these mammals to move in moderately deep snow. In deep, soft snow these species must resort to packing down trails and runways.

Hibernation and Estivation

Many mammals pass through unfavorable climatic periods by becoming inactive. When the animal is reacting thus to cold conditions, the period is called hibernation; when reacting to dry or hot conditions, the period is called estivation. The result of these adaptations is a time of dormancy, permitting the mammal to pass through an unfavorable climatic change with little expenditure of energy. Many studies of hibernation (Kayser, 1961; and Lyman and Dawe, 1960) have produced a storehouse of facts, but the basic problem of the environmental stimulus to hibernate remains a mystery. Few studies of estivation exist, but these suggest that the physiological processes are similar to those during hibernation. Indeed, some mammals may pass from estivation into hibernation.

Kinds of Hibernators

Many species hibernate. The monotremes, Echidna and Platypus, hibernate for periods up to ten days during the winter months (June to September). Unfortunately the absence of physiological observations prevents comparison with other mammals. Several marsupials have periods of dormancy with lowered temperature, but the details of physiological processes are not known. Rodents provide numerous examples of hibernation, and the process has been extensively studied in many species. Woodchucks (*Marmota monax*), ground squirrels of many kinds, dormice, jumping mice, jerboas, hamsters, and gerbills are known to hibernate. Insectivores also hibernate (hedgehogs (*Erinaceus europaeus*) and tenrecs (*Tenrec ecaudatus*)); although perhaps entrance into a state of torpidity is a better description of the process. Bats are notorious hibernators, and most species in the temperate zones spend the winter in caves for this purpose. However, many tropical species of bats do not and probably cannot hibernate. Among carnivores several types of hibernation occur. Badgers and skunks in many cases sleep a great deal during winter. Raccoons may hole up for many days, while bears sleep most of the winter but do not truly hibernate since their temperature remains normal.

Preparation

Before entrance into hibernation, a long period of preparation occurs. The best-known forms such as ground squirrels and woodchucks store up large quantities of fat. Others, such as bats and hamsters, accumulate moderate amounts or none at all. In addition, the mammal seeks an appropriate place. Bats migrate to caves, bears find hollow trees, woodchucks select a burrow. Not all individuals begin hibernation simultaneously. Indeed, in ground squirrels some individuals of the population may not hibernate at all in certain areas.

Physiological Processes

The actual mechanisms which initiate hibernation have not been identified, but there is basically a fluctuation and drop in the body temperature, with a decline in the rate of metabolism prior to dormancy. In hibernation many mammals curl into a tight ball, with the head placed beneath the tail. The body temperature follows the environmental temperature, which in many burrows is around 5 to 8°C. The heart rate is slowed, auriculo-ventricular dissociation occurs, and the blood pressure drops. These changes are associated with a decline in metabolic rate to 1/3 to 1/100 of the resting metabolic rate when the animal is in a homeothermic state. During hibernation the RQ is near 0.7, indicating that the animal is using stored fat for energy.

Hibernators seem to possess certain physiological modifications which are distinct from nonhibernators. For instance, hibernating mammals can be chilled to much lower temperatures than other mammals, and survive. In addition, their nerves can function at lower temperatures. The woodchuck, for instance, can tolerate a colonic temperature of 3°C, while most mammals cannot survive rectal temperatures much below 15°C. Nerves of nonhibernators usually stop functioning at about 8 to 9°C, while nerves of the hamster will function down to 3.4°C (Lyman and Chatfield, 1955).

Arousal

The process of waking from hibernation is dramatic. Slowly the rate of respiration and the body temperature begin to increase. Due to differential vasoconstriction, the temperature in the cranial part of the body leads the caudal part, so that in the hamster near the midpoint in the waking process, the cranial may be 20°C warmer than the caudal portion. Immediately before the waking process, the A-V dissociation disappears; this is followed by an increase in the heart rate and blood pressure. Glycogen is used as a source of energy and the metabolic rate rapidly rises. In eight hours the chilled animal can be fully awake and active.

Eventually the mammal comes out of its burrow, den, or cave and becomes truly active. During hibernation, ground squirrels and woodchucks wake up once or twice a week. In the spring their waking periods increase in duration. Arousal also occurs if the mammal is experimentally chilled to temperatures below freezing. These temperatures would result in death unless arousal occurred.

Adaptive Value

Hibernation permits many species to endure a difficult season. Some hibernate when food is scarce and/or the temperature is low. Others sleep while the environment is hot and dry. The deposits of fat, at least in the woodchuck, are not only used during hibernation (when metabolism is low) but also after arousal when green vegetation is sparse. The adaptive value is to permit the woodchuck to survive periods of snow and cold after arousal in February in temperate regions. It appears that some species have an automatic physiological device (an interior "clock") to stimulate arousal in the spring. The woodchuck, for example, is deaf and blind and completely insulated from the environment during hibernation. If he lacked some sort of a clock, he would never wake up! The mechanism is not understood at present. Other species may respond to environmental clues.

REFERENCES

Allen, G. M. 1939. Bats. Harvard Univ. Press. 368 pp.

Baumgartner, L. L. 1939. Food of the fox squirrel in Ohio. Ohio Wildlife Research Station Release, No. 108. 7 pp. (mimeo.).

Beddard, F. E. 1900. A Book of Whales. New York, G. P. Putnam's Sons. 320 pp.

Benedict, F. G. 1936. The physiology of the elephant. Carnegie Inst. of Wash. Publ. No. 474. 302 pp.

Bissell, H. D., B. Harris, H. Strong, and F. James. 1955. The digestibility of certain natural and artificial foods eaten by deer in California. Calif. Fish and Game 41: 57-78.

Bourliere, F. 1956. The Natural History of Mammals. 2nd ed. New York, Alfred A. Knopf, Inc. 364 pp.

Brody, S. 1945. Bioenergetics and Growth. Baltimore, Waverly Press. 1023 pp.

Brown, E. R. 1961. The black-tailed deer of western Washington. Wash. State Dept. Game Biol. Bull. 13. 124 pp.

Christian, J. J. 1950. Behavior of the mole (*Scalopus*) and the shrew (*Blarina*). J. Mamm. 31: 281-287.

Conaway, C. H. 1952. Life history of the water shrew (*Sorex palustris navigator*). Amer. Midl. Nat. 48: 219-248.

Connell, C. C. 1959. Seasonal lipid levels in three population groups of an old field ecosystem. Ph.D. Thesis. Univ. of Georgia.

Cowan, I. McT., A. J. Wood, and W. D. Kitts. 1957. Feed requirements of deer, beaver, bear, and mink for growth and maintenance. Trans. 22nd N. Amer. Wildlife Conf.: 179-188.

Dusi, J. L. 1949. Methods for the determination of food habits by plant microtechnics and histology and their application to cottontail rabbit food habits. J. Wildlife Mgt. 13: 295-298.

Eden, A. 1940. Coprophagy in the rabbit. Nature (London) 145: 36-37.

Eisentraut, M. 1936. Beitrag zur Mechanik der Fledermausfluges. Zeitschr. f. Wiss. Zool. 148. 159-188.

Fisher, K. C. 1958. An approach to the organ and cellular physiology of adaptation to temperature in fish and small mammals. In, Physiol. Adaptations. Amer. Soc. Physiol. (Washington): pp. 3-49.

Forbes, E. B., L. F. Marcy, A. L. Voris, and C. E. French. 1941. The digestive capacity of the white-tailed deer. J. Wildlife Mgt. 5: 108-114.

Golley, F. B. 1960. Energy dynamics of a food chain of an old-field community. Ecol. Monog. 30: 187-206.

Golley, F. B. 1961. Studies of energy flow in *Sigmodon hispidus*. Paper presented before Amer. Soc. Mamm., Univ. Illinois.

Griffin, D. R. 1958. Listening in the Dark. Yale Univ. Press. 413 pp.

Griffin, D. R. 1959. Echoes of Bats and Men. Garden City, N.Y., Doubleday & Co., Inc. 156 pp.

Grossman, M. I. 1955 Integration of current views on the regulation of hunger and appetite. Annals N. Y. Acad. Sci. 63: 76-91.

Harder, W. 1949. Zur Morphologie und Physiologie der Blinddarmes der Nagetiere. Verhandlung der Deutschen Zool. in Mainz.

Hart, J. S. 1957. Climatic and temperature induced changes in the energetics of homeotherms. Canad. Rev. Biol. 16: 133-174.

Hildebrand, M. 1959. Motions of the running cheetah and horse. J. Mamm. 40: 481-495.

Hildebrand, M. 1960. How animals run. Sci. Amer. 202(5): 148-157.

Howard, W. E. 1957. Amount of food eaten by small carnivores. J. Mamm. 38: 516-517.

Howell, A. B. 1930. Aquatic Mammals; Their Adaptations to Life in the Water. Springfield, C. C. Thomas. 338 pp.

Howell, A. B. 1944. Speed in Animals; the Specialization for Running and Leaping. Univ. Chicago Press.

Ingeburg, F., U. Hadden, and W. Harder. 1951. Zur Ernährungsphysiologie der Nagetiere: Uber die Bedeutung der Coecotrophie und der Zusammensetzung der Coecotrophie. Pflugers Archiv. 253: 173-180.

Irving, L. 1939. Respiration in diving mammals. Physiol. Rev. 19: 112-134.

Irving, L. and J. Krogh. 1954. Body temperatures of arctic and subarctic birds and mammals. J. Applied Physiol. 6: 667-680.

Irving, L., P. F. Scholander, S. W. Grinnell. 1942a. Significance of the heart rate to the diving ability of seals. J. Cell. Comp. Physiol. 18: 283-297.

Irving, L., P. F. Scholander, S. W. Grinnell. 1942b. The regulation of arterial blood pressure in the seal during diving. Amer. J. Physiol. 135: 557-566.

Kanwisher, J., and A. Senft. 1960. Physiological measurements on a live whale. Science 131: 1379-1390.

Kayser, C. 1961. The Physiology of Natural Hibernation. New York, Pergamon Press. 325 pp.

Kellog, R. 1928. The history of whales—their adaptation to life in water. Quart. Rev. Biol. 3: 29-76, 174-208.

Layne, J. N. 1954. The biology of the red squirrel, *Tamiasciurus hudsonicus loquax* (Bangs) in Central New York. Ecol. Monog. 24: 227-267.

Layne, J. N., and A. H. Benton. 1954. Some speeds of small mammals. J. Mamm. 35: 103-104.

Lyman, C. P., and P. O. Chatfield. 1955. Physiology of hibernation in mammals. Physiol. Rev. 35: 403-425.

Lyman, C. P., and A. R. Dawe. 1960. Mammalian hibernation. Bull. Mus. Comp. Zool. 124: 1-549.

Miyao, T., T. Kitazawa, and M. Morozumi. 1960. On the relation of the lengths of large intestine and caecum against the length of small intestine in rats. Dobutsu-gaku Zasshi 69(5): 19-24.

Morrison, P. R. and F. A. Ryser. 1952. Weight and body temperature in mammals. Science 116: 231-232.

Morrison, P. R., M. Pierce, and F. A. Ryser. 1957. Food consumption and body weight in the masked and short-tail shrew. Amer. Midl. Nat. 57: 493-501.

Murie, A. 1944. Wolves of Mount McKinley. USDI, Fauna Series No. 5. 238 pp.

Parry, D. A. 1949a. The anatomical basis of swimming in whales. Proc. Zool. Soc. (London) 119: 49-60.

Parry, D. A. 1949b. The swimming of whales, and a discussion of Gray's paradox. Brit. J. Exp. Biol. 26: 24-34.

Pearson, O. P. 1947. The rate of metabolism of some small mammals. Ecol. 28: 127-145.

Pruitt, W. O., Jr. 1960. Animals in the snow. Sci. Amer. 202(1): 60-68.

Rorig, G. 1905. Über den Nahrungsverbrauch einer Spitzmaus. Arb. Kaiserl. Gesundh. 4: 121-122.

Sealander, J. A., Jr. 1952. Food consumption in *Peromyscus* in relation to air temperature and previous thermal experience. J. Mamm. 33: 206-218.

Scheffer, V. B. 1958. Seals, Sea Lions and Walruses: A Review of the Pinnipedia. Stanford Univ. Press. 179 pp.

Schmidt-Nielsen, K. 1959. Physiology of the camel. Sci. Amer. 201: 140-151.

Schmidt-Nielsen, K., and B. Schmidt-Nielsen. 1952. Water metabolism of desert mammals. Physiol. Rev. 32: 135-166.

Scholander, P. F. 1940. Experimental investigations on the respiratory function in diving mammals and birds. Hvalraadets Skrifter, No. 22, Det Norske Vidinskaps Akademii, Oslo.

Scholander, P. F. 1955. Evolution of climatic adaptation in homeotherms. Evol. 9: 15-26.

Scholander, P. F., V. Walters, R. Hock, and L. Irving. 1950. Body insulation of some arctic and tropical mammals and birds. Biol. Bull. 99: 223-236.

Scholander, P. F., R. Hock, V. Walters, F. Johnson, and L. Irving. 1950. Heat regulation in some arctic and tropical birds and mammals. Biol. Bull. 99: 237-258.

Sharp, H. 1962. Nutrition and energy balance studies of the rice rat, *Oryzomys palustris*. MS, Thesis. Univ. of Georgia.

Springer, S. 1937. Observations on *Cryptotis floridana* in captivity. J. Mamm. 18: 237-238.

Svihla, R. D. 1929. Habits of *Sylvilagus aquaticus littoralis*. J. Mamm. 10: 315-319.

chapter five

THE EVOLUTION OF MAMMALS

IN AN EARLIER SECTION random mutation and selection were shown to be of fundamental importance in the evolution of species. The evolution of higher categories, genera, families, and orders can also be explained in terms of these processes. Here our objective will be to identify some of the major trends in the evolution of the mammals. In particular, we will discuss two processes: (1) the development of variety, or the branching of the phylogenetic tree (kladogenesis in the sense of Rensch, 1959) and (2) the development of complexity and versatility (progressive evolution or anagenesis—Rensch, 1959). In the first case we are concerned with the forms that were present in the evolutionary history of the mammals and in the second, with the direction of evolution.

In Chapter 2 the morphology and natural history of the orders of living mammals were briefly discussed. However, these living mammals represent only a small portion of the diverse forms which have belonged to the Class Mammalia. Simpson (1945) has pointed out that 44 per cent of all orders, 54 per cent of all families and 67 per cent of all genera are known only as fossils. These fossils then provide the facts of mammalian history, while our knowledge of the ecology, physiology, genetics and morphology of the soft parts of living mammals permit us to explain the facts of history, with the reasonable assumption that ecological, physiological, and genetic processes have remained unchanged throughout that history. Before considering trends of evolution, let us first evaluate the nature of the fossil evidence.

THE NATURE OF THE FOSSIL EVIDENCE

Fossils are usually found in beds or strata of sedimentary rock. Sedimentary rock is composed of material eroded from some pre-existing land surface, transported to its place of accumulation by rivers, the sea, wind, or ice, and deposited. Fossilization occurs since live animals or their carcasses may be trapped and rapidly buried in these sediments. After the sediment has reached its final resting place with the buried animals, it may undergo important changes before it is transformed into rock. For instance, sediment may be cemented into stone by the precipitation of materials such as calcium carbonate, or it may be chemically reduced or recrystallized. Later these beds of sedimentary rock may be uplifted and thereby become available for study by the paleontologist.

Bias of Sampling

Obviously all animals do not have an equal chance to become preserved, nor are all fossils equally available for study. Thus, the fossil record is only a sample of all the mammals which have lived in the past. In order to understand the population which this sample represents, the bias of the sample must be identified (Simpson, 1960a). First, there is the bias of preservation associated with the ecological characteristics of the individual species. Since fossils are found in sedimentary materials, animals that live where sediments are being formed have the best chance to become fossilized. Animals living on the eroding uplands seldom become fossils unless they are washed downstream by rivers and buried in alluvial deposits. In addition, not all individuals or parts of the same individual are equally fossilizable. Bones and teeth have the best chance of becoming fossilized—the soft parts are almost never preserved.

Second, bias is also associated with conditions of burial and subsequent preservation. We might expect that a group of fossils within the same bed of rock would represent a group of animals which lived together when alive (a biocenosis) but this is not always the case. In some instances the bodies of animals from several biocenoses have become grouped after death and form an aggregation called a thanatocenosis. Finally, after burial, the fossil-bearing sediments may be destroyed by erosion or by metamorphosis of the rock. Often there are major breaks in the column of sediments and the fossils in strata represented by these breaks are lost, unless they can be discovered in other, more complete, stratigraphic columns.

Third, there is bias associated with the collection of fossils. A fossil-bearing stratum must be exposed in a rock outcrop, roadcut, quarry, well, or some other place on dry land to be available to collectors. Where the exposed rock is greatly weathered or covered by vegetation, as in the tropics, the opportunity for collecting is greatly decreased. Finally, the collector can seldom follow the strata in a local column very far, and it is necessary to correlate the strata of many columns in order to make relatively complete collections.

Fourth, bias may also be associated with the processes of discovery. For instance, it is much easier to recognize fossils of large mammals than small mammals. Actually, for satisfactory collection of small fossils it may be necessary to break up the rock matrix and sieve the material for fossil bones and teeth, while larger fossils may be chipped from the rock outcrop or even recognized in the rock on the ground surface.

Fifth, not all areas of the globe have been equally searched. There has been some collecting on every continent, but vast regions in Central Asia, Africa, South America, and Australia are relatively unknown.

This consideration of bias of the fossil record may leave the reader with the impression that the sources of bias are so considerable that any generalizations made from a sample of fossils are suspect. Actually, this is not so. The very fact that we can recognize and account for bias aides us in making satisfactory generalizations. We can seek out more unbiased samples and we can allow for bias in otherwise unsuitable materials.

Determining the Age of Fossils

A further problem is to determine the age of the fossils or of the rock in which the fossils are located. Relative age is not difficult to determine since rockbeds lying close to the surface usually are deposited later than those below them. When strata have been tipped at a steep angle or turned over by warping and folding of the rock, careful examination will usually allow the geologist to distinguish the younger from the older beds. For instance, the grading of particles can be used for this purpose. Large particles are deposited toward the bottom of a stream or lake bed, with finer particles above the larger. If this condition is reversed in a stratum of rock, it is certain that the stratum has been overturned in some way.

The absolute time in years is much more difficult to determine. One method of estimating the absolute age of strata is to estimate the rates at which sediments form. For instance, Weller (1960) states that the

Thames River carries one-half million tons of mineral salts daily. These salts are mostly calcium carbonate eroded from limestone uplands. The surface of the limestone region is being lowered at a rate of 1 in. per 13,000 years. If the area of deposition of the salts on the sea bottom is known, then the rate of deposition and the age of the sediment can be calculated.

Recently, the study of radioactive isotopes has been applied to these problems. Radioactive isotopes are forms of elements which are unstable and give off particles and electromagnetic rays which can be detected with special equipment such as the Geiger counter. Each radioactive element disintegrates at a certain rate which is independent of the environment, and is gradually transformed into a stable form. The time for one-half of the activity of the isotope to be expended is called the half-life.

If a radioactive isotope was incorporated into the rock when it was formed and there was no subtraction or addition of materials which would alter the proportion of radioactive parent to daughter, then that proportion is a direct measure of the time elapsing since formation of the rock. The most useful method for old rocks today is the ratio of uranium or thorium or both, as parents, to lead as the daughter. More recently, methods using isotopes of rubidium, potassium, calcium, and carbon have been developed. Carbon [14], because of its rapid disintegration rate (half-life 5760 years), is only useful for geologically young materials deposited during the last 50,000 years. Recently the potassium[40]-argon[40] decay scheme has proved spectacularly successful in dating the age of the primitive tool-maker, *Zinjanthropus,* discovered by L. S. B. Leakey in Olduvai Gorge, Tanganyika, at 1,750,000 years.

By careful and detailed mapping of many columns of sedimentary rock throughout the world, stratigraphers have been able to recognize distinct eras, periods, and epochs, in the earth's history. These are based on the types of fossil life found in the strata and represent major changes in the life of the planet. The geological time scale and the absolute age of the divisions based on the most recent evidence (Kulp, 1961) are shown in Table 5-1.

TRENDS IN EVOLUTION

Examination of the fossil record suggests that the appearance of new forms of mammals is somewhat similar to the growth of individuals

TABLE 5-1.   The Geologic Time Scale

Era	Period	Epoch	Beginning of Interval (million years)
Cenozoic	Quaternary	Pleistocene	1
	Tertiary	Pliocene	13
		Miocene	25
		Oligocene	36
		Eocene	58
		Paleocene	63
Mesozoic	Cretaceous		135
	Jurassic		181
	Triassic		230
Paleozoic	Permian		280
	Carboniferous		345
	Devonian		405
	Silurian		425
	Ordovician		500

or populations. That is, after the point of origin, there is first a slow increase in the number of new forms, then a very rapid increase, followed by a diminishing appearance of new types and sometimes extinction (Table 5-2). The periods of origin, rapid expansion, specialization, and extinction will be considered below.

TABLE 5-2.   Number of New Families and Orders per Geological Epoch *

Geological Epoch	Number of Families	Number of Orders
Jurassic	7	3
Cretaceous	5	2
Early Tertiary	144	25
Paleocene and Eocene	102	19
Late Tertiary	46	1
Miocene	31	

* After Rensch, 1959.

The Origin of Mammals

During the later portion of the Paleozoic era the pelycosaur reptiles began a surge of evolutionary expansion which led to reptiles with premammalian characteristics. The pelycosaurs in the Permian gave rise to a broad group, the therapsid reptiles, which were the progenitors of the mammals. True mammals can be identified in late Triassic and

Jurassic, but during the lower and middle Triassic a number of mammal-like reptiles or reptile-like mammals were present. The question of the origin of mammals depends upon a decision as to which of these early forms were mammals and which were reptiles.

Since most of the fossil remains from these early periods consist of skull fragments, lower jaws, and teeth, most decisions about mammal phylogeny must rest on comparisons of tooth structure, jaw attachment, ear ossicles, and structure of the lower jaw. Using these structures, true reptiles can be distinguished from true mammals by the following characters (Figure 5-1).

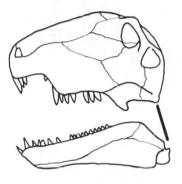 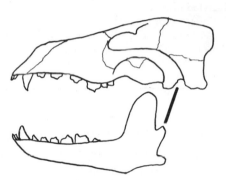

| PELYCOSAUR | MODERN |
| REPTILE | MAMMAL |

Figure 5-1. Diagrams Contrasting the Skull of a True Reptile with That of a True Mammal. Note the articulation of the lower jaw, indicated by the heavy line, and the number of bones in the mandible.

Reptile:
    (1) Articular-quadrate suspension of lower jaw.
    (2) No dentary-squamosal joint between lower jaw and skull.
    (3) One bone (stapes) in middle ear.
    (4) Mandible of more than one bone.

Mammal:
    (1) No articular-quadrate suspension.
    (2) Dentary-squamosal joint present.
    (3) Three ossicles in middle ear.
    (4) Mandible of one bone (the dentary).

During the Triassic transition period fossils with various combinations of all four key characters were present. Simpson (1959) has recognized nine different groups of mammals or mammal-like reptiles: Theria (Pantotheria), Symmetrodonta, Triconodonta, Docodonta, Morganucodontidae, Multituberculata, Tritylodontidae, Haramyidae, and Monotremeta (Table 5-3).

TABLE 5-3. Jaw Articulation, Number of Ear Ossicles, and Nature of the Mandible in the Eight Orders of Mammals or Premammals Probably Present in Late Triassic *

Order	Articular-Quadrate Suspension	Dentary-Squamosal Joint	Number of Ear Ossicles	Number of Bones in Mandible
Docodonta	yes	yes	1	many
Morganucodonta	yes	yes	1	many
Tritylodonta	yes	yes	1	many
Symmetrodonta	yes	yes	3	many
Pantotheria	no	yes	3	1
Triconodonta	no	yes	3	1
Multituberculata	no	yes	3	1
Monotremata	no	yes	3	1

* Haramyidae are known only from isolated teeth (Simpson, 1959).

Simpson (1959) suggests that there were four crossings from the therapsid reptile to the mammal line: (1) Symmetrodonta-Pantotheria-later Theria, (2) Triconodonta, (3) Docodonta (with Morganucodontidae)-Monotremata, and (4) Multituberculata. A minimal hypothesis would reduce these to two crossings, associating Symmetrodonta, Triconodonta, Docodonta, Monotremes, and Morganucodontidae with one crossing, Multituberculata with another, and considering Tritylodonts and Haramyids as reptiles. A maximal view would consider all nine groups making separate crossings. Figure 5-2 summarizes these hypotheses.

Each hypothesis outlined above leads to the conclusion that the mammals had a polyphyletic rather than a monophyletic origin. Since this conclusion appears to violate the taxonomic rule that each major taxonomic group must be monophyletic, there have been several recent attempts to re-examine the evidence for mammal origin. (See Van Valen, 1960; Reed, 1960; and Simpson, 1960b).

The conservative view suggests that the four criteria discussed above are most significant for distinguishing reptiles from mammals. Where these criteria do not separate the forms (see Table 5-3) the presence of a dentary-squamosal joint between the skull and lower jaw dis-

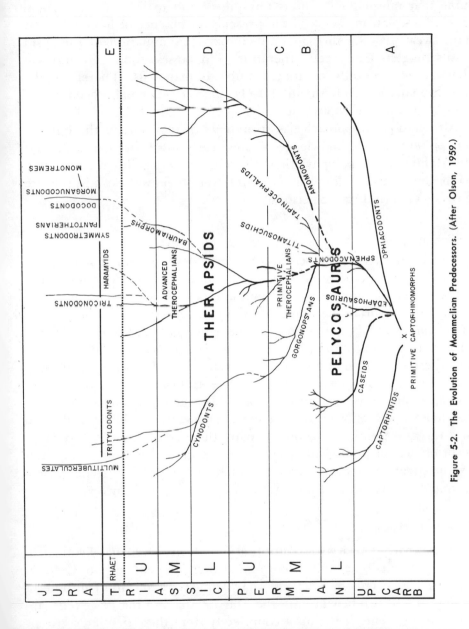

Figure 5-2. The Evolution of Mammalian Predecessors. (After Olson, 1959.)

tinguishes the mammals from the reptiles. Another approach is to assume that morphology reflects physiology and to infer from changes in skull and jaw morphology the presence or absence of homeothermy, hair, sweat glands, vibrissae, and vivipary. Examination of therapsid fossils suggests that several therapsids did possess some physiological characteristics usually attributed only to mammals. Therefore, the transitional therapsids should be classified as mammals, making the class Mammalia monophyletic.

Although each approach has arguments in its favor, in the light of our present state of knowledge of these early fossils, we conclude that the Mammalia are polyphyletic with from two to possibly nine individual orders of mammals crossing the line from therapsid stock in the late Triassic or early Jurassic periods.

Radiation

Radiation refers to the periods of intense development of new forms. Radiation may be the result of a combination of high rate of mutation, intense selection, proper size of population, and proper habitat conditions. Two important periods of radiation in the developmental history of mammals can be recognized in the Paleocene and Eocene—over a time-span of about 30 million years. Preceding these periods of radiation there was a long period of slow development. First, in the Jurassic, six orders of mammal were probably present: Triconodonta, Symmetrodonta, Pantotheria, Multituberculata, Docodonta (and Morganucodontidae), and Monotremata. These were generally small, about the size of a rat, and were omnivorous. During the Age of Reptiles any large form of mammal life would have been in danger of being devoured by the great carnivorous reptiles which dominated the scene. These mammals are recognized largely by tooth structure (Figure 5-3).

Cretaceous Mammals

In the early Cretaceous, Pantotheria, Multituberculata, Symmetrodonta, Triconodonta, and Monotremata were present; in late Cretaceous times the primitive Triconodonta, Symmetrodonta, and Pantotheria disappear and two new groups, the Marsupialia and the Placentals, appear on the scene. It is almost completely from these two later groups that our mammal fauna of today is derived. The four late Cretaceous orders were characterized as follows:

Multituberculata: The order Multituberculata was a highly special-ized and successful group which first appeared in Jurassic times and persisted to the Eocene. The structure of the skull and teeth indicate that these primitive mammals were herbivores, analogous to the pres-ent-day rodents, and that they reached relatively large size for Jurassic mammals—some may have been as large as the woodchuck (*Marmota monax*). The skull was massive and stoutly built and the dentition was

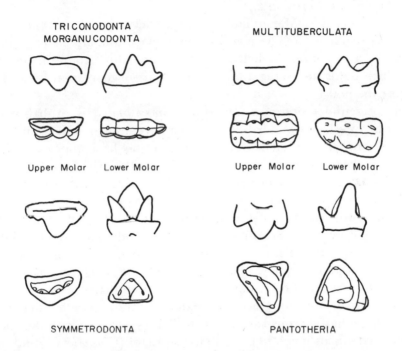

Figure 5-3. Diagrams of the Tooth Structure of Some Jurassic Orders of Mammals. (Redrawn from Simpson, 1935.)

quite specialized. A pair of incisors were enlarged above and below, with small lateral incisors sometimes persisting in the upper jaw. The canines were lost. Following the diastema was a well-developed row of molar teeth. These molars were elongated with two or three parallel rows of cusps (Figure 5-3). In the lower jaw, in many multituberculates, the posterior premolar was modified into an enlarged cutting tooth. Although the order flourished throughout the early history of mammals, the evolutionary stem was sterile and did not give rise to any later groups of modern mammals.

Monotremata: The Monotremata was a highly specialized, yet primitive order which is essentially unidentified as fossils. Unlike other, living mammals, the monotremes have characteristics of both reptiles (young born in eggs, imperfect temperature regulation) and mammals (mammary glands, and hair). They presumably arose, separately from other Theria, from therapsid reptile stock. Recently Kermack and Mussett (1958) have suggested that they were derived from the Morganucodonta and the Docodonta.

Marsupialia: The Marsupialia probably developed from Pantothere stock independently of the placental mammals. Marsupials are characterized by a pouch on the belly of the female, which contains the teats and which holds the young after birth. A pair of marsupial bones help support the pouch.

The present-day opossum (*Didelphis marsupialis*) is probably very similar in appearance and habits to the Cretaceous marsupials, and gives us an idea of how this element of the fauna may have appeared. These animals were probably omnivorous and partly arboreal. From this primitive type a variety of marsupials evolved in South America and Australia, where they were free from competition with placental mammals. In South America placental carnivores were absent, and marsupials evolved a variety of carnivorous forms including a marsupial sabertooth tiger. In Australia, the primitive marsupials were free to radiate extensively since only a few placental rodents and bats were able to invade the Continent. The radiation of Australian marsupials eventually paralleled many of the placental mammals and included marsupial wolves, large herbivorous kangaroos, wallabies, large rodent-like forms, gliding marsupials much like the flying squirrel (*Glaucomys*), and marsupial moles. However, the marsupials were never able to invade the air or sea. Throughout the rest of the world the marsupials have remained subordinate to the placental mammals.

Placental Mammals: The placental mammals differ from the marsupials in that they do not have a pouch or marsupial bones and the young are nourished *in utero* through the placenta. Primitive placental mammals are known from the Cretaceous of Mongolia and North America, and the fossil skulls indicate that these animals were small and presumably insectivorous. Our modern Insectivora (shrews, moles, and hedgehogs) retain many primitive characters, and the early placental mammals are sometimes considered as unspecialized Insectivora.

The Time of Origin and Derivation of the Orders of Mammals.   (The position of the name indicates the age of the earliest fossil.)

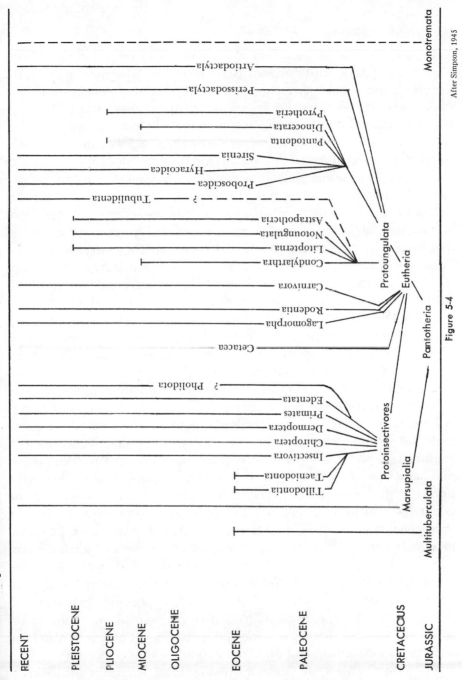

Figure 5-4

After Simpson, 1945

The Paleocene Radiation

Throughout the Mesozoic era the reptiles retained a dominant position in the fauna, while mammals remained for the most part small, secretive, and subordinate elements. Following this period of reptile dominance, the fossil record shows an abrupt change: the ruling reptiles lose their dominance and the mammals increase greatly and become the dominant form of life on earth (Figure 5-4). Simpson (1937) has drawn the analogy to this replacement of reptiles by mammals as the lowering of the curtain on one cast of actors, and then its immediate rise on a different cast—but in the same roles. The increase in mammals did not come from the four late Cretaceous orders equally, but from an extensive radiation of the Placental mammals. At least sixteen orders of mammals were present in the Paleocene epoch, and although the faunas from North America, Asia, Europe, and South America are not the same, they show a common ancestry. These orders include the Multituberculata, Marsupialia, Insectivora, Primates, Taenidonta, Carnivora, Condylarthra, Pyrotheria, Tillodonta, Edentata, Notoungulata, Astrapotheria, Dinocerata, Rodentia, Lagomorpha, and Dermoptera. Most of these early mammals were similar in appearance. The skulls had long, narrow brain-cases and a long, slender rostrum, with the orbits near the middle of the skull. The fore and hind limbs were of equal length, the trunk was rather long, and the tail long and heavy. All were pentadactyl and most were plantigrade. These primitive mammals had a heterodont dentition, with a dental formula of incisors 3/3, canines 1/1, premolars 4/4, molars 3/3. Every known Paleocene mammal has a similar pattern of the molar teeth or can be traced through a known sequence to an older type which does, with the exception of the edentates which have degenerate teeth when they appear in the Paleocene. This pattern, which was ancestral for the later placental mammals, consisted, on the lower molars, of an elevated anterior portion (trigonid) with one outer cusp (protoconid) and two inner cusps (paraconid and metaconid) and a lower posterior portion (talonid) with three cusps on its elevated rim (entoconid, hypoconid, hypoconulid) (Figure 5-5). The upper molars had three main cusps: one inner (protoconule) and two outer (paracone and metacone). There may also have been two intermediate cuspules (protoconule and metaconule).

The typical Paleocene fauna was made up of abundant Multituberculates, occupying the ecologic role of the later rodents, primitive

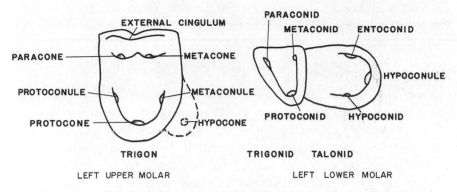

Figure 5-5. Diagram of the Tooth Structure of a Generalized Paleocene Mammal. (Redrawn from Simpson, 1937.)

primates in arboreal habitats, large fossorial taenidonts, carnivorous creodonts, and the terrestrial herbivorous Condylarthra and Pyrotheria. All of these types survived the Paleocene but gradually diminished in importance, and except for some primates and creodonts, none survived to the end of the Eocene.

The sudden appearance of the Paleocene fauna suggests that it did not develop in North America where most of the fossils of this period have been found, but rather immigrated into North America from some other continent. However, the source of these hypothetical immigrants is unknown (Simpson 1937).

The Eocene Radiation

In North America, and probably in Europe and Asia, a modern mammalian fauna gradually replaced the Paleocene fauna. This modern fauna was the result of a second radiation which gave rise to all of our present-day orders and many families. These new forms were not derived from the Paleocene fauna but developed from a stock common to both, probably living in Asia, which immigrated into North America where they replaced the primitive forms. The completeness of the replacement of the Paleocene fauna by the Eocene mammals is shown by the fact that the most abundant Eocene mammals did not even belong to the same orders as the dominant Paleocene mammals.

In South America conditions were considerably different. The land connection between North and South America was broken in late Cretaceous or early Tertiary, and the Paleocene fauna persisted and developed unmolested to the Pliocene. The type of change which took place in North America during Paleocene-Eocene time occurred in South America in Pliocene-Pleistocene time. The phenomena were the same in both instances.

The Causes of Radiation

From this discussion we can see that the radiation of the mammals was a successive rather than an explosive process. The intensified rate of development of new forms of mammals may be explained by an increased rate of mutation and/or intensified natural selection. Although mutation rates may have been increased by the high temperatures in the early Tertiary, it is more likely that, in the warm and temperate climates prevailing over the earth, favorable mutations were expressed more readily than when a cold season interrupted the life cycles of the animals. Actually, the assumption of a higher mutation rate is not needed to explain the radiation; the natural mutation rate provides a wealth of variety and we only need to assume an intensified selection.

Natural selection leading to the dominance and radiation of mammals came about in part for three reasons. First, the evolution of angiosperms in the late Mesozoic provided new food, shelter, and habitats which mammals could utilize. Many times during the evolution of living organisms, formation and development of heterotrophs followed the development of autotrophs. For instance, the mammals first emerged following the appearance of ferns, cycads, and conifers in the Paleozoic. Terrestrial snails, many types of insects and birds, as well as mammals, all showed radiations in the early Tertiary. Apparently the new ecological conditions resulting from angiosperm evolution were detrimental to the ruling reptiles but provided suitable conditions for other terrestrial animals.

Second, natural selection was especially effective where the range of the animal was sufficiently expanded, so that the form met new conditions of selection. Peripheral populations may become adjusted to different conditions from those surrounding the central populations, and then, if some form of isolation intervenes, the peripheral forms may develop into new species. This process is clearly seen on islands, and presumably was very significant where the Paleocene fauna expanded and migrated into new areas.

Third, even if the niches were already occupied by animals, they may have been reconquered by stronger competitive types, which is actually the same situation as though the habitats had not been occupied at all. The mammals were more adaptable, more active and more intelligent than the reptiles they replaced. The placental mammals were superior in brain performance and in the care of the young to the more primitive types present in the late Cretaceous, and could successfully replace them. An example of this process has been observed in Australia in historical times. There the marsupials radiated extensively, free from competition with placental mammals, and developed climbing, jumping, running, burrowing, herbivorous, insectivorous, and carnivorous forms; however, as soon as man introduced placental mammals into the Australian continent, many of these marsupials were displaced.

The Period of Specialization

Following the period of radiation there is a phase of specialization during which no new types (higher categories) are formed, but many types show increasing evolutionary adaptation to various aspects of the environment. The phase of specialization appears to be the result of two contrasting tendencies. First, the new niches are gradually filled, leaving fewer opportunities for development without active competition. And second, since trends in adaptation during a radiation phase may lead to suboptimum structures, during the phase of specialization there may be improvement of the types, permitting successful competition for the occupied niches.

An example of the improvement of structural type is seen in the development, in Carnivora, of the carnassial teeth suited for cracking bones (Rensch, 1959). Several kinds of adaptation occurred in Eocene carnivores (Creodonta). In some, the second upper and third lower molars were enlarged, and developed cutting edges; in others the first upper and second lower molars were enlarged. In both cases, however, these specialized teeth could not be enlarged beyond a certain point, since they were placed too far to the rear in the jaw. Animals with this type of dentition soon disappeared, and only those which used the fourth upper premolar and the first lower molar for cracking bones persisted. In these the teeth were far enough forward to enlarge and develop into the efficient carnassial teeth of our present-day Felidae.

During a phase of radiation, many experiments in combination of structures are tried. These experiments are to be expected, since muta-

tion is essentially a random process. Later, during the phase of specialization, many of the experiments prove unsuccessful and are eliminated.
The history of the Perissodactyla illustrates this phenomenon clearly. In
the Eocene, primitive Perissodactyla appeared. These gave rise to
several lines of descent, one leading to the present-day horses and the
other to the tapirs and rhinocerotes. In addition, several other forms
were derived from the primitive horse stock. First, the Titantotheres
tended to a large size, with horn-like processes on the skull and very
unprogressive teeth. The molars in these animals had a zig-zag-shaped
pattern of enamel folds on the buccal side of the crown, but on the lin-
gual side the crowns were blunt. However, the blunt side was lower than
the enamel folds, and could not be used until the enamel wore down to
their level. Second, the Chalicotheres had teeth similar to the Titantotheres, with a typical Perissodactyla skull and skeleton; however, instead
of hooves on the feet this group had claws which may have been used as
root-digging organs. These various combinations of characters did not
prove successful, and led to extinction of the Titantotheres and other
types in the Oligocene and Miocene in North America and Europe,
and to that of the Chalicotheres in the Pleistocene in Africa and Asia.

Extinction

This brings us to a consideration of the disappearance or extinction
of animal forms. Extinction may come about by competition with newly
developed or newly arrived superior types. The replacement of the
Paleocene orders by advanced placental mammals is an illustration of
this type of extinction. On a continental scale the replacement of South
American and Australian marsupials by advanced placental mammals
provides a further example. More recently, release of the mongoose
(*Herpestes auropunctatus*) on the island of Jamaica caused the extinction of several species of rodents, reptiles, and birds.

Extinction may also occur in certain species as a consequence of their
own evolution. In many of the mammals there has been a tendency to
become increasingly specialized for a certain set of conditions. However, the specialist loses the ability to respond to a variety of conditions.
For instance, excessive development of special organs, such as the enlarged antlers of the Irish elk (*Megaceros*), may handicap the species
in adapting to new conditions. Actually, random mutation could lead
to a return to the earlier, less specialized form, but the chance of this
occurring is so low that irreversibility of evolution is the rule.

EVOLUTIONARY PROGRESS

Because of the great number of variations arising as a result of random mutations of morphological and physiological characters, and the extensive variety in conditions of habitat and environment, one might expect evolution to be an erratic process following a zig-zag path by favoring certain characters or combinations of characters at random, and eliminating others. However, in general, this is not so. In many lines of descent definite evolutionary trends may be recognized. And further, in many instances, these trends show a progressive tendency, with an increase in complexity, in efficiency of the vital processes, and in plasticity.

Increase in Body Size

A very general tendency in almost every mammalian ancestry has been a progressive increase in body size. The giant forms which probably evolved from small ancestors represent the end types of phyletic stems or branches. This tendency, called Cope's Rule, is especially well established in the Artiodactyla. The recent types of camels and llamas originated from rabbit-sized Eocene ancestors which also gave rise, via another line, to animals the size of the rhinoceros. In the Cervidae, the Miocene ancestors were small, being the size of a roe deer, and gave rise to the Pleistocene giants, *Megaceros* and *Alces latifrons*. The early forms of the Giraffidae were also small. These same trends can be seen in almost all groups for which a fossil record is available, with the exception of certain species living in very small habitats, or that fly. In flying forms a large size would be a disadvantage since the area of the wing only doubles when the weight triples.

The Advantage of Large Size

Since random mutation should give rise to both large and small varieties, there has also been in almost all lines of descent a parallel tendency toward small types of animals. Yet the small or dwarf forms are not, and appear never to have been, very successful or numerous. Large size seems to have been an advantage throughout the history of mammals. There are a number of reasons why largeness might be a positive value in selection. First, large forms are more vigorous and resistant. In mammals, where there are several young born per litter, the weakest embryos have a greater tendency to die in utero or at birth.

After birth, the struggle for food and care begins. The smallest young will often be pushed aside by the more vigorous siblings, and quite often the weaker will be stunted or may die as a consequence. In adult animals, the larger and more vigorous will be more often successful in the keen competition for food, for shelter, or escape. In sexual competition the larger male is favored where fighting among males is an essential part of the behavior pattern. The smaller males may have less chance to breed successfully and may be killed in combat.

Second, large species may be more competitive since they occupy wide ecological niches. When interspecies competition develops between a large and small form, the larger may have an advantage since it may range over a wider area of habitat and thereby have a greater chance to find suitable aggregations of food and other requirements.

Third, due to the effects of allometric growth, the body and organ proportions of larger types differ from those of small forms, and may be of positive selective value. According to Rensch (1959) the growth ratios of single organs and structures in relation to the whole body remain constant for certain periods. An organ or structure can grow more quickly than the whole body (positive allometry), more slowly (negative allometry), or at the same rate (isometry). In some instances these growth gradients may remain contant throughout the life of the animal and in other cases several different growth gradients may follow one another or may change from positive to negative allometry or vice versa. These changes often coincide with birth, puberty, and so forth. For instance, in many mammals the head grows with positive allometry during prenatal life, but after birth grows with negative allometry. If body size is enlarged and therefore growth is accelerated or the period of growth prolonged, then allometric growth becomes more apparent. Organs with positive allometry will become larger and eventually excessively large, while organs with negative allometry will become smaller and eventually vestigal.

Growth in Organs of Attack and Defense

Rensch has pointed out that in many mammals the organs for attack or self defense show positive allometry. For instance, after loss of the milk teeth, the permanent teeth must grow more quickly than the body as a whole, and with increasing body size the permanent teeth may become excessively large. This tendency is not particularly evident where the premolars and molars are concerned, since excessive growth of these teeth disturbs articulation of the jaws and would be disadvantageous. However, the incisors and canines are not similarly restricted, and in many large forms—elephants, walruses, hippopotamuses, pigs, cats, etc.—excessive growth of these teeth is seen. For instance, the early Proboscidea had a complete set of teeth with only slightly enlarged incisors. By the Oligocene, *Palaeomastodon* had enlarged to about the size of a small elephant and four tusks had developed from the incisors. From these evolved the large Miocene and Pleistocene mastodons, in which the lower incisors were missing. In some of the largest Proboscidea the tusks were no longer useful for defense but curved backward in great arcs. In the cats a similar tendency is observed, but in this case it involves the canines. The trend here leads to the huge stabbing canines of the sabertooth tiger (*Smilodon*).

Another set of structures for defense associated with the skull, the horns or antlers, grow with positive allometry. In very small types of Miocene deer the antlers are a little longer than the skull, but with increasing body size these grow into huge structures reaching the excessive size seen in *Megaceros*.

Growth of the Brain

The skull and brain also show these same kinds of relationships. The facial portion of the skull tends to grow relatively faster than the head as a whole, so that in large mammals the skull is longer than in small forms (compare the cat with the lion). The brain grows with negative postnatal allometry, and in general the size of the brain in large species is relatively smaller than in related small species. The different portions of the brain also grow with different ratios and thus, in large species of mammals, the brain stem (the brain without the pallium and cerebellum) is relatively smaller than in small, related species. From this it would seem probable that the larger forms would be capable of more complicated associations, be more plastic, and have better memory than the small forms. In addition, there may be more neurons and dendrites in the brain of large forms, since increase in size is usually the result of increased numbers of cells rather than increased cell size.

Chemical Differentiation

Associated with the tendency to growth in size and complexity of organs and structures is a tendency toward increasing chemical differentiation. The formation of new forms often means an alteration in the chemical background of the body (as shown by precipitation tests and paper chromatography) arising from the large variety of possible proteins, and other organic compounds.

Further Advantages of Size

Large mammals may also be more successful than their small relatives for physiological reasons. In large forms the rate of metabolism is proportionately less, due partly to a relatively smaller loss of body heat. Larger species may therefore have an advantage in cooler regions. In the glacial period there was a widespread evolution of large or giant forms in most mammalian orders. Some of the best known of these are the giant Mammoths (*Elephas primigenius* and *E. imperator*), giant beaver (*Castoroides*); and giant sloths (*Megatherium*). Giant forms developed not only in North America and Europe but also in South America, Australia, and other areas. The development of so many large forms was surely not accidental and probably reflects the advantage of the larger forms in a cooling climate.

Finally, large mammals usually live longer than related small forms. Increased longevity would be a favorable character since the animals would have a longer time to find the best habitat, to gather individual experience, to accumulate antibodies, and to adapt in other ways to the variety of conditions found in the natural systems.

Of course, we must not overlook the fact that selection affects the growth pattern of certain organs. For instance, hoofed mammals living on the steppes must be able to run rapidly to escape from predators, and the selection for quick, long-legged forms may act against the trend of allometric growth. All hooved animals arose from small omnivorous or insectivorous Cretaceous ancestors, whose legs probably grew with negative allometry before birth, resulting in young with relatively short legs. These would be a disadvantage on the steppes, and selection probably acted against this tendency, resulting in a positive allometry in the legs before birth (as in present-day Artiodactyla and Perissodactyla).

Evolutionary progression also involves increased efficiency of performance, and versatility. In part, this may be brought about through simplification or concentration of control in fewer centers.

The Trend Toward Complexity

It appears that there is a progressive tendency in all natural systems, individuals, populations, species, and ecosystems (see Margalef, 1957) toward complexity of structure and function. The reason for this tendency is because complexity leads to stability and therefore improved survival. The simple system is subject to violent oscillations and possible death because of its less efficient regulatory mechanisms but, in addition, it is also capable of rapid growth and development if the resources permit. These simple systems are the invaders or pioneers in changing nature. A trend toward complexity is not an unmixed blessing, since overspecialization may result and inhibit sufficient response to normal fluctuations of the environment, thus leading to failure and extinction. The trend to overspecialization is universal, and since most systems are unable to control this tendency to complexity, there is a continuing wave of developing forms arising from the simple and small systems and moving toward complexity and overdevelopment.

Parallel Evolution

Finally, we might consider the common tendency for faunas derived from different ancestors to develop forms with similar morphology and ecology in widely separated areas. These parallelisms may arise from several different sources. First, they may be due to similar hereditary factors, such as parallel mutation. Identical genes could result in parallel mutation; mutation of homologous genes could also lead to this phenomenon (as in albinism and melanism, observed in many populations of mammals). If mutation occurs in characters carrying strong correlative effects on other organs and structures (such as body size) the resulting forms may show marked similarity.

Second, and possibly of more importance than similar heredity, is parallelism arising from parallel selection of analogous rather than homologous structures and organs. For example, there are striking similarities in the teeth of mammals eating the same kinds of food, in the body shape in those living in the same habitats, and in the faunas of different geographical areas and habitats. There are a limited number of kinds of food, a limited efficiency in using these foods, and a limited number of ecological roles (niches) in any natural system. These limits place very strong selective pressure on the available genetic material, with the result that mammals of widely different ancestry do similar jobs with similar structures in all parts of the earth.

REFERENCES

Kermack, K. A. and F. Mussett. 1958. The jaw articulation of the Docodonta and the classification of Mesozoic mammals. Proc. Royal Soc., B. 148: 204-215.

Kulp, J. L. 1961. Geologic time scale. Science 133: 1105-1114.

Margalef, D. R. 1957. Information theory in ecology. Mem. d. l. Real. Acad. Ciencias y Artes d. Barcelona 23: 375-449.

Olson, E. C. 1959. The evolution of mammalian characters. Evolution 13: 344-353.

Reed, C. A. 1960. Polyphyletic or monophyletic ancestry of mammals, or: What is a class? Evolution 14: 314-322.

Rensch, B. 1959. Evolution Above the Species Level. London, Methuen & Co. Ltd. 419 pp.

Simpson, G. G. 1935. The first mammals. Quart. Rev. Biol. 10: 154-180.

Simpson, G. G. 1937. The beginning of the age of mammals. Cambridge Philosoph. Soc., Biol. Rev. 12: 1-47.

Simpson, G. G. 1945. The principles of classification and a classification of mammals. Bull. Amer. Mus. Nat. Hist. 85: 1-350.

Simpson, G. G. 1959. Mesozoic mammals and the polyphyletic origin of mammals. Evolution 13: 405-414.

Simpson, G. G. 1960a. The history of life. In, Evolution after Darwin. Vol. 1. The Evolution of Life, Sol. Tax, Ed. Univ. Chicago Press. pp. 117-180.

Simpson, G. G. 1960b. Diagnosis of the classes reptilia and mammalia. Evolution 14: 388-392.

Van Valen, L. 1960. Therapsids as mammals. Evolution 14: 304-313.

Weller, J. M. 1960. Stratigraphic Principles and Practice. New York, Harper & Bros. 725 pp.

chapter six

ZOOGEOGRAPHY

ZOOGEOGRAPHY IS CONCERNED with describing and understanding special patterns of the distribution of animals. The emphasis, especially in the past, has been almost solely on a description of distribution over space; a more recent objective has been to understand the use of space through time. The interaction of space and time is especially significant to evolutionary theory, since geographical isolation may prevent gene flow between populations. Modern students of zoogeography are primarily interested in the place and time of origin and the subsequent history of the movement of taxa.

DISTRIBUTION PATTERNS

Early workers in zoogeography were very active in categorizing the distribution patterns of individual taxa into generalized geographical groupings. It became obvious to the students of mammals in the 18th and 19th centuries that the mammal fauna of the world was not uniform over the continents but, rather, was grouped into relatively homogeneous units which were separated from other units by regions of transition. These homogeneous units were termed faunal regions (Figure 6-1). Although faunal regions are usually shown on maps as sharply delimited units, they actually represent averages of the individual patterns of distribution of the taxa in the fauna. Therefore, we would expect that some of the individual taxa would range far beyond the boundaries of a particular faunal region, while others would be confined to only a portion of a region. The reality of these geographical units is attested to by the fact that most zoogeographers have proposed

133

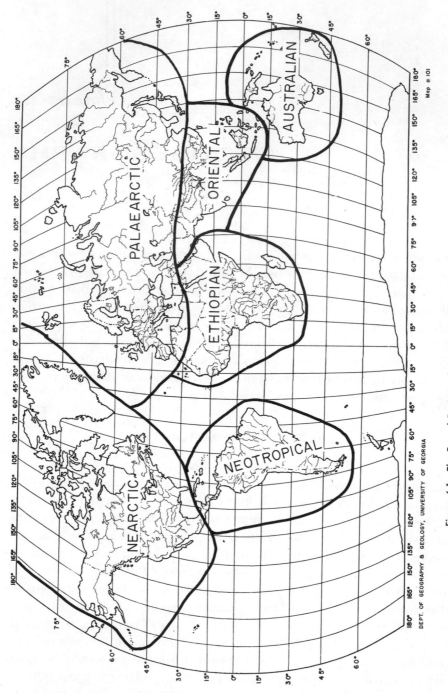

Map # IOI

DEPT. OF GEOGRAPHY & GEOLOGY, UNIVERSITY OF GEORGIA

Figure 6-1. The Faunal Regions of the World. (Modified from Sclater, 1858.)

the same general areas as regions, even though they have not agreed on their limits. For a history of ideas about faunal regions Wallace (1876), Lydekker (1896) and Schmidt (1954) might be consulted.

Sclater's (1858) divisions, somewhat modified by later workers and reported by Darlington (1957), form a suitable basis for a description of mammalian distribution. The commonly accepted system is:

Realm Megagea: the main part of the world:

  (1) Ethiopian Region: Africa, except the northern corner, with part of southern Arabia.
  (2) Oriental Region: tropical Asia, with associated continental islands.
  (3) Palearctic Region: Eurasia above the tropics.
  (4) Nearctic Region: North America, except the tropical part of Mexico.

Realm Neogea

  (5) Neotropical Region: South and Central America.

Realm Notogea

  (6) Australian Region: Australia with New Guinea.

In addition, the Palearctic and Nearctic are often combined into the Holarctic region.

Data for Study of Distribution Patterns

The basic data for description and comparison of faunal regions are lists of genera and species, and maps of their ranges of distribution. These lists are available for most parts of the world, but the value of the lists varies greatly because the study of nomenclature of the mammals in the light of modern taxonomy has not been equal everywhere, and because individual taxonomists have different bases for making taxonomic decisions (some are "lumpers" and some are "splitters"). If the species lists are reliable, or if the bias in the lists can be recognized and corrected for, they can be used to determine the degree of commonness or resemblance between faunas. A number of workers, including Simpson (1953) and Burt (1958), have reduced these lists to mathematical indices of resemblance or dissimilarity. There are various ways to do this. For instance, Simpson (1953) uses $100\ C/N_1$, where C is the number of genera in common to the two faunas and N_1 is the total number of genera in the smaller of the two. Burt suggests

TABLE 6-1. Living Mammals of the Ethiopian Faunal Region and Their Zoogeographic Relationships *

Groups	Relationships
Otter shrews	Exclusive family
Golden moles	Exclusive
Hedgehogs	Eurasia
Elephant shrews	Almost exclusive
Shrews	World-wide
Fruit bats	Old-World tropics
Insectivorous bats	
Mouse-tailed bats	Northeastern Africa, southern Asia
Sheath-tailed bats	Tropical
Hollow-faced bats	Oriental
Big-eared bats	Oriental
Horseshoe bats	Oriental
Vespertilionid bats	World-wide
Free-tailed bats	Tropical world-wide
Loris	Oriental
Old-world monkeys	Oriental
Great apes	Oriental
Scaly anteater	Oriental
Dogs	World-wide
Weasels	World-wide
Civet cats	Oriental and Palearctic
Hyenas	Asia
Cats	World-wide
Aardvark	Exclusive order
Elephants	Oriental
Hyraxes	Almost exclusive
Horses	Palearctic
Rhinocerotes	Oriental
Pigs	Eurasia
Hippopotamuses	Exclusive
Tragulid	Oriental
Giraffes	Exclusive
Bovids	Eurasia and a few in North America
Rabbits	World-wide
Squirrels	World-wide
Anomalurids	Exclusive
Spring haas	Exclusive
Cricetids	World-wide
Bamboo rats	Oriental
Murids	Old-World
Dormice	Palearctic
Jerboas	Palearctic
Old-World porcupines	Oriental

* Modified from Darlington (1957).

that $(C/(N_1 + N_2 - C) \times 100$, where C and N are as above and N_2 is the total number of genera in the larger fauna, might be more appropriate, especially when the two faunas are equal in size. The source of zoogeographical data should be remembered when we use these indices, since reduction of lists of taxa to numbers implies a high degree of taxonomic accuracy which may or may not be present. Actually many workers still rely strongly on their personal familiarity with the fauna when determining the degree of resemblance between regions (Burt, 1958).

Ethiopian Region

Table 6-1 gives a general list of the living mammals of the Ethiopian faunal region, as described by Darlington (1957) in his detailed study of the zoogeography of the vertebrates. The list shows that in general the Ethiopian mammals are strongly related to those in the Oriental region, but that the region also has important endemic groups which have no living relatives outside Africa. The region is bounded by ocean, except on the north where it is bounded by the Sahara desert. The mammals in the northwest corner of Africa (Morocco and Algeria) are more European in their relationships, while in the deserts between north and central Africa the fauna is specialized and transitional between Europe and Africa. Southwestern Arabia also has a fauna transitional to the Ethiopian region. Within the region the greatest diversity of species is found in the central tropical area, with a strong reduction of diversity northward toward the deserts and a less strong reduction southward.

Oriental Region

The Oriental region is ecologically like the Ethiopian, and the mammal fauna is quite similar (Table 6-2). In addition, the fauna shows resemblances to the Palearctic. Relatively few endemics are confined to the Oriental region and the boundaries are not sharply defined. A transition area occurs in the dry country of northwestern India, while the Himalaya mountains form a natural barrier to the north. In the south-China area occurs a wide transition zone with the Palearctic. To the south and east, the islands of Ceylon, Formosa, Sumatra, Java, Borneo, and the Philippines are included in the region. Beyond Java and Borneo the Oriental fauna forms a limited transition with the Australian.

TABLE 6-2. Living Mammals of the Oriental Fauna Region and Their Relationships *

Groups	Relationships
Spiny hedgehog	Ethiopian and Palearctic
Hairy hedgehog	Exclusive
Shrews	World-wide
Moles	Palearctic
Fruit bats and insectivorous bats	Ethiopian
Flying lemur	Exclusive
Tree shrews	Exclusive
Lorisids	Ethiopian
Tarsiers	Exclusive
Old-world monkeys	Ethiopian
Apes	Ethiopian
Scaly anteaters	Ethiopian
Dogs	World-wide
Bears	Palearctic and Nearctic
Weasels	World-wide
Civet Cats	Old-World
Hyena	Ethiopian
Cats	World-wide
Elephant	Ethiopian
Tapir	Neotropical
Rhinocerotes	Ethiopian
Wild pigs	Ethiopian and Palearctic
Chevrotains	Ethiopian
Deer	Palearctic and Nearctic
Bovids	Ethiopian and Palearctic, Nearctic
Rabbits	World-wide
Squirrels	World-wide
Flying squirrels	Palearctic and Nearctic
Cricetids	World-wide
Bamboo rats	Ethiopian
Murids	Old-World
Spiny dormice	Exclusive
Old-World porcupines	Ethiopian

* Modified from Darlington (1957).

Palearctic Region

The Palearctic region is largely north-temperate in climate, with a heterogeneous vegetation including deciduous forest, grassland, arid desert, northern coniferous forest, and tundra. The fauna (Table 6-3)

TABLE 6-3. Principal Palearctic Mammals and Their Relationships *

Groups	Relationships
Hedgehogs	Ethiopian and Oriental
Shrews	World-wide
Moles	Nearctic
Vespertilionids (mainly)	World-wide
Dogs	World-wide
Bears	Oriental and Nearctic
Pandas	Exclusive subfamily
Weasels	World-wide
Cats	World-wide
Horses	Ethiopian
Pigs	Ethiopian and Oriental
Camel	Neotropical
Deer	Oriental and Nearctic
Bovids	Ethiopian, Oriental, Nearctic
Pikas	Nearctic
Rabbits	World-wide
Squirrels	World-wide
Flying squirrels	Oriental, Nearctic
Beaver	Nearctic
Cricetids	World-wide
Mole-rats	Almost exclusive
Murids	Old-World
Dormice	Ethiopian
Seleviniids	Ethiopian
Jumping mice	Exclusive
Jerboas	Nearctic

* Modified from Darlington (1957).

is related to the Oriental and, especially in the north, to the Nearctic. As a whole, the fauna is less diverse than the tropical faunas to the south; the areas of greatest diversity are in China, where there is a resemblance to the Oriental, and in the Mediterranean region, where there is a resemblance to the Ethiopian. Within the Palearctic, diversity of mammals is greatest in the warmest areas and decreases toward the north (to as low as eight species in the highest continental arctic), toward high mountains, and toward the deserts (which cover a large portion of interior Asia). The Palearctic region appears to be a transition between the faunas of the old-world tropics and North America. It has few endemics of its own.

Nearctic Region

The Nearctic region is similar to the Palearctic in terms of climate and vegetation, and the fauna shows many resemblances, especially in the north (Table 6-4). In addition, other groups are shared with the Neotropical. These relationships suggest that the Nearctic fauna is transitional between the Palearctic and Neotropical regions. However, it is not entirely a transitional fauna since a number of endemic genera, especially rodents, are also present. The fauna is richest in the south, and diversity progressively decreases to the arctic. The region forms a complex transition zone with the Neotropical in southern Mexico.

TABLE 6-4.   Principal Groups of Living Nearctic Mammals and Their Relationships *

Groups	Relationships
Opossum	Neotropical
Shrews	World-wide
Moles	Palearctic
Armadillo	Neotropical
Vespertilionid bats	World-wide
Leaf-nosed bats	Neotropical
Long-legged bats	Neotropical
Free-tailed bats	Tropical world
Dogs	World-wide
Bears	Palearctic and Neotropical
Raccoons	Neotropical
Weasels	World-wide
Cats	World-wide
Peccaries	Neotropical
Deer	Palearctic and Neotropical
Antelope	Exclusive
Bovids	Palearctic, Oriental Ethiopian
Pikas	Palearctic
Rabbits	World-wide
Sewellel	Exclusive
Squirrels	World-wide
Flying squirrel	Palearctic and Oriental
Pocket gophers	Neotropical
Pocket mice	Neotropical
Beaver	Palearctic
Cricetid rodents	World-wide
Jumping mice	Palearctic
Porcupine	Neotropical

* Modified from Darlington (1957).

Neotropical Region

The Neotropical region is largely tropical forest, but extends southward through temperate forest and grassland to the cold, wet region of Tierra del Fuego. The mammal fauna (Table 6-5) is a complex of very distinct and exclusive groups, and others shared with the Nearctic. The fauna shows greatest diversity in the central tropical areas, with a reduc-

TABLE 6-5.   Principal Living Neotropical Mammals and Their Relationship *

Groups	Relationships
Opossums	Nearctic
Caenolestid marsupials	Exclusive
Shrews	World-wide
Sheath-tailed bats	Tropical
Fish-eating bats	Exclusive
Leaf-nosed bats	Nearctic
Vampire bats	Exclusive
Long-legged bats	Nearly exclusive
Smoky bats	Exclusive
Disk-winged bats	Exclusive
Vespertilionid bats	World-wide
Free-tailed bats	Tropical world-wide
Monkeys	Exclusive families
Anteaters	Exclusive
Sloths	Exclusive
Armadillo	Nearctic
Dogs	World-wide
Bears	Nearctic, Palearctic
Raccoons	Nearctic
Weasels	World-wide
Cats	World-wide
Tapirs	Oriental
Peccaries	Nearctic
Camels	Palearctic
Deer	Nearctic and Palearctic
Rabbits	World-wide
Squirrels	World-wide
Pocket gophers	Nearctic
Pocket mice	Nearctic
Cricetids	Nearctic, Old-World
Porcupines	Nearctic
Hystricomorph rodents	Exclusive families

* Modified from Darlington (1957).

tion and mixture with Nearctic forms northward through the smaller area of central America and a reduction southward toward cooler climate.

Australian Region

The Australian region is partly tropical and partly south-temperate, with a large area of arid desert in the interior of the Australian continent. The mammal fauna includes the Monotremes (an exclusive subclass), Marsupials (six exclusive families), rodents of the family Muridae, fruit bats related to old-world forms, and six families of insectivorous bats which also occur elsewhere. The very primitive mammal fauna of monotremes and marsupials is largely endemic; the rodents and bats show resemblances with similar groups in the Oriental region.

Conclusions

From this brief discussion of the distribution of living mammals arranged in faunal regions, it is apparent that the greatest variety of mammals is found in the tropics and that there is a progressive reduction of diversity toward the north and south and toward desert areas. The faunal regions of the old-world tropics have a great deal in common, and both have contributed to the fauna of Palearctica. This fauna is largely transitional between the Old- and New-World tropics, while that of Nearctica is transitional between the Palearctic and the Neotropical regions. All three southern regions share faunas with the regions north of them (but only to a very slight extent in the case of Australia) and have a high percentage of exclusive groups. Therefore, the general pattern of distribution of living mammals is a band of rich and fairly similar faunas in the tropics of the Old World, with a world-wide band of similar transitional faunas across the north temperate and arctic regions (Holarctica). Three regions extending to the south in the New and Old Worlds have a number of exclusive groups.

Once the pattern of distribution of living mammals is recognized, the reasons for the development of the observed pattern can be considered. Study of the zoogeographic history of mammals requires information on the place of origin of the taxa and the pattern of movements between the time of origin and the present.

PLACE OF ORIGIN

It is an extremely difficult task to determine the time and place of origin of a group of animals. There are several reasons for this. First, a new form does not develop in an explosive process of evolution and suddenly appear on the scene; instead, origin occurs on a continuum of differentiation. This makes it almost impossible to determine the exact point in time and space when a new form is different from its parents. Because of this fact Burt (1958) suggests that "phase of origin" be used rather than "time of origin." A second problem is that although the fossil record is extremely good for mammals compared with other classes of vertebrates, it is far from complete, especially for those periods when mammals radiated extensively. Failing a satisfactory fossil record, the zoogeographer must resort to criteria based on the present-day distribution of mammals.

Criteria for Determining Place of Origin

The criteria for determining the place of origin of a taxon take into consideration both the fossil record and the pattern of distribution of living mammals. First, the earliest fossil record of a group indicates the place of origin. Obviously the fossil record is the basic source of information here; however, since the record is incomplete, fossils may easily give an incorrect impression of past distribution. Second, a record of earlier progenitors in the proposed area is an indication of the place of origin. This criterion, coupled with the first, is the ultimate basis for definition of a center of origin. Third, the area of greatest taxonomic diversity of a particular group indicates its place of origin. This criterion is based on the reasoning that a group has had time to adapt (hence is of greatest antiquity) in the area of most extensive diversity. But this may not necessarily follow, since it is usual to find the highest variety of adaptation in habitats affording the greatest variety of niches. Therefore, to use this criterion, one may have to correct the degree of diversity by the opportunity to diversity. Fourth, the area where the individuals show the highest development, or are least primitive, is the place of differentiation of the group. This criterion is based on the premise that greatest adaptation takes place at the center of origin, while primitive forms continue to exist in regions peripheral to the center. It is apparent that the criteria based on present-day distribution patterns are only of value as support for hypotheses based on a record of fossils. Without sufficient fossil data, these criteria could easily lead the investigator astray. For instance, camels are now found only in the Neotropical and Oriental regions, yet had their greatest development in the Nearctic region.

Conclusions on the Center of Origin of Mammals

As might be expected from this brief discussion of criteria, various investigators have come to different conclusions about the center of

TABLE 6-6. Time and Place of Earliest Appearance of Mammal Orders in the Fossil Record *

Order	Time of Appearance	Place of Appearance
Multituberculata	Triassic	Europe, Africa, and North America
Triconodonta	Jurassic	Europe and North America
Docodonta	Jurassic	Europe and North America
Symmetrodonta	Jurassic	Europe and North America
Pantotheria	Jurassic	Europe and North America
Monotremata	Pleistocene	Australia
Marsupialia	Cretaceous	North America
Insectivora	Cretaceous	North America and Asia
Dermoptera	Paleocene	North America
Chiroptera	Eocene	North America and Europe
Primates	Paleocene	North America
Tillodontia	Paleocene	North America
Taeniodonta	Paleocene	North America
Edentata	Paleocene	North America
Rodentia	Paleocene	North America
Carnivora	Paleocene	North America
Condylarthra	Paleocene	North America
Pantodonta	Paleocene	North America
Dinocerta	Paleocene	North America and Asia
Perissodactyla	Eocene	North America and Europe
Artiodactyla	Eocene	North America and Europe
Lagomorpha	Paleocene	Asia
Proboscidea	Eocene	Africa
Notoungulata	Paleocene	South America and Asia
Pholidota	Oligocene	Europe
Hyracoidea	Oligocene	Africa
Tubulidentata	Pliocene	Europe and Asia
Litopterna	Paleocene	South America
Astrapotheria	Eocene	South America
Pyrotheria	Eocene	South America
Sirenia	Eocene	Africa and Jamaica
Cetacea	Eocene	North America

* Compiled from Simpson (1935), Savage (1958), and Darlington (1957).

origin of the mammalian orders. Matthew (1915), assuming that the most advanced members of a group were near the center of origin and that evolution was more progressive at this point, decided that the Holarctic region was the center of evolution of land vertebrates, while tropical regions are refugia for primitive forms. Other workers have opposed this view. For instance, Darlington (1957) proposed an old-world tropical center of origin for mammals; his conclusions were based partly on the observation that the old-world tropical faunas (particularly the Oriental) have relatively few endemics and have dominant relationships with the faunal regions surrounding them. Darlington defines dominance as being conspicuously successful, numerous, and diverse in adaptation. It seems unlikely that this disagreement can be resolved at the present time. Examination of the earliest records for the orders of mammals (compiled from Simpson (1935), Savage (1958), and Darlington (1957), shown in Table 6-6, suggest that the largest proportion of orders originated in North America or in Holarctica. However, these conclusions probably reflect the more abundant collections of fossils from North America and Eurasia—there have been relatively few fossil collections made in the tropical regions.

The problems of determining origin become less acute, although still difficult, for categories lower than orders, since their time of origin is less remote. Simpson (1947) has discussed evidence for the origin of the families of North American mammals which mainly occurred in the Oligocene. Figure 6-2 (from Savage, 1958) summarizes Simpson's conclusions. Living genera originated from Miocene to Pleistocene, at least in the Nearctic region. Living Nearctic species are mainly autochthonous, and developed from the Pleistocene to the present.

DISPERSAL OF MAMMALS

Mammals can survive dispersal only when they move to an area within their physiological and ecological tolerances. In living mammals these tolerances can be studied directly by experiment and observation, but in fossil forms the determination of tolerance limits is largely a matter of speculation. Various authors differ in the emphasis they place on biotic and physical environmental factors influencing movements of mammals. For instance, Darlington (1957) suggests that climate (temperature and seasonal fluctuations) was a primary influence in directing

The Origin and Dispersal of Living Nearctic Mammalian Families.

	Palearctic	REGIONS Nearctic	Neotropical
Didelphidae	E ←	──── L ────	→ L
Soricidae	L ← ── ? ──	L ──	→ L
Talpidae	L ──	→ L	
Phyllostomatidae		L ← ── ? ──	L
Vespertilionidae	L ── ? ──	→ L ──	→ L
Molossidae	L ── ? ──	→ L ──	→ L
Hominidae	L ──	→ L ──	→ L
Dasypodidae		L ← ──	L
Ochotonidae	L ── ? ──	→ L	
Leporidae	L ──	→ L ──	L
Aplodontidae	E ← ──	L	
Sciuridae	L ← ── ? ──	L ──	L
Geomyidae		L	
Heteromyidae		L ──	→ L
Castoridae	L ← ──	L	
Cricetidae	L ── → ? ← ──	L ──	→ L
Muridae	L ──	→ L ──	→ L
Zapodidae	L ──	→ L	
Erethizontidae		L ← ──	L
Canidae	L ── → ? ← ──	L ──	→ L
Ursidae	L ──	→ L ──	→ L
Procyonidae	L ── → ? ← ──	L ──	→ L
Mustelidae	L ── ? ──	→ L ──	→ L
Felidae	L ── ? ──	→ L ──	→ L
Tayassuidae	L ── → ? ← ──	L ──	→ L
Cervidae	L ── ? ──	→ L ──	→ L
Bovidae	L ──	→ L	
Antilocapridae		L	

E—extinct, L—living   From Savage, 1958

Figure 6-2

the dispersal of mammals over the entire planet. In contrast, Burt (1958) suggests that biotic or ecological factors were more significant; climate being important in its indirect effects on vegetation and soil. In addition to these ecological and climatic limitations, there have been actual physical barriers, and these are more amenable to analysis.

Barriers

Mammals arose from land reptiles, and only in a very few instances have they developed the ability to move in salt water or air. Therefore, salt water forms a very significant barrier to movement for most mammals, and, alternatively, a highway for the few aquatic forms. On land, high mountains and deserts may also serve as effective physical barriers to some members of the mammal fauna.

However, barriers are seldom completely limiting to all types of mammals. Most barriers act as filters to part of the fauna and allow those forms capable of surviving their peculiar environmental conditions to cross them. The land-bridge which existed at various times in the past between Siberia and Alaska across the Bering Strait is an example of a filter barrier. Although any mammal which could walk on land could cross this bridge, the cooler climatic conditions acted as a filter against those tropical mammals which did not have the ability to resist cold.

Some mammals have accidentally crossed barriers. Simpson (1953) calls this type of movement "sweepstakes dispersal," and it may be extremely important, especially in the population of islands. Mammals which can swim, cling to floating rafts of vegetation, or "hitch a ride" with exploring man, may move across salt water in a more or less accidental fashion. Australia was probably populated by mammals through sweepstakes dispersal.

A comparison of the distribution of living orders (Tables 6-1 to 6-5) and the places of the earliest record of orders (Table 6-6) shows that the mammals have moved widely over the surface of the earth. Movement between faunal regions continues at the present time, but is greatly reduced between the Palearctic and Nearctic regions and the Oriental and Australian regions because of water barriers. In addition partial barriers in the form of arid lands are present between the Oriental and Ethiopian and between the Ethiopian and Palearctic regions. What has been the nature of these barriers and transition areas in the past? In order to answer this question it is necessary to consider the historic patterns of continents and climates during the geological periods when mammals were present.

Continental Patterns

Most authorities agree that since the origin of the mammals in the Mesozoic, the position of the continental land masses has remained unchanged, although the general shape and surface of the continents has undergone dramatic variation. According to Dunbar (1949) the Mesozoic era began with a general emergence of the continents and widespread aridity. The land later subsided, and more moist conditions prevailed in the Jurassic. During the Cretaceous the continents sank to a low level and were partly flooded by shallow seas. Toward the end of the Cretaceous the land rose again. During the portion of the Mesozoic when mammals were in existence, land connections probably occurred between North and South America, Asia and North America, Eurasia and Africa, and possibly Asia and Australia (Darlington, 1957). Some authorities also suggest connections between North America and Europe across the north Atlantic Ocean; between Madagascar and Africa; and between Africa, Australia, and South America through Antarctica. However, these latter land-bridges are not necessary to explain the distribution of mammals, and their existence has not been accepted by the majority of geographers.

During the Cenozoic the continents did not change greatly in shape. The rise in the height of the continents which began in late Cretaceous times continued, and reached a maximum in the Pleistocene to recent epochs, when connections existed between North and South America, North America and Asia, and Eurasia and Africa. Prior to the Pliocene, South America was isolated from North America. Australia was isolated through the Cenozoic. Associated with the rising land surfaces was intense mountain-building activity. In Eurasia the Tethys Sea extended across the whole of southern Europe and Asia during the early part of the Tertiary, making northern Europe a peninsula. From this area the Alps and Himalayas arose, causing complex geographical changes. In North America shallow seas covered parts of the southeastern coastal plain and Mississippi valley, but the continental pattern was modified by the rise of the Appalachian system of mountains in the east and the birth of the Rocky Mountains in western North America. In South America, the Andes are principally of Tertiary

origin and reached their present height in the late Tertiary and Pleistocene. Finally in the Pleistocene, continental glaciers made great areas
of the land surface uninhabitable for mammals. These areas were
located primarily in North America and in northern Europe and in
Asia. Changes in sea level were associated with glaciation, since the
great masses of ice accumulated vast quantities of water and caused a
lowering of the sea level. Along the Atlantic coast of North America
fluctuations in sea level may have been on the order of 100 meters Thus
part of the continental shelf became available for mammal migration,
and off-shore islands were available for colonization by land mammals.

Climatic Patterns

Although we are unable to measure past climates directly, we can
reconstruct climate by assuming that the physiological tolerances of
plant and animal taxa to the environment have not changed. In the
early Mesozoic tree ferns, cycads, conifers, and other ancient plants
were dominant on the earth. These were replaced in the Cretaceous by
the broad-leaved trees (Angiosperms) which had a long history during
the Mesozoic (Axelrod, 1960). In the Cretaceous, plants such as tree
ferns, palms, figs, and cycads lived in Greenland and Alaska, indicating
that subtropical climatic conditions existed far north on the continents.
During the late Mesozoic and early Cenozoic, tropical forest also occurred far into the present-day temperate regions. During the early
Cenozoic there were broad climatic zones of vegetation, but these were
much wider than at present and probably did not include the extreme
types, such as tundra, as distinct communities. Tropical to temperate
forest occurred over most of the earth's surface.

Cooling of the climate began in the Oligocene and ultimately re-
sulted in widespread glaciation characteristic of the Pleistocene epoch.
Associated with these cooling conditions was the evolution of the herbaceous plants (Barghoon, 1953) which probably had a great effect on the
evolution and distribution of seed-eating and herbivorous mammals.
During this part of the Tertiary, rising mountain systems in North
America captured moisture on their westward slopes and caused drier
conditions on the leeward side. The grasses probably developed in response to these changes in moisture on the plains east of the Rocky
Mountains and were a major influence in the development of the mod
ern ungulates. With deteriorating climates and the appearance of

herbaceous floras, the world climatic zones of vegetation became increasingly pronounced during the Tertiary. Finally, Pleistocene glaciation caused a mixing of floras and faunas and an eclipsing of the climatic zones. Northern elements were moved far south of their present range.

Summary

Sometime during the age of mammals land-bridges permitted exchange of mammals between every faunal region, with the exception of Australia. These land connections were not present everywhere at the same time, nor for equal lengths of time. The complex pattern of connection and separation was extremely significant to the movement of mammals. Climatic zones of vegetation were probably not as pronounced as at present, and tropical or semitropical conditions existed far into the present-day temperate regions. These conditions gradually changed as the climate deteriorated, until the Pleistocene ice sheets completely upset the ancestral distribution patterns of many forms in the Palearctic and Nearctic regions. The effects of glaciation were probably much less important in the other faunal regions.

Movements to Islands

Since the pattern of mammal distribution on islands so clearly illustrates the effect of barriers, we will consider island patterns before we take up patterns of movement between continents. As mentioned earlier, very few mammals can tolerate salt water for a long period of time and, therefore, islands that have not been connected to the mainland are invaded only by flying mammals, those carried by man, and those that can travel on rafts of vegetation or by other accidental means. Accidental dispersal in most cases is limited to small mammals and fairly hardy species. For instance, the island of Madagascar, which has been separated from Africa and Asia by water gaps, was inhabited by small forms such as insectivores, lemurs, cricetid rodents, viverrids, and a pigmy hippopotamus. The semiaquatic hippopotamus was the largest mammal to invade Madagascar. Rodents appear to be the land mammals with the greatest tolerance for salt water or the ability to move by accidental means. Rodents have universally penetrated farthest from land, and some of their dispersal distances are truly astonishing. For example, on the Galapagos Islands, 600 miles from South America, an endemic cricetid rodent (*Oryzomys*) is present. This same genus also reached the island of Jamaica over a long water gap.

Patterns of Island Distribution

Invasion of islands depends largely on their distance from the continental land mass. The major island distribution patterns may be recognized as (1) continental islands which are recently formed with more or less reduced continental faunas, (2) fringing archipelagos which lie near the continents and have a reduced continental fauna, and (3) isolated single islands and archipelagos.

Continental Islands

The British Isles are continental islands and illustrate the effect of successive water gaps on dispersal. The British Isles consist of two islands, Great Britain and Ireland, which lie on the continental shelf and were connected to the mainland by a land-bridge during glaciation and up to about 7000 years ago. Ireland was separated from Great Britain somewhat earlier than Britain from the mainland. Britain has four shrews, a hedgehog, mole, red fox, and wildcat; six mustelids; two native deer; three native hares and rabbits; eleven rodents; twelve bats; and, in historic times, the wolf, brown bear, wild boar, and beaver (Darlington, 1957)—a fair sample of the fauna of the continent. Ireland on the other hand, has or had the hedgehog and red fox, one shrew, six mustelids, one deer, two native hares and rabbits, some of the rodents and bats of Britain, the wolf, bear, and boar. These faunas are mainly a result of post-Pleistocene immigration across the land-bridge, with only a part of the post-Pleistocene continental fauna reaching Britain and only a part of the British fauna reaching Ireland. Thus the smaller fauna of Ireland is due to its earlier separation from the continent, its greater distance from the mainland, and probably also to its less diverse topography.

Fringing Archipelagos

The Greater Antilles in the West Indies are examples of the fringing-archipelago type of island dispersal. The Greater Antilles, consisting of Cuba, Hispaniola, Jamaica, and Puerto Rico, are made of volcanic and marine limestone and may never have been connected to the continents. The flightless land mammals are very few, and most are known only as fossils. The distribution of these on the islands declines in a direction away from the point of entry, similar to the condition in the British Isles. Five or six groups of mammals (two insectivores, one or two small ground sloths, two hystricomorph rodents) appear to have entered the

Antilles by way of Cuba, where they are most abundant, and some have spread to Hispaniola and finally to Puerto Rico (one insectivore, one sloth, and two groups of rodents, all extinct). Four other groups (a monkey, two other hystricomorph rodents, and a cricetid rodent) appear to have entered by way of Jamaica, with only one group of rodents extending to Hispaniola, Puerto Rico, and other islands. The distance from the mainland and the problem of crossing the salt water barrier limited the number and size of the species able to cross to the Greater Antilles. A larger proportion of rodents occur in the island faunas, indicating greater dispersal ability of rodents under these difficult conditions.

Isolated Islands

The problem of overcoming the distance to isolated oceanic islands is very great for land mammals. For instance, the Hawaiian Archipelago, lying about 2000 miles from North America, has only one native mammal, a bat (*Lasiurus*), derived from America. Iceland in the North Atlantic, 155 miles from Greenland and a much greater distance from Europe, lies far north, and was essentially covered by ice during the Pleistocene. Its land-mammal fauna consists of one rodent, the long-tailed field mouse (*Apodemus sylvaticus*), the arctic fox (*Alopex lagopus*), and the amphibious polar bear (*Thalarctos maritimus*). All of these animals probably crossed the formidable water gap accidentally on floating ice—the polar bear still frequently does.

Influence of the Size of the Islands

In addition to the role of salt water barriers as limiting factors on the size of island fauna, the area of land capable of supporting animals may be significant. On small islands this influence would act to reduce the survival of large mammals, even if they did manage to reach the island. Furthermore, the breeding stock and the genetic variability of an island species could be limited by the size of the island, and the influence of genetic drift might be exaggerated. For these reasons island species may be unable to meet competition of new invaders which might arrive by accidental means of dispersal.

Continental Patterns of Dispersal

We can generalize from the exceedingly complex distribution patterns of the individual groups of mammals to a relatively simple world-wide pattern for the mammal fauna of the Cenozoic. This pattern is essentially a history of movements from a center of origin in the old-world tropics or the Holarctic region southward into southern Africa, Australia, and South America, and a series of interchange movements between the Palearctic and Nearctic faunal regions. The history of dispersal and invasion of the individual faunal regions can be considered in the light of the over-all pattern.

Dispersal on the Southern Continents

Ethiopian Region: The earliest fossil mammals of Africa (Egypt) come from the upper Eocene and lower Oligocene strata and are a mixture of contemporaneous European forms and distinct African groups. Darlington (1957) suggests that this mixture indicates that Africa was connected in early Tertiary times with Eurasia, received the ancestral stocks of mammals then, subsequently was isolated, and later, in the Eocene, was reconnected. In the period of isolation orders such as the Proboscidea and Hyracoidea developed. The mammals of the Ethiopian region dispersed southward into the more temperate and smaller area of South Africa. They also moved from Africa into the Oriental and Palearctic regions and from there to the New World. Some of the Proboscidea ultimately reached South America.

Australian Region: Mammals from the Oriental region moved southward into Australia across the water gaps between the island archipelagoes following an island pattern of dispersal. Ancestors of the marsupials came some time in the period from the Cretaceous to early Tertiary, by island-hopping through the East Indies (Table 6-7). Murid rodents arrived in Australia from Asia in a series of waves from the Miocene to Recent, and radiated extensively, forming a number of endemic genera. Bats moved to the continent from Asia continuously throughout the Tertiary. New Guinea was the major center of bat differentiation, and there was a diffusion of bats from New Guinea to Australia and toward Asia. The ancestors of the monotremes probably arrived in late Triassic or Jurassic times; the monotremes themselves, in all probability, never occurred outside of the Australian region. There has been very little dispersal of the Australian fauna toward the Oriental region. The main Australian fauna stops at New Guinea; a small part occurs on the Aru, Kei, and Moluccas Islands; and only the marsupial, *Phalanger,* reaches Celebes and Timor in the zone of overlap with the Oriental fauna.

TABLE 6-7.   Stratification of the Australian Mammal Fauna *

Time of Appearance	Animal Stratum	Groups Included
Late Pleistocene to Recent	late island-hoppers	rabbits and other historical introductions, Dingo dogs, some rats.
Miocene		
	middle island-hoppers	Old-World rats, bats
Paleocene-Eocene		bats
Late Cretaceous and Paleocene	old island-hoppers	marsupials
Late Triassic or Jurassic	archaic immigrants	monotremes

* After Simpson, 1953 and 1961.

Neotropical Region: The movements of mammals into the remaining southern continent, South America, is much more complicated. In the Paleocene epoch marsupials, edentates, and ungulates were present in South America. These were a portion of the early Tertiary fauna of North America which crossed a water gap into the southern continent (Table 6-8). The insectivores and carnivores which were also present in North America in the Paleocene failed to make the crossing. Although throughout most of the Tertiary South America was separated from North America by a water gap, possibly consisting of a series of islands in the region of Central America, certain other groups periodically crossed this barrier. A hystricomorph rodent reached South America probably in the late Eocene; monkeys appear in the Miocene; procyonids reached South America before the end of the Miocene; bats probably arrived throughout the Tertiary. When the land connection between North and South America was established in the Pliocene there was a dispersal of faunas in both directions. For example, prior to the connection, South America had 29 families of terrestrial mammals and North America had 27 families, but only two of these were common to both. In the Pleistocene, North and South America had 22 families in common.

The South American fauna was profoundly influenced by the southward dispersal of North American forms. In the ancient fauna the insectivore and carnivore types were derived from marsupials, and the

TABLE 6-8. Stratification of the Mammal Fauna of Latin America *

Time	Stratum	Groups Introduced	Differentiation in Latin America
Late Miocene to Recent	late island hoppers and immigrants	deer, camel, peccaries, tapirs, horses, mastodons, cats, weasels raccoons, bears, dogs mice, squirrels, rabbits, shrews	
Late Eocene to Oligocene	old island hoppers	protogomorph rodents, advanced lemuroids	caviomorph rodents New-World monkeys
Earliest Paleocene	ancient immigrants	ferungulates	litopterns notoungulates astrapotheres pyrotheres
		palaeanodonts	xenarthrans ground sloths tree sloths armadillos glyptodonts
		didelphoids	

* After Simpson, 1950.

large herbivore types from primitive ungulates. After the connection with North America, a shrew, a genus of rabbit, a squirrel, a genus of pocket mouse, several stocks of cricetid rodents, three canids, a bear, some procyonids, four mustelids, three or more cats, three or four elephants, two horses, tapirs, peccaries, camels, and deer invaded South America. These northern carnivores and herbivores partially replaced the marsupial carnivores and eliminated the South American ungulate orders of Litopterna, Notoungulata, Astrapotheria, and Pyrotheria. Some elements of the South American fauna also moved northward, but these did little more than add to the diversity of the North American fauna. South American mammals dispersing into North America included three families of ground sloths, two stocks of armadillos, two stocks of glyptodonts, the porcupine, two capybaras, and possibly the opossum.

Dispersal in Holarctica

The exchange of mammals between the Palearctic and Nearctic regions is much more complex than the other dispersal patterns considered above. The interchange of mammals took place across the Bering Strait over a distance of what is now about 75 miles, from Cape Prince of Wales to East Cape. The climatic and ecological conditions on the land-bridge varied during the Tertiary and had an important effect on the dispersal of particular mammals. The climate in the region of the land-bridge grew progressively colder through the Tertiary, and the groups exchanged between the faunal regions were generally those adapted to cooler climates. The land-bridge was interrupted periodically during the Cenozoic, the interruptions probably occurring during the Paleocene, middle Eocene, middle to late Oligocene, and the early Pliocene (Simpson, 1947). Early Tertiary to Late Tertiary-Pleistocene crossings in both directions are indicated for some members of the families Soricidae, Mustelidae, Canidae, Felidae, Castoridae, Leporidae, and the subfamily Microtinae. The Talpidae and Tayassuidae apparently made early crossings, while the Hominidae, Sciuridae, Aplodontidae, Zapodidae, Ochotonidae, Cervidae, and Bovidae made late ones (Burt, 1958).

A number of groups did not make the move between continents. These included the old-world viverrids (civets and mongooses), fruit bats, higher primates (except man), murid rodents, gliroid rodents, and true pigs. New-world forms which did not use the land-bridge include the raccoons, ringtails, prairie dogs (Sciuridae), pocket gophers, kangaroo rats, pocket mice, porcupines, antelopes, and mice of the subfamily Cricetinae. The living New-World prairie dogs, pocket gophers, kangaroo rats, pocket mice, and the prong-horn antelope are adapted to a relatively arid habitat and may have been ecologically limited from crossing the land-bridge. The porcupine came to North America from South America in the Pliocene, and probably did not have time to reach the Bering Strait area. Presumably the porcupine could cross if a land-bridge were in existence today. The raccoons and ringtails probably were restricted from the region of Alaska by low temperatures. Why the murid rodents, which are highly adaptable in their region, did not make the crossing is unknown.

Resemblance of Faunas

Simpson (1953) has used an index of resemblance (100 C/N_1) to compare the Holarctic faunas, and his findings indicate the importance of Asia as a transitional area for mammals dispersing east and west. The generic resemblance of central Asia to North America and Europe during the late Eocene is about the same (index of 17 and 15), while the resemblance between North America and Europe is much less so (index of 5). This indicates that there was interchange between Asia and Europe and North America in both directions, but that the connection between Europe and North America was through Asia and not by a direct route. The few genera common to Europe and North America also occur in Asia. The index of resemblance also shows that Africa and South America do not share any genera of ancient mammals, and this can only mean that these continents were never connected during the age of mammals.

Summary of Dispersal Patterns

The patterns of dispersal of the mammals are summarized in Figure 6-3. The major movements have been from the largest land masses of

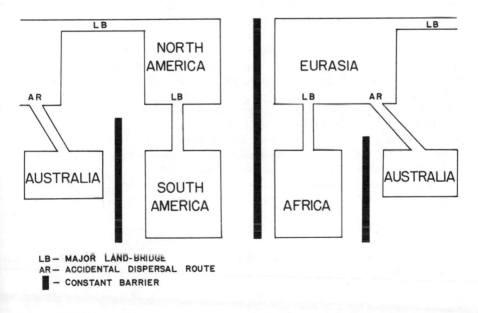

LB— MAJOR LAND-BRIDGE
AR— ACCIDENTAL DISPERSAL ROUTE
▌ — CONSTANT BARRIER

Figure 6-3. Summary of the Distribution Patterns During the Age of Mammals. (Redrawn from Simpson, 1953.)

Eurasia and central Africa toward south Africa, Australia, North America, and through North America to South America. North America has also been the base for dispersal toward Eurasia and to South America. The distribution patterns of the mammals can be fully explained with the land-bridges and transition areas discussed above. Other connections, as between Europe and North America, and hypotheses such as drifting continents are not needed to explain the zoogeography of the mammals.

REFERENCES

Axelrod, D. I. 1960. The evolution of flowering plants. In, Evolution after Darwin. Vol. 1. The Evolution of Life, Sol Tax, Ed. Univ. Chicago Press: pp. 227-305.

Barghoon, E. S. 1953. Evidence of climatic change in the geologic record of plant life. In, Climatic Change: Evidence, Causes and Effect, Shapley, *et al.*, Eds. Harvard Univ. Press: pp. 235-248.

Burt, W. H. 1958. The history and affinities of the recent land mammals of western North America. In, Zoogeography. AAAS Publ. 51: pp. 131-154.

Darlington, P. J., Jr. 1957. Zoogeography: the Geographical Distribution of Animals. New York, John Wiley & Sons, Inc. 675 pp.

Dunbar, C. O. 1949. Historical Geology. New York, John Wiley & Sons, Inc.

Lydekker, R. 1896. A Geographical History of Mammals. Cambridge Univ. Press. 400 pp.

Matthew, W. D. 1915. Climate and evolution. Ann. New York Acad. Sci. 24: 171-318.

Savage, D. E. 1958. Evidence from fossil land mammals on the origin and affinities of the western Nearctic fauna. In, Zoogeography, AAAS Publ. 51: pp. 97-129.

Schmidt, K. P. 1954. Faunal realms, regions and provinces. Quart. Rev. Biol. 29: 322-331.

Sclater, P. L. 1858. On the general geographical distribution of the members of the class Aves. J. Proc. Linnean Soc. Zool. 2: 130-145.

Simpson, G. G. 1935. The first mammals. Quart. Rev. Biol. 10: 154-180.

Simpson, G. G. 1947. Holarctic mammalian faunas and continental relationships during the Cenozoic. Bull. Geol. Soc. Amer. 58: 613-688.

Simpson, G. G. 1950. History of the fauna of Latin America. Amer. Sci. 38: 361-389.

Simpson, G. G. 1953. Evolution and Geography. Condon Lectures, Oregon State System of Higher Education. 64 pp.

Simpson, G. G. 1961. Historical zoogeography of Australian mammals. Evolution 15: 431-446.

Wallace, A. R. 1876. The Geographical Distribution of Animals. The Macmillan Co. (London). 2 vols.

chapter seven

REPRODUCTIVE PROCESSES

FOR AN UNDERSTANDING of the life history of mammals, it is necessary to review such important basic reproductive phenomena as birth rates, breeding season, and behavior. It is not the purpose of this section to cover in detail the physiological processes of reproduction, but to point out the features of primary importance to a mammalogist. The first part of the chapter will summarize anatomical and physiological information to be found in detail in various texts (Arey, 1960; Hall, 1959; Turner, 1960); a compendium of information is available in the third edition of "Sex and Internal Secretions," edited by W. C. Young (1961). Then there will be a discussion of the number of young produced by mammals; and finally there will be a discussion of the factors influencing that number.

ANATOMY

Development

First, it seems desirable to describe briefly the development of the gonads and of the reproductive ducts. In the early embryo a urogenital ridge develops on the dorsal part of the coelom. Thickened strips of mesothelium contain small cuboidal cells into which migrate the sex cells from the future mesentery of the gut. Within this thickened area develop the sex cords, and eventually the whole gonad becomes suspended by a mesentery. The gonads subsequently differentiate into an outer cortex and an inner medulla. The tissues of the gonad undergo several reorganizations, eventually resulting, in the female, in the de-

159

velopment of the cortex and the atrophy of the medulla. The converse occurs in the male. The germ cells, which originated in the entoderm, lie within the cortex of the female or medulla of the male and develop into definitive ova or sperm through a series of stages.

The ducts of both male and female develop from the more posterior part of the urogenital ridge. Actually the female ducts develop some-what later in embryogeny than do the male ducts. The urogenital ridge separates into cords longitudinally, the lateral cord becoming the vas deferens and the medial cord becoming the oviduct. In the female the vas deferens regresses although some bits of tissue may remain throughout life. The oviduct separates into three portions: the anterior part adjacent to the ovary becomes a coiled narrow tube; the middle part (uterus) is much broader and generally straight; the lower part (vagina) forms by junction of uteri from each side.

In the male, gonadal development proceeds in the beginning as in the female, but the medullary tissue becomes the testis and the cortical tissue rarely develops. The ducts also develop as in the female, but the lateral duct (vas deferens) takes over the function of carrying the sperm to the exterior, and the oviduct atrophies.

Female Organs

The female has more complex reproductive organs than does the male, although the glands are simple. The primary organ is the ovary which is connected to the exterior by a set of ducts. In addition there are certain genitalia and mammary glands (Figures 7-1, 7-2, 7-3, 7-4).

Ovary

In the mature female the ovary contains many small ova and some larger ones undergoing development within follicles. Surrounding the follicles are special interstitial cells that supply estrogenic hormones. The follicle, when mature, is a relatively large, spherical body enclosing an ovum. The sphere is partly hollow and the ovum lies in a layer of cells that protrudes from its walls. An important feature from the viewpoint of life history of mammals is that some follicles may lack ova (anovular) while others may have several ova (polyovular). At ovulation the walls of the follicle rupture and the ovum flows into the coelom and is picked up by the oviduct. Promptly the follicle begins to change into a corpus luteum. This structure develops from the granulosal and thecal layer adjacent to the now-empty center of the follicle. The corpus is present during the gestation period, but after parturition regresses and eventually remains as a small body of connective tissue called a corpus albicans. The number of corpora lutea is an important measure of the number of ova that have been ovulated and thus of how many embryos may have been produced. At any time during the sexual life some of the follicles may regress and thus become atretic. Atresia may occur at any stage in the development of the follicle from the earliest period almost until the final phase. An important point for the

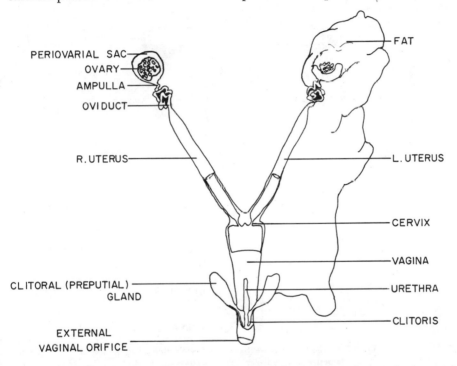

Figure 7-1. The Reproductive Organs of a Female Rat Partly Dissected to Contrast Appearance in Freshly-opened Mammal (right) and Dissected Organs. (Redrawn from Turner, 1960.)

life history of mammals is the possible occurrence of pseudopregnancy. Probably this condition is rare in nature, but without careful study the pseudopregnant female cannot be distinguished from the pregnant female by study of the ovary alone.

Among the orders of mammals some ovarian conditions are noteworthy. In monotremes the left ovary is larger than is the right. The egg of the monotreme is very similar to that of a bird or reptile since

it contains a large quantity of yolk. Atresia of the monotreme egg follows the avian pattern. In marsupials large numbers of ova are shed at
one time, and the loss before implantation may be very high. Among
the insectivores, the European mole (*Talpa europea*) presents a peculiar
situation since the ovary may be intersexual. During the nonbreeding
season the medulla may become very large and push the cortex to the
anterior part of the gonad. Then during the breeding season the cortex
becomes active and produces ova. In bats a somewhat similar situation

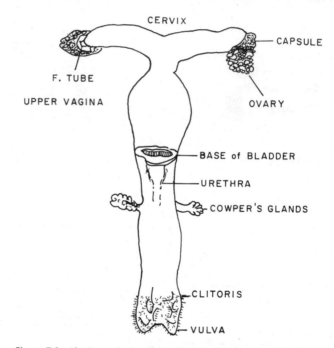

Figure 7-2. The Reproductive Tract of a Female Hedgehog, Representative of Insectivora. (From Deanesley, 1934.)

occurs, although the increase is due primarily to interstitial cells in the
ovary rather than extensive development of the medulla. In many bats
the left ovary is functional and the right ovary is atrophic. Among
rodents polyovuly is common. Some seals ovulate from one ovary one
year and from the other in a subsequent year. Walruses alternate ovarian
activity biennially. Elephants ovulate during pregnancy. Other orders
of mammals present only detailed differences from the typical picture
as given above.

Ducts

In a sexually mature mammal the vagina passes through a series of cellular changes called the estrous cycle. This sequence has been most intensively investigated among rodents, but somewhat similar changes have been found in many other mammals. The importance of the estrous cycle in the life history of mammals is its government of the actual time of mating. In the so-called typical cycle as found in laboratory rats, the first stage is called **proestrous**. At this time some follicles

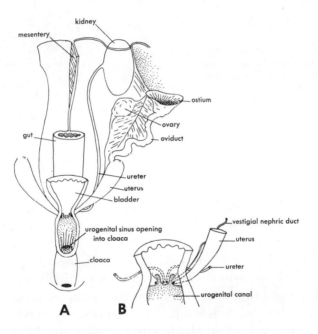

Figure 7-3. Reproductive Organs of Echidna. A, female in ventral view; B, details of connections to urogenital canal. (From Jollie, Malcolm, 1962. Chordate Morphology. New York, Reinhold Pub. Corp.)

are essentially mature. In the vaginal epithelium there are a number of nucleated cells, but leukocytes are absent. In the estrous condition, which appears some twelve hours later, the vagina shows flat squamous cells lacking nuclei. At this time the female will receive the male. **Metestrous** begins eight to ten hours later, when the leukocytes slough off the vaginal epithelium. During the final stage of the cycle, the

diestrous, the vaginal epithelium contains many leukocytes and some squamous nucleated cells. In the typical polyestrous animal, cycles continue one after another, often with great regularity. In species that cease breeding for a period within the breeding season or change into the nonbreeding phase, the vagina closes, atrophies, and loses its cellular exudates. This condition is called **anestrous.**

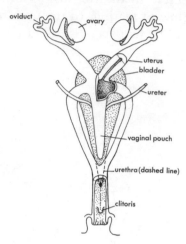

Figure 7-4. Reproductive Organs of Female Kangaroo. (From Jollie, Malcolm, 1962. Chordate Morphology. New York, Reinhold Pub. Corp.)

The uterus during the breeding period undergoes a series of changes. The resting uterus is generally small without extensive vascularization of the endometrium (the inner cell layers). Just after ovulation the endometrium begins a remarkable series of changes in preparation for implantation of the ovum. The layer becomes highly vascularized and thickened. Several days after ovulation the ovum implants in the endometrium and begins to develop. The structure formed by the endometrium at the site of implantation is called the placenta. Pseudopregnant animals show the same endometrial changes; but, of course, no embryo is present. This sequence of changes in the uterus occurs during pregnancy, but in the regular estrous cycle there are also minor changes in the uterus. The principal one occurs in rodents, for at the time of ovulation the uterus becomes very much enlarged and is called a balloon uterus. The menstrual cycle of primates is a special case in which the uterine endometrium becomes very much thickened and sloughs off about midway between ovulations, resulting in bleeding. The dog also has bleeding, but it occurs prior to ovulation.

The type of implantation is important in understanding the lives of mammals principally because the number of sites may be detectable in the uterus long after parturition and thus indicates how many embryos had been present. The circulatory relationships between mother and fetus show a progressive series of changes allowing for a more direct exchange of gases and nutrients from the maternal circulation to the fetal circulation. In some forms materials must pass through three cell layers of the fetal and three cell layers of the maternal tissue. In other species cell layers disappear. In the most specialized type the only layer left is the endothelium of the blood vessels themselves, so that essentially the transfer is from a sinus on the maternal side through the fetal cell wall. Along with these changes are differences in the formation of the placenta on the maternal side and in particular its attachment to the uterus. In a number of forms the placenta is deciduous, meaning that maternal tissues are actually pulled away at the time of birth. Such mammals have placental scars at the site of each placenta. Other mammals have less intimate connections so that no scar is formed at the site. The shape of the placenta differs greatly among mammals. In some the placenta is diffuse, completely surrounding the embryo and attached on all sides of the uterus; in others the placenta consists of several separate patches called cotyledons. In dogs the placenta is a band or girdle around the embryo. In rodents and some others the placenta is discoid, consisting simply of a circular structure attached on one side of the uterus.

Other Structures

Of some importance in understanding the lives of mammals is a knowledge of the clitoris, a partial homologue of the penis. A significant feature is the presence of a bone (os clitoris) in some species.

The mammary glands are another helpful feature in the study of the lives of mammals. Primitively the glands occurred in two parallel rows on each side of the lower surface. In marsupials the nipples occur in a ring (Figure 7-2). In some species the number has been reduced so that there may be mammary glands only in the posterior part, as in cows, or in the anterior part, as in primates. Many species maintain two long rows. Usually the glands are ventral, but in some hystricomorph rodents the nipples occur on the side. The glands themselves when active consist of a series of ducts ending in little bulbs that secrete the milk. Histological study of the condition of the mammary gland can reveal the estrous condition as well as the lactation condition of the female.

Male Organs

The male organs consist of the primary elements, the testes, that produce sperm and the endocrines, and various accessory glands (Figures 7-5, 7-6, 7-7).

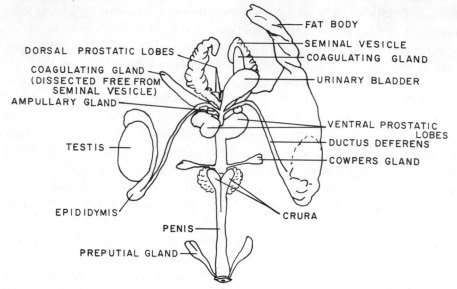

Figure 7-5. The Internal Organs of a Male Rat Showing the Reproductive Glands as Well as the Location of Other Endocrine Glands. (Redrawn from Turner, 1960.)

Testis

The testis contains a large number of long, coiled tubules containing sperm and separated from each other by a few interstitial cells. The tubules join together and eventually pass out from the testis to form the epididymis, which is at first a series of coiled tubes, but which eventually attaches to the vas deferens. The sperm are formed from cells along the edge of the tubules and pass through several stages before becoming the definitive, long-tailed spermatozoa. Waves of sperm-formation lasting perhaps a day pass down the tubules and result in the production of millions of sperm.

The orders of mammals show only relatively minor differences in the reproductive organs of the males. Naturally, the monotreme presents the greatest number of peculiarities; the testes are kept in the abdomen at all seasons of the year. The sperm flow through the vas deferens to a urogenital sinus with an arrangement of valves so that at

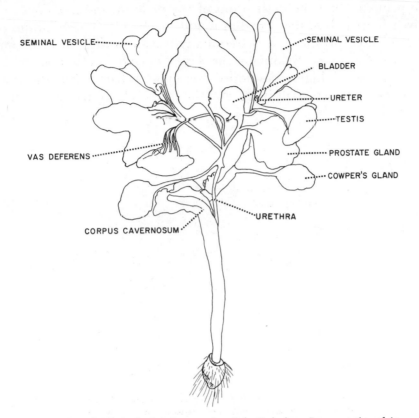

Figure 7-6. The Reproductive Organs of a Male Hedgehog, Representative of Insectivores. (From Allanson, 1934.)

the time of copulation only the sperm are ejaculated. Marsupials have a definite scrotum for maintaining the testes exterior to the body and a very long urethral connection of the vas deferens. Some of the insectivores have abdominal testes, whereas others have a scrotum which keeps the testes outside the abdomen. A specialization in the epididymis produces a gland which appears to be a reservoir for sperm. The prostates (Figure 7-6) are very large. Bats have a very large special sac called the cremaster for maintaining the testes outside of the body. Like the insectivores, they have a special place for the storage of sperm. Primates generally have extra-abdominal testes, although in the primitive lemurs and monkeys the testes do not descend until sexual maturity. Edentates generally have intra-abdominal testes in keeping with their relatively low body temperature. Rodents, perhaps, have been studied even more than primates, and the description of the male organs given above is derived largely from the situation found in rodents. The baculum (os penis) is often present and is frequently used as a help in taxonomic decisions. Carnivores maintain the testes outside the abdomen and generally have a highly developed baculum. Whales keep the testes within the abdomen at all times, and the penis is held in a sac, external

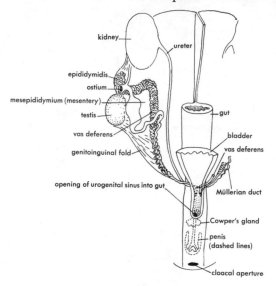

Figure 7-7. The Reproductive Organs of a Male Echidna.
(From Jollie, Malcolm, 1962. Chordate Morphology. New York, Reinhold Pub. Corp.)

to the body. The odd-toed ungulates have external testes and a number of special glands associated with the sperm. Lagomorphs hold the testes in the abdomen during the nonbreeding season. The even-toed ungulates present no peculiarities of great interest.

Glands

Accessory to the gonad are a number of sex organs that facilitate insemination or maintain the viability of the sperm. The seminal vesicles are relatively large, paired organs lying on either side in the lower part of the abdomen close to the junction of the vas deferens and the bladder. The prostate generally has three lobes, one being dorsal, and the other two a ventral pair. Another gland, the bulbourethral or Cowper's, is still farther posterior and is associated with lubrication of the urethra.

Secondary Sex Characters

Anatomical features found normally in only one sex are called secondary sex characters. A great variety of these are present in mammals, but by no means as many as those found in birds. Perhaps the most conspicuous examples are the antlers in male deer. Other secondary sex characters are certain skin glands found only in males of some species, or the brilliant color of the skin in some primates as, for example, the mandrill. Teeth may differ in number or shape. In a few cases there may be a difference between the sexes in the color of the fur. A rather constant secondary character is the baculum or penis bone found in a large number of mammalian males. Secondary sex characters are useful in mammalogy, since they serve as taxonomic guides and as a means of identifying age and sex.

PHYSIOLOGY

The study of the secretions of endocrine glands has made tremendous progress in the last generation in clarifying the control of reproductive processes. For the mammalogist this physiological knowledge is vitally important in understanding the extent of the breeding season and the number of animals born. For this reason a brief introduction to the knowledge of hormones is given here.

Pituitary Hormones

First it is necessary to note the anatomy of the lower part of the brain. The hypothalamus connects closely with an organ called the pituitary. Actually, the pituitary is derived from two separate parts: the posterior part is an evagination from the brain; and the anterior part develops from the primitive gut. The two parts join together in early life and externally appear to be one organ. However, the connection with the brain is different for the two parts. The posterior section is connected by nerves that go up into the hypothalamus, but the anterior is connected only by a portal blood system. So far, no neural connection has been demonstrated between the anterior part of the hypothalamus and the anterior pituitary. Neural secretory material comes through the portal system to the anterior portion of the pituitary, where it is stored. Similarly, neural material is stored in the posterior part.

For the control of reproduction, the anterior portion of the pituitary is more vital. The hypothalamus is controlled by an assortment of nervous stimuli, some coming from the animal itself and others depending on the length of day. The pituitary itself contains in the anterior part a large number of different hormones. These hormones may differ chemically from species to species but generally have very similar functions within each species. The follicle-stimulating hormone (FSH) is stored in the pituitary and controls the growth and maturation of ovarian follicles as well as the production of sperm. Another hormone (luteinizing, or LH) controls ovulation as well as the formation of the corpora lutea. The luteinizing hormone acts together with the follicle-stimulating hormone in the development and production of both ova and sperm. Another type of hormone (adrenocorticotrophic hormone or ACTH), after release, stimulate another gland. It controls the cortex of the adrenal gland but has no effect on the medulla. Apparently ACTH has little effect on one layer of the adrenal gland called the glomerulosa. Still other hormones are provided by the pituitary. Thyrotropin influences growth and many other metabolic functions. Prolactin (luteotropin) is the only hormone manufactured in the anterior pituitary. It controls the development of the mammary glands, maternal behavior, and maintains the corpus luteum. Another hormone of somewhat minor importance, sebotropin, occurs in the pituitary and apparently controls the secretion of the sebaceous glands, which are important in maintaining the pelage in proper condition. Still another hormone, somatotropin, is important in growth but has little to do directly with reproduction.

The posterior part of the pituitary elaborates a number of hormones dealing with water balance, urine production, and other metabolic features. One hormone (oxytocin) is important in reproduction since it maintains the contractions of the uterus necessary in the movement of sperm before fertilization. It also controls the letting down of milk from the mammary glands. Unfortunately, since relatively few species have been studied intensively, most of our knowledge of mammalian hormones depends on studies of rodents and primates.

Ovulation

An important feature in the control of reproduction is whether or not ovulation is spontaneous. A mammal is said to ovulate spontaneously if the release of the ovum occurs routinely without external stimulation. The contrast occurs in the cycle, on the one hand, of a rat, which ovulates approximately every fourth day irrespective of external conditions; and, on the other hand, of a cat, which comes into estrous and remains in estrous until some external episode stimulates ovulation. The various orders of mammals differ considerably in this respect. Primates ovulate spontaneously. Many carnivores are nonspontaneous; others, such as the dog, are spontaneous. The rodents are entirely spontaneous ovulators so far as is known, except for the transitional cases mentioned below, and show very much the type of hormone conditions described above. Among the even-toed ungulates ovulation is spontaneous in the sow, cow, ewe, and doe. The lagomorphs are nonspontaneous ovulators requiring an effective stimulus. Recently the classical division into spontaneous and nonspontaneous has been modified by certain transitional cases. For example, ovulation of rats is controlled to a certain extent by the length of day. The estrous cycle of mice and ewes is influenced by the appearance of a male.

Implantation

The anatomical features of implantation were described briefly above. The hormonal control of these changes is highly complex and only partly understood. Certainly progesterone is involved, and perhaps other hormones are also. A peculiar phenomenon is the development of delayed implantation in many of the weasel family and also in some seals, bears and even deer. The ovum ovulates, is fertilized, develops to the blastocyst stage, but then lies dormant in the uterus of the female for a matter of months until suitable length of day results in the proper conditions for growth. Some mustelids such as the mink copulate early in the spring and have only a short period of delayed implantation. However, the ovum does not implant within the uterus until the length of day has set the suitable conditions, irrespective of the time of copulation.

A phenomenon that produces a similar result occurs in bats. In some species copulation takes place in the fall before hibernation, and the sperm are stored in the uterus. Fertilization occurs in the spring and implantation promptly follows. This phenomenon is called delayed fertilization, in contrast to delayed implantation.

PRODUCTION OF YOUNG

The preceding sections have described the physiological basis for reproduction. This schematic background can be applied to a wide variety of mammals, although it is based upon the relatively few species that have been studied in the laboratory. However, for mammalogical work, the current knowledge of physiology helps us to understand the reproductive processes in general that determine the production of young. The total number of animals produced during the year or a breeding season depends upon a number of features resulting from the physiology. The number of embryos, the frequency of pregnancy, the success of lactation, and the length of breeding season, all combine to determine the total of production. Many of these aspects are discussed from a different viewpoint in Chapter 8.

Births

The first statistic of importance is the number of young born. Unfortunately it is extremely difficult to get an accurate figure of this quantity, since the observer would have to be on hand almost at the instant of birth to be sure that the true number was counted. A few studies have permitted exact counts, but except for species that produce only one young, the information is very meager. However, the number of embryos present in the female can easily be determined simply by collecting some of the animals and counting the embryos. Nevertheless, many pitfalls in interpretation may occur. Since there may be some loss of embryos during pregnancy, it is important to know whether the count includes all embryos that were implanted or merely those that were carried to term. Generally speaking, of course, the count is the average in a random sample of pregnant females, considered to occur at the midpoint of pregnancy.

Still another problem is the determination of pregnancy. In most species the fertilized ovum undergoes considerable development before implantation. Only after implantation can the observer detect the presence of an embryo by inspection of the uterus. While techniques for washing out the unimplanted blastocysts exist, these are tedious and are rarely practiced. Therefore, in practice one usually counts only what can be called the "visible" embryos. For example, in the rat as studied in the laboratory, implantation occurs on about the seventh day after conception and the embryos begin to produce a visible swelling at about that time. Since parturition occurs on about the 21st day, the animal would be "visibly pregnant" for only 14 out of 21 days of true pregnancy. In actual practice the use of counts of the visible embryos is entirely satisfactory, since the important question is how many young are born, and these counts help in approximation. Information on the number of embryos was summarized by Asdell (1946), but since that time a large amount of new data has become available. A few examples (Table 7-1) will be cited from the extensive literature in the specialized journals. One point of considerable interest is that closely related species living in the same area may have different numbers of embryos. The meadow vole had 4.5 embryos in Ohio while the prairie vole had 3.4 (DeCoursey, 1957). Similarly, the long-tailed deer mouse had 4.6 embryos while the brush mouse had 3.1 (Jameson, 1953). Many species of bats, seals, monkeys, and apes normally have only one young a year. But twins or even triplets are occasionally recorded for certain species—deer, harbor seals, and some primates.

The litter order also affects litter size. Domestic rats and mice regularly show an increase to about the third or fourth litter (Mathewson, *et al.*, 1959). Captive meadow voles (Poiley, 1949) increased from 3.33 young for the first litter to 4.89 at the eighth.

Pregnancies

The number of pregnancies clearly is important in determining the production of young during a year. The first item to be considered is the proportion of females that are pregnant at any one time. For example, 72 per cent of the opossums (McKeever, 1958) had young in the pouch. Of course young in the pouch is not true pregnancy, but is its equivalent for a marsupial. Cottontails (Lord, 1961) over a period of three years averaged 60 per cent pregnant. Mule deer (McConnell, 1960) were 98 per cent pregnant as adults. Other examples will be cited later when more detailed analyses are made.

A simple figure of the percentage pregnant in a sample is inadequate to determine the important point, namely, how many litters are born per year. However, it is possible to calculate the number of pregnancies per hypothetical average female for a given period of time (Emlen and Davis, 1946). By this method or some modification, several authors have determined the number of pregnancies per year (Table 7-1). Variation may be expected from place to place and year to year. The California vole (Greenwald, 1957) produced 4.4 pregnancies in one year and 5.6 in another year. Many species, of course, have only one pregnancy per year. For example, many carnivores such as foxes and bobcats, and many ungulates such as deer and moose, and many aquatic mammals such as seals, bear young only once a year.

TABLE 7-1. Reproductive Performance of Selected Mammals

Species	Remarks	Embryos (mean)	Incidence of Pregnancy *	References (senior author only)	
Opossum	Missouri	8.9	. . .	Reynolds	(1945)
(Dilelphis	Maryland	8.2	. . .	Llewellyn	(unpub)
marsupialis)	Kansas	7.4	. . .	Fitch	(1953)
	California	7.2	. . .	Reynolds	(1952)
	California	7.1	. .	McKeever	(1958)
	Texas	6.8	. . .	Lay	(1942)
	Florida	6.5		Burns	(1956)
Eastern Mole	spring	3.91	1	Conaway	(1959)
(Scalopus aquaticus)					
Salt Marsh Shrew	. . .	5.16	.	Johnston	(1957)
(Sorex vagrans)					
Mongoose	Feb-July	2.7	2	Pearson	(1953)
(Herpestes					
auropunctatus)					
Coyote	New Mexico	5.54	. . .	Young	(1951)
(Canis latrans)					
Gray Fox	April	4.9	1	Wood	(1958)
(Urocyon					
cinereoargenteus)					
Bobcat	Jan-Sept	3.2	1	Gashwiler	(1961)
(Lynx rufus)					
Walrus	. . .	1.0	1	Loughrey	(1959)
(Odobenus rosmarus)					
Woodchuck	April	3.98	0.8	Snyder	(1960)
(Marmota monax)					
Fox Squirrel	Michigan	3.02	. . .	Allen	(1943)
(Sciurus niger)					
Red Squirrel	New York	4.2		Layne	(1954)
(Tamiasciurus					
hudsonius)					
Gray Squirrel	England	2.87	. . .	Shorten	(1951)
(Sciurus carolinensis)					
Pocket Gopher	Florida	1.52	.	Wing	(1960)
(Geomys pinetus)					
Pocket Gopher	75% year-	6.4	1	Hansen	(1960)
(G. bursarius)	lings				
Pocket Gopher	. . .	3.40	1	Vaughn	(1960)
(G. bursarius)					
Deer Mouse	. . .	4.6	. . .	Jameson	(1953)
(Peromyscus					
maniculatus)					
Brush Mouse	. . .	3.1	. .	Jameson	(1953)
(Peromyscus boylli)					
Cotton Mouse	Sept-May	3.7	. . .	Pournelle	(1952)
(P. polionotus)					
Meadow Vole	. . .	4.48	. . .	DeCoursey	(1957)
(Microtus					
pennsylvanicus)					

TABLE 7-1.   Reproductive Performance of Selected Mammals (*Continued*)

Species	Remarks	Embryos (mean)	Incidence of Pregnancy *	References (senior author only)	
Prairie Vole (*Microtus ochrogaster*)	. . .	3.40	. . .	DeCoursey	(1957)
California Vole (*M. californicus*)	peak in Apr	4.2	4.4 to 5.6	Greenwald	(1957)
Creeping Vole (*M. oregoni*)	. . .	3.11	. . .	Cowan	(1954)
Red-backed Vole (*Clethrionomys rutilus*)	Finland	6.00	. . .	Kalela	(1957)
Water Vole (*Arvicola terrestris*)	Feb-Sept	4.5	4.4	Wijngaarden	(1954)
Bank Vole (*Evotomys glareolus*)	March-Oct	4.0	. . .	DeLost	(1955)
Sagebrush Vole (*Lagurus curtatus*)	. . .	5.27		James	(1954)
Muskrat (*Ondatra zibethica*)	4 years	3.46	. . .	O'Neil	(1949)
Muskrat (*O. zibethica*)	22 years	7.49		Errington	(1957)
Gerbil (*Tatera afra*)	wild adults	4.06	. . .	Measroch	(1954)
Gerbil (*Tatera brantsi*)	wild adults	2.94	. . .	Measroch	(1954)
Vizcacha (*Lagidium peruanum*)	Nov-Aug	1.0	2.0	Pearson	(1949)
Audubon Cottontail (*Sylvilagus auduboni*)	Jan-Aug	2.9	. . .	Sowls	(1957)
Black-tailed Jack Rabbit (*Lepus californicus*)	Jan-Aug	2.3	4.27	Lechleitner	(1959)
European Hare (*Lepus timidus*)	Jan-Aug	1.9	. . .	Reynolds	(1959)
Snowshoe Hare (*Lepus americanus*)	. . .	3.82	2.75	Rowan	(1956)
Mule Deer (*Odocoileus hemionus*)	yearling	1.23	1	McConnell	(1960)
Mule Deer (*O. hemionus*)	3 to 8 year old	1.77	1	McConnell	(1960)
Mule Deer (*O. hemionus*)	yearling	1.11	1	Robinette	(1955)
Mule Deer (*O. hemionus*)	adult	1.61	1	Robinette	(1955)
Moose (*Alces americana*)	late Sept	1.12	1	Edwards	(1958)

* Incidence means the average number of pregnancies during the breeding season for a female.

From the above type of information the number of embryos produced in a year can be determined, but, as indicated above, the actual number of births and of lactations is poorly known. In principle the same procedures can be used with lactation as with pregnancy to determine how frequently during a year a female lactates. Prevalence of lactation is based on expression of milk from the nipples. The same method as above will serve when modified to include a different numerical value for the denominator. Almost the only work done on frequency of lactation is a study in rats summarized by Davis (1953) showing that females had about six lactations per year.

Breeding Season

Another problem of importance in the production of young is the duration of the breeding season, which lasts from the beginning of courtship till the last young are weaned. In some species (woodchucks) the interval may be only a few weeks, but in others (deer) courtship and copulation occur in the fall and calving follows in the spring. In such forms "breeding season" may refer only to the fall part. Some species in one way or another have continuous breeding throughout the year. In many parts of the temperate zone some rats (Davis, 1953) can be found pregnant in any month of the year. The males have sperm at all times. In many tropical areas a number of rats breed in the wild throughout the year (Harrison, 1955), and other rodents in the tropics may have a continuous season as well. Spiny rats (Davis, 1945) were found pregnant in small numbers in every month of the year in the forests of Brazil. Some squirrels and perhaps a shrew (Harrison, 1955) may breed at all times of the year, although there is a definite decline in activity from October to March. However, generally speaking, there may be seasonal peaks and troughs in the frequency (Figure 7-8). In the temperate region variation occurs from year to year. The meadow vole (Hamilton, 1941) was found breeding throughout the winter in one out of four years, and the bank vole (*Evotomys glareolus*) bred in certain winters (Baker, 1930). Many isolated cases of this phenomenon could be cited. Another situation occurs in the gopher (*Geomys bursarius*) (Miller, 1946), which bred throughout the year in irrigated alfalfa fields in California, while in the adjacent nonirrigated fields the breeding season was limited. The European rabbit (*Oryctolagus cuniculus*) introduced into New Zealand breeds in all months, although the lowest period is in April and May. This example is puzzling, because in the

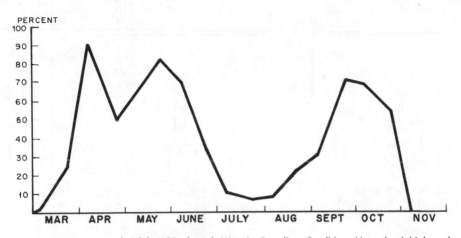

PERCENT

Figure 7-8. Percentage of Adult White-footed Mice in Breeding Condition. Note the initial peak followed by a drop due in part to simultaneity of lactation. (From Burt, 1940.)

northern temperate regions there is a definite season of breeding, with its maximum in the spring in April and May. An interesting case is the mountain viscacha (Pearson, 1949) that breeds at altitudes from 12 to 17 thousand feet at all seasons of the year. Elephants breed at any time during the year.

The examples mentioned above illustrate a continuous breeding season, although in many cases there are definite peaks and valleys in the frequencies of the pregnancies. Most mammals have a discontinuous season that may be divided in several different ways. Some forms have several distinct periods of breeding, partly due to synchrony at the times of conception. The cottontail rabbit (Schwartz, 1942; see Figure 7-9), produced a series of alternating pregnancies and lactation periods. A high proportion of the females became pregnant suddenly in February, produced their litters, weaned them, and then became pregnant again. In one sense the breeding season was continuous, but the periods of pregnancy were discrete. The males have functional testes throughout the season (Figure 7-10).

Some species that have only one pregnancy per year obviously have a discontinuous breeding period. Foxes in Georgia (Wood, 1958) conceived in January and gave birth to their young about April 1. Woodchucks in Pennsylvania (Snyder and Christian, 1960) produced about 90 per cent of their litters within ten days around April 10 (Figure 7-11). Ground squirrels (Moore, *et al.*, 1934) also have a single breeding

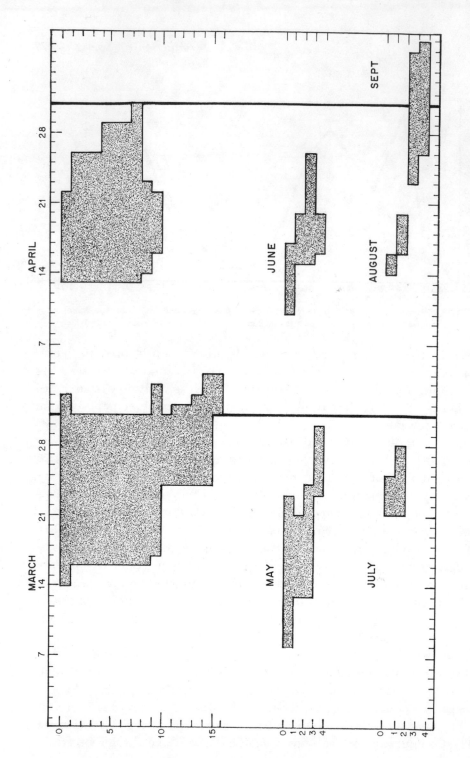

Figure 7-9. Discontinuity of Breeding in Cottontails. Note that the synchrony gradually disappears. (From Schwartz, 1942.)

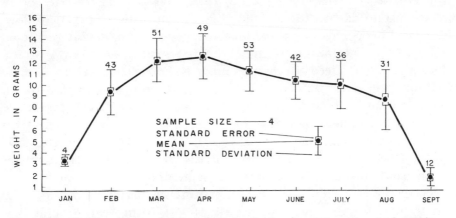

Figure 7-10. The Size of Testes of Cottontails During the Breeding Season. (From Lord, 1961.)

REPRODUCTIVE CYCLE OF SOUTHERN WOODCHUCK

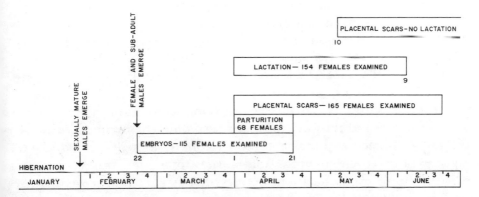

Figure 7-11. Sequence of Reproductive Conditions in Female Woodchucks. (From Snyder and Christian, 1960.)

period. Many other cases could be mentioned, especially those found among ungulates.

Perhaps the more usual situation is that as the season begins, several pregnancies follow without rigorous spacing, thus giving a steady increase to a maximum followed by a decline at the end of a season. Muskrats (Errington, 1957) show a peak in many places in the spring. The meadow vole (DeCoursey, 1957) as well as the prairie vole have a definite season from March to October. The mountain pocket gopher in Colorado (Hansen, 1960) breeds from March to May. The cotton mouse in Florida (Pournelle, 1952) breeds from August till the following May. The percentage of pregnancies ranged from 7 in August to 69 in December and down to 17 in May. A water rat in southern Australia (McNally, 1960) breeds from September to February, but each female has only one litter per year. The gerbils in South Africa (Allanson, 1958) show an interesting contrast. One species breeds throughout the year, while in the same area the second species breeds from April through February. The cottontail rabbit in Arizona (Sowls, 1957) breeds from January to August, whereas in more northern climates (Lord, 1961) it breeds from March to September.

Some species, instead of having a continuous period of considerable length, may breed at two separate times within the year. Several Brazilian opossums (Davis, 1945) breed at six months' intervals, having only one litter each time. The gray and fox squirrels in Illinois and in many other areas of the United States (Brown and Yeager, 1945) have a litter in February or March and a second litter in August or September. Between litters the animals become sexually inactive, and not all individuals breed at both seasons in the same year.

From the above information it is clear that mammalian species differ greatly in the number of young produced during the year. Some are limited to small numbers and have only slight variability, dependent on place, season, or year. Other species, especially rodents, differ greatly in the time of year and the number of young, as well as in the number of pregnancies, and thus may produce very different numbers of individuals at different times. Species that have a high reproductive capacity can recover promptly from a catastrophe, but may encounter the dangers of overpopulation. Species that have a low reproductive capacity and breed during all the year maintain level populations. A variety of important factors determine these variations.

FACTORS AFFECTING REPRODUCTION

Differences in the number of young from year to year or place to place depend upon numerous factors in the environment acting through the long chain of physiological processes outlined above. In most cases the actual course of events is sketchily known, although a correlation between a factor and the number of young may be apparent. This part of the chapter will illustrate some types of relations between the factors in a mammal's environment and its reproduction. The study of the relation of environmental conditions to reproduction is in its infancy, primarily because experiment and analysis are difficult. Laboratory experiments have only limited applicability to natural populations, and field studies suffer from lack of suitable controls. Another hindrance is the necessity that the factor being analyzed be the limiting factor at the particular time and place. For example, suppose the relation of number of litters of muskrats to food supply is being examined. For such experiments it is essential that all other factors (water, dens or houses, space, etc.) be in excess or optimal. Since the limiting factor is difficult to detect and changes frequently, it is understandable that successful field studies are rare. Further discussion of this topic occurs in Chapter 8.

Food

Some good data on the relation of natural food supply to reproduction are available. Captive English field voles (*Microtus agrestis*) (Baker and Ranson, 1933) fed diets that simulated winter supplies (hay and seeds) and summer conditions (growing grass), did not differ in reproduction. As another example, the extent of reproduction of white-tailed deer (*Odocoileus virginiana*) (Cheatum, *et al.*, 1950) correlated with condition of range. The range conditions in five parts of New York State were classified from best to worst. The number of embryos declined respectively, from 1.7 to 1.1. Presumably the range condition correlated with the food supply so that deer in poor range had poor food, but it is possible that population density was also a factor. Breeding of rats (*Rattus rattus*) stopped (Gomez, 1960) in Venezuela when, in the dry season, the food decreased. While it is certain that food supply is important to breeding, unfortunately its effect is usually confounded with many other seasonal events.

Temperature

The important role of temperature in reproduction of lower vertebrates is well documented, but there is little proof of a direct effect of temperature on birds or mammals. House mice (Laurie, 1946) living in a cold-storage warehouse, bred as well as those living in warmer places. Indeed, significantly more embryos per female occurred in the cold warehouse, presumably due to the ample diet there of frozen meat. Captive English field voles (Baker, *et al.*, 1933) had fewer pregnancies at 5°C than at 18°C, although the fecundity of the male was not affected. However, cotton mice (Pournelle, 1952) at high temperatures (89 to 101°F) in the laboratory, lacked sperm in 3 to 4 weeks. European rabbits (Brambell, 1944) in the cold spring of 1942 had a low number of pregnancies. It seems likely that the action of temperature on the reproduction of warm-blooded vertebrates usually occurs indirectly through other factors. Nevertheless, studies at extremes of temperature are warranted.

Light

The length of the day or shortness of the night is known to control reproduction in some mammals. Some effect of light periods occurs in field voles (Baker, *et al.*, 1932). Females kept for a year at 9 hours' light per day had fewer pregnancies and embryos than did females kept at 15 hours'. However, no differences occurred in reproduction between voles kept at 6 hours' and at 15 hours' light when food was abundant (Marshall, *et al.*, 1956). Similarly, no effect of light was noticed in another species of vole (Cowan, *et al.*, 1954). However, white-footed mice (Whittaker, 1940) were affected by light conditions. At low intensities the mice reproduced even at low temperatures. Blinded mice, however, were not sterile. The fact that so many mammals are nocturnal raises the problem of how, in an evolutionary sense, light could come to have a relation to reproduction. For mustelids and ungulates the relation of short days (or, probably, long nights) is well known. Experimental manipulation shows that some mustelids come into reproductive condition as days get long, and that ewes (*Ovis domestica*) come into estrous as days get short. Presumably deer resemble ewes.

Some other aspects of light have been examined only slightly. Apparently intensity itself has little effect if any. One study on moonlight reports an outbreak of conceptions in several Malayan rats just before full moon (Harrison, 1952). A few studies (Baker, 1930; Lord, 1961) suggest that the amount of sunshine is correlated in some cases with an early breeding season.

Other Environmental Factors

The effects on reproduction of such other environmental factors as rain and disease are poorly known. Rain presumably always acts through the vegetation. The Ord kangaroo rat (*Dipodomys ordi*) (McCulloch, *et al.*, 1961) bred at different months in different years in association with rainfall. In Arizona the white-tailed deer (McCabe, *et al.*, 1951) drop their fawns in August after the rains begin in July. Disease usually acts on reproduction through metabolism in general, but may directly affect reproduction. In many cases even a disease that has a high fatality rate will not affect reproduction directly. In epidemics of myxomatosis among rabbits (Marshall, *et al.*, 1955) there was no effect on fecundity of the population. However, it is possible the drastic decline in population permitted an increase of reproduction to compensate for loss due to disease.

Latitude

Many environmental variables correlate with latitude, and thus it is no surprise that the litter size often does the same. Such features as length of day, rainfall, temperature, and insolation change from the equator to the poles. Generally, the size of litter increases from south to north. Examples occur in marsupials (see Table 7-1) and placental mammals (Lord, 1960). The relation was statistically significant in rabbits, voles, deer mice, tree squirrels, and shrews. However, several hibernating and fossorial prey species and predators showed no significant change in litter size with latitude. Perhaps the large litter size in northern regions is necessary to compensate for a high mortality in winter among the active species. Experimental studies of the populations and their reproduction are needed to unravel these mysteries.

Age or Size at Sexual Maturity

Sexual maturity may be defined by a variety of criteria depending upon the feasibility of observations. For many mammals it is possible to use external characters that can be examined without harming the individual. Thus in rodents, the perforation of the vaginal orifice or the descent of the testis are feasible measures for studies of live animals. The percentage having these characters may be plotted against weight (Figure 7-12) or length on special paper called "50 per cent point." A useful statistic, then, is the weight at which 50 per cent of the mammals are sexually mature, i.e., have the characters. For animals that are killed, other definitions can be used, such as presence of sperm, or in females, of corpora lutea.

The age at sexual maturity is known in a general way for most kinds of mammals. Cottontails, deer mice, and many other mammals breed at or before one year of age. However, some large mammals and primates wait several years before breeding. For example, the prevalence

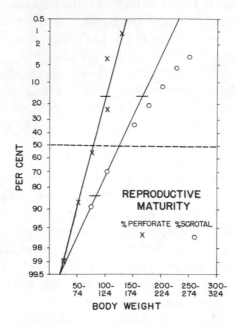

of pregnancy in elk (*Cervus canadensis*) according to age (Kittams, 1953) was as follows: None of 37 1½-year-olds had been pregnant (as judged by presence of corpora lutea); but 4 per cent of 39 2½-year-olds and about 85 per cent of the older elk cows had corpora lutea. Yearling mule deer (Robinette, *et al.*, 1955) averaged 1.32 fetus per pregnant doe and only 84 per cent were pregnant. In 2-year-olds the average was 1.77, and 99 per cent were pregnant. A similar change with age occurred in another population (McConnell, *et al.*, 1960). Of yearlings, 24 per cent had twins and 66 per cent were pregnant. Of 2-year olds, 50 per cent had twins and 94 per cent were pregnant. The percentages were even higher in older animals. Among woodchucks (Snyder, *et al.*, 1960) only half the yearlings became pregnant but almost all adults bore young. Fur seals (Abegglen, 1959) showed a peak in pregnancy with age (Table 7-2). Foxes, however (Wood, 1958) showed no difference in pregnancies with age although an increase in embryos from 4.76 to 5.75 occurred (Table 7-3). Cottontails (Lord, 1961) showed a peak in pregnancies but a steady increase in litter size (Table 7-4).

The problem of age at maturity becomes complex in short-lived species that have a long breeding season. A mouse born in early spring may breed the same year (Dice, *et al.*, 1951) at an age of 4 months, per-

TABLE 7-2. Percentage of Pregnant Northern Fur Seals, by Age—
Pribilof Islands, 1956-1957 *

Age (years)	Females	Per Cent Pregnant
2	35	0
3	458	1
4	1821	11
5	2767	52
6	1893	74
7	1267	78
8	1025	71
9	784	69
10	454	65
10+	2751	48
Totals:	13255	52

* From Abegglen, *et al.*, 1959.

TABLE 7-3. Breeding Performance by Age Classes of Foxes *

Age (years)	Foxes Examined	Number Pregnant	Embryos (mean)	Foxes Post Partum	Placental Scars
1	78	25	4.76	36	4.19
2	39	11	5.27	19	4.44
3	22	4	5.75	11	4.60
4	3	0	. . .	1	5.00

* From Wood, 1958.

TABLE 7-4. Age—Specific Reproduction of Cottontails *

Age class	Embryos (mean)	Per Cent Pregnant	Number Females
Juvenile	4.72	31	20
1 year	5.44	77	130
2 years	5.87	70	31
3 years	6.00	68	13

* From Lord, 1961.

haps; but an individual born in late spring may not mature before the
winter and, hence, not breed till the next spring at an age of 9 months.
These individuals are very different in chronological age, but are the
same physiological age in respect to reproduction. In rats there is evi-

dence (Davis, *et al.*, 1951) that at some seasons (spring and fall) the females breed at a smaller size (younger?) than in other seasons.

Another aspect is that the age at first breeding may be related to the density of population. Consider a comparison of a stationary rat (*Rattus norvegicus*) population with an increasing one. Perforce the former is more dense than the latter. In stationary populations in Baltimore, 8.7 per cent of small rats (180 to 199 mm long) were pregnant in contrast to 24.4 per cent of the same size in increasing populations. For larger rats the differences between the two population levels were much less. These data are interpreted as an indication that in less dense (increasing) populations the rats breed at a younger age than in more dense populations.

Compensation for Loss

Some species, especially large mammals, are unable to breed a second time in a season to compensate for loss of young. But others such as rodents may start over and commonly produce another litter at once after loss of a litter. Wild European rabbits also have a second litter (Brambell, 1944) to compensate for loss.

Optimum Litter Size

The average number of progeny may be the result of a compromise between a tendency for the most productive individuals to leave more progeny and the tendency for individuals in a large litter to have poor survival because of inadequate care by parents (Lack, 1954). For mammals less milk will be available for each individual in a large litter than in a small one. More data, especially from wild mammals, are needed to place this hypothesis in proper perspective.

In this connection it is worth referring to the relation of the number of young to their size. It is often claimed that in domestic rats the average weight of the young decreases as the number increases, but Huggett and Widdas (1951) did not find a decrease in weight of fetus with increase in litter size. Data for wild mammals are scanty. In humans the average weight decreases with increase of litter size, and duration of gestation is increased as litter weight increases.

Sex Ratio

Various species of animals differ in the sex ratios of adults, but a shortage of one sex is usually taken care of by some arrangement of breeding behavior or by temporary changes in behavior. Among mammals some species (foxes) are monogamous, but most kinds are promiscuous. Actually, there is no evidence that in nature a shortage of one sex directly limits the birth-rate in mammals. However, this result could occur, if, for example, by chance only males invaded an area. Apparently, compensatory behavior takes care of the situation in most cases, because under natural conditions the unbalance in sex ratio is rarely extreme.

BEHAVIORAL ADAPTATIONS

Certain aspects of behavior pertain directly to the production of young and will be discussed here rather than in Chapter 10.

In monogamous species, which retain the same mate for several years or for a lifetime, there is seldom a problem of locating a mate. In polygynous species the problem may be more acute, depending on the number of males and females. During the breeding season the males search for receptive females, often by following olfactory clues which are deposited by the females. Visual and auditory clues may also be used, but in densely vegetated habitats they are of less value to the male. The white-tailed deer is an example of a species in which males and females live separately. During the breeding season or rut, males will occasionally be seen running through the woods with their noses to the ground searching for receptive females. When the male locates the odor of a female he will try to follow the trail to her, but if the female is not receptive she will actively repulse the male and run away. If the female is receptive she will nuzzle, lick, and rub against the male and then will stand quietly while the male mounts. Copulation may occur several times before intromission is successful (Golley, 1957). Following copulation, the male and female appear to lack interest in each other. Many insectivores and rodents also exhibit this type of behavior.

Many mammals, for example elk and seals, congregate during the breeding season in small or large aggregations of both sexes. Since the females are together, the problem of locating a receptive female is reduced. In these groups the male seems to be more concerned with satisfying the drive to herd the females and to breed. In elk, the females and young live in herds and family groups, while the males, which may live together during most of the year, become antagonistic toward one another during the breeding season. Males will herd harems of females and young, and drive away other bulls. When a female comes into heat, the herd male will breed with her. In fur seals (*Callorhinus ursinus*) the males arrive first at the breeding grounds and establish their territories. When the females arrive, they are grouped into harems which are defended by the males. Herding and breeding with a large harem is a demanding task, and during the course of a breeding season fresh bulls can usually defeat the herd bulls or at least drive away some of the females to form other harems. It is interesting to note that in red deer (*Cervus elaphus*) when danger threatens, the male dominance breaks down and the herd, including the bull, follows the dominant female—who leads them away from the source of disturbance (Darling, 1937).

Finally we can recognize polygynous species which live together throughout the year in groups which include both males and females. Many primates exhibit this type of social behavior. In these the female, when receptive, makes herself conspicuous by provocative gestures, movements, and by sexual swelling and coloration. These receptive females may be covered by a number of males during the heat period. In Panama the male howler monkeys (*Alouatta palliata*) within the clan display no antagonism toward other males over the receptive female.

These different types of behavior suggest there has been an adaptive trend toward reduction of the difficulty of locating a mate. This problem is especially acute in those species in which the males and females live solitary lives. In these, the population density affects the chance of a male meeting a female, and at very low density levels a female may pass through several heat periods without breeding. Density may also influence success of breeding in those species which form breeding herds or harems, since, in these, males may require the stimulation of fighting and defense activity to complete the breeding cycle. In the polygamous clans and monogamous families the problem of locating a receptive female is essentially eliminated.

BREEDING EFFICIENCY

Throughout the mammals there are trends towards improved efficiency for survival. However, not all groups become efficient in the same features. Some develop protective devices, such as running or fighting (Chapter 4), or physiological tricks such as hibernation. These processes generally reduce the mortality rate, and the species can persist even though the birth rate may be low. However, some species have stressed the development of efficiency of reproduction and, so to speak, have ignored the mortality rate. Rodents, for example field voles, have only trivial protective devices. Predators have little difficulty in catching voles and even extirpating the population. But some voles escape and outsmart the predators by outbreeding them. Numerous specific aspects of reproduction can be mentioned: early sexual maturity (1 month), frequent estrous periods and a postpartum estrus, promiscuity, and a highly efficient type of placenta. The litter size is not remarkable, but obviously does not need to be. By these means high reproductive rates can compensate for high mortality rates.

REFERENCES

Abegglen, Carl E., and Alton Y. Roppel. 1959. Fertility in the northern fur seal, 1956-57. J. Wildlife Manag. 23(1): 75-81.

Allanson, Marjorie. 1934. Seasonal reproductive organs of the male hedgehog. Phil. Trans. Roy. Soc. B223: 277-303.

Allanson, Marjorie. 1958. Growth and reproduction in the males of two species of gerbil, *Tatera brantsii* (A. Smith) and *Tatera afra* (Gray). Proc. Zool. Soc. London. 130(3): 373-396.

Allen, Durward L. 1943. Michigan Fox Squirrel Management. Lansing, Mich., Game Div., Dept. of Conservation. 405 pp.

Arey, L. B. 1954. Developmental Anatomy. W. B. Saunders Co. 680 pp.

Asdell, S. A. 1946. Patterns of Mammalian Reproduction. Comstock Pub. Co. 437 pp.

Baker, J. R. 1930. The breeding season in British wild mice. Proc. Zool. Soc. London (1): 113-126.

Baker, J. R., and R. W. Ranson, 1932-33. Factors affecting breeding of the field mouse (*Microtus agrestis*). I. Light. Proc. Roy Soc. London B110: 313-322. II. Temperature and food. Proc. Roy. Soc. London B112: 39-46.

Brambell, F. W. R. 1944. The reproduction of the wild rabbit *Oryctolagus cuniculus* (L.) Proc. Zool. Soc. London 114: 1-45.

Brown, L. G., and L. E. Yeager. 1945. Fox squirrels and gray squirrels in Illinois. Bull. Ill. Nat. Hist. Surv. 23(5): 449-536.

Burns, R. K., and Lucille M. Burns. 1956. Vie et reproduction de l'opossum américain *Didelphis marsupialis virginiana* Kerr. Bull. Soc. Zool. France 81(4): 230-246.

Burt, W. H. 1940. Territorial behavior and populations of some small mammals in southern Michigan. Misc. Publ. Mus. Zool. Univ. Mich. 45: 1-58.

Cheatum, E. L., and C. W. Severinghaus. 1950. Variations in fertility of white-tailed deer related to range conditions. Trans. N. A. Wildl. Conf. 15: 170-190.

Conaway, C. H. 1959. The reproductive cycle of the eastern mole. J. Mamm. 40(2): 180-194.

Cowan, Ian McT., and Margaret G. Arsenault. 1954. Reproduction and growth in the creeping vole, *Microtus oregoni serpens* Merriam. Canad. J. Zool. 32: 198-208.

Darling, F. F. 1937. A Herd of Red Deer. Oxford Univ. Press. 216 pp.

Davis, David E. 1945. The annual cycle of plants, mosquitoes, birds, and mammals in two Brazilian forests. Ecol. Monog. 15: 243-295.

Davis, David E. 1953. The characteristics of rat populations. Quart. Rev. Biol. 28(4): 373-401.

Davis, David E., and Octavia Hall. 1951. The seasonal reproductive condition of female Norway (brown) rats in Baltimore, Maryland. Phys. Zool., 24(1): 9-20.

Deanesly, Ruth. 1934. The reproductive cycle of the female hedgehog. Phil. Trans. Roy. Soc. B223: 239-276.

DeCoursey, G. E., Jr. 1957. Identification, ecology, and reproduction of *Microtus* in Ohio. J. Mamm. 38(1): 44-52.

Delost, P. 1955. Etude de la biologie sexuelle de Campagnol des Champs (*Microtus arvalis P.*). Arch. Ant. Microsc. et Morpholi Exptl. 44(2): 150-190.

Dice, L. R., and Walter E. Howard. 1951. Distance of dispersal by prairie deer mice from birthplaces to breeding sites. Cont. Lab. Vert. Biol. Univ. Mich. 50: 1-15.

Edwards, R. Y., and R. W. Ritcey. 1958. Reproduction in moose population. J. Wildl. Manag. 22(3): 261-268.

Emlen, J. T., and David E. Davis. 1948. Determination of reproductive rates in rat populations by examination of carcasses. Physiol. Zool. 21(1): 59-65.

Errington, P. L. 1957. Of population cycles and unknowns. Cold Spring Harbor Symp. on Quant. Biol. XXII: 287-300.

Fitch, H. S., and L. L. Sandridge. 1953. Ecology of the oposssum on a natural area in northeastern Kansas. Univ. Kansas Publ. Mus. Nat. Hist. 7(2): 305-338.

Gashwiler, Jay S., W. Leslie Robinette, and Owen W. Morris. 1961. Breeding habits of bobcats in Utah. J. Mamm. 42(1): 76-84.

Golley, Frank B. 1957. Gestation period, breeding and fawning behavior of Columbian black-tailed deer. J. Mamm. 38(1): 116-120.

Gomez, Juan C. 1960. Correlation of a population of roof rats in Venezuela with seasonal changes in habitat. Amer. Mid. Nat. 63(1): 177-193.

Greenwald, Gilbert S. 1957. Reproduction in a coastal California population of the Field Mouse Microtus californicus. Univ. Calif. Pub. Zool. 54(7): 421-446.

Hall, Peter F. 1959. The functions of the endocrine glands. W. B. Saunders Co. 290 pp.

Hamilton, W. J., Jr. 1941. Reproduction of the field mouse Microtus pennsylvanicus (Ord.). Cornell Univ. Agric. Exper. Station. 237: 1-23.

Hansen, Richard M. 1960. Age and reproductive characteristics of mountain pocket gophers in Colorado. J. Mamm. 41(3): 323-335.

Harrison, J. L. 1952. Moonlight and pregnancy of Malayan forest rats. Nature 170(4315): 73-74.

Harrison, J. L. 1955. Data on the reproduction of some Malayan mammals. Proc. Zool. Soc. London 125(2): 445-460.

Huggett, A. St. G., and W. F. Widdas. 1951. The relationship between mammalian foetal weight and conception age. J. Physiol. 114(3): 306-317.

James, William B., and Ernest S. Booth. 1954. Biology and life history of the sagebrush vole. Walla Walla College Publ. Dept. Biol. Sci. 4: 1-20.

Jameson, E. C., Jr. 1953. Reproduction of deer mice (*Peromyscus maniculatus* and *P. boyeli*) in the Sierra Nevada, California. J. Mamm. 34(1): 44-58.

Johnston, Richard F., and Robert L. Rudd. 1957. Breeding of the salt marsh shrew. J. Mamm. 38(2): 157-163.

Kalela, Olavi. 1957. Regulation of reproduction rate in subarctic populations of the vole *Clethrionomys rufocanus* (Sund.). Ann. Acad. Sci. Fennicae A. IV. 34: 1-60.

Kittams, Walter H. 1953. Reproduction of Yellowstone elk. J. Wildl. Manag. 17(2): 177-184.

Lack, D. 1954. The regulation of animal numbers. Oxford Univ. Press. 343 pp.

Laurie, E. M. O. 1946. The reproduction of the house mouse (*Mus musculus*) living in different environments. Proc. Soc. London, B133 (872): 248-281.

Lay, D. W. 1942. Ecology of the opossum in eastern Texas. J. Mamm. 23(2): 147-159.

Layne, James N. 1954. The biology of the red squirrel, *Tamiasciurus hudsonicus loquax* (Bangs), in central New York. Ecol. Monog. 24: 227-267.

Lechleitner, R. R. 1959. Sex ratio, age classes and reproduction of the black-tailed jack rabbit. J. Mamm. 40(1): 63-81.

Lord, Rexford D. 1960. Litter size and latitude in North American mammals. Amer. Mid. Nat. 64(4): 488-499.

Lord, Rexford D. 1961. Magnitudes of reproduction in cottontail rabbits. J. Wildl. Manag. 25(1): 28-33.

Loughrey, Alan G. 1959. Preliminary investigation of the Atlantic walrus. Wildl. Manag. Bull. 1(14): 1-122.

Marshall, A. J., and O. Wilkinson. 1956. Reproduction in the Orkney vole (*Microtus orcadensis*) under a six-hour day-length and other conditions. Proc. Zool. Soc. London 126(3): 391-395.

Marshall, I. D., A. L. Dyce, W. E. Poole, and Frank Fenner. 1955. Studies in the epidemiology of infectious myxomatosis of rabbits. IV. Observations of disease behaviour in two localities near the northern limit of rabbit infestation in Australia, May 1952 to April 1953. J. Hyg. 53(1): 12-25.

Mathewson, Sue Flick, David E. Davis, and John J. Christian. 1959. Effect of constant length of day on reproduction in albino mice. J. Hyg. 57(2): 193-197.

McCabe, R. A., and A. Starker Leopold. 1951. Breeding season of the Sonora white-tailed deer. J. Wildl. Manag. 15(4): 433-434.

McConnell, Burt R., and Paul D. Dalke. 1960. The Cassia deer herd of southern Idaho. J. Wildl. Manag. 24(3): 265-271.

McCulloch, C. Y., and J. M. Inglis. 1961. Breeding periods of the Ord kangaroo rat. J. Mamm. 42(3): 337-344.

McKeever, Sturgis. 1958. Reproduction in the opossum in southwestern Georgia and northwestern Florida. J. Wildl. Manag. 22(3): 303.

McNally, J. 1960. The biology of the water rat *Hydromys chrysogaster geoffroy* (Muridae: Hydromyinae) in Victoria. Aust. J. Zool. 8(2): 170-180.

Measrock, Veronica. 1954. Growth and reproduction in the females of two species of gerbil. *Tatera brantsi* (A. Smith) and *Tatera afra* (Gray). Proc. Zool. Soc. London 124(3): 631-658.

Miller, Milton A. 1946. Reproductive rates and cycles in the pocket gopher. J. Mamm. 27(4): 335-358.

Moore, C. R., G. F. Simmons, L. T. Wells, M. Zalesky, and W. O. Nelson. 1943. On the control of reproductive activity in an annual-breeding mammal (*Citellus tridecimlineatus*). Anat. Rec. 60: 279-289.

O'Neil, Ted. 1949. The muskrat in the Louisiana coastal marshes. La. Dept. Wildlife and Fisheries. 152 pp.

Pearson, Oliver P. 1949. Reproduction of a South American rodent, the Mountain Viscacha. Am. J. Anat., 84(1): 143-174.

Pearson, Oliver P., and Paul H. Baldwin. 1953. Reproduction and age structure of of a mongoose population in Hawaii. J. Mamm. 34(4): 436-447.

Poiley, Samuel M. 1949. Raising captive meadow voles (*Microtus p. pennsylvanicus*). J. Mamm. 30(3): 317-318.

Pournelle, G. H. 1952. Reproduction and early post-natal development of the cotton mouse, *Peromyscus gossypinus gossypinus*. J. Mamm. 33(1): 1-20.

Reynolds, Harold C. 1945. Some aspects of the life history and ecology of the opossum in central Missouri. J. Mamm. 26(4): 361-379.

Reynolds, Harold C. 1952. Studies on reproduction in the opossum (*Didelphis virginiana virginiana*). Univ. Calif. Publ. Zool. 52(3): 223-284.

Reynolds, J. K., and R. H. Stinson. 1959. Reproduction in the European hare in southern Ontario. Can. J. Zool. 37(5): 627-632.

Robinette, W. Leslie, J. S. Gashwiler, Dale A. Jones, and Harold S. Crane. 1955. Fertility of mule deer in Utah. J. Wildl. Manag. 19(1): 115-136.

Rowan, Ward, and B. Keith. 1956. Reproductive potential and sex ratios of snowshoe hares in northern Alberta. Can. J. Zool. 34(4): 273-281.

Schwartz, Charles W. 1942. Breeding season of the cottontail in central Missouri. J. Mamm. 23(1): 1-16.

Shorten, Monica. 1951. Some aspects of the biology of the grey squirrel (*Sciurus carolinensis*) in Great Britain. Proc. Zool. Soc. London 121(2): 427-459.

Snyder, Robert L., and John J. Christian. 1960. Reproductive cycle and litter size of the woodchuck. Ecology 41(4): 647-656.

Sowls, Lyle K. 1957. Reproduction in the audubon cottontail in Arizona. J. Mamm. 38(2): 234-243.

Turner, C. D. 1960. General Endocrinology (third edition). W. B. Saunders Co. xi + 511 pp.

Vaughan, Terry A. 1962. Reproduction in the plains pocket gopher in Colorado. J. Mamm. 43(1): 1-13.

Whittaker, W. L. 1940. Some effects of artificial illumination on reproduction in the white-footed mouse, *Peromyscus leucopus noveboracensis*. J. Exp. Zool. 83: 33-60.

Wijngaarden, A. v. 1954. Biologie en Bestrijding van de Woelrat, *Arvicola terrestris terrestris* (L.) in Nederland. Proc. Plantenziektenkundige Dienst (Wageningen) 123: 13-147.

Wing, Elizabeth S. 1960. Reproduction in the pocket gopher in north-central Florida. J. Mamm. 41(1): 35-43.

Wood, John E. 1958. Age structure and productivity of a gray fox population. J. Mamm. 39(1): 74-86.

Young, Stanley P. 1951. The Clever Coyote. Stackpole Co. 411 pp.

Young, William C. (Editor). 1961. Sex and Internal Secretions. Williams & Wilkins. 1609 pp. (2 volumes).

chapter eight

MAMMALIAN POPULATIONS

ADVANCES in recent years in the collection of data about mammals have permitted examination of the changes in populations. Populations are complex aggregations, with a seemingly infinite number of regulatory factors acting on the species. A population is usually defined by mammalogists as a group of mammals belonging to the same species. Often there exist some types of coordination or interaction. For example, individuals may warn each other, defend an area, or merely live in the same region. However, such features are not necessary in determining a population, especially in the newer taxonomy.

The regulation of a population may be accomplished by almost any factor in the environment, including other members of the same species. Some regulatory factors may be extremely rare (earthquakes, for example) while others, such as food supply, may be common. For present purposes any factor that affects the numbers of a mammalian group may be called a regulatory factor. But the factor that at a particular time and place is restricting the growth or rate of growth is called the "limiting factor." For example, in a certain area in Tennessee a lake was formed after an earthquake. At the moment, the quake limited the population of mammals; but soon more usual factors such as food or competition reassumed the role. The regulatory factors are numerous, and shift their effects with bewildering speed.

EQUILIBRIUM

The result of the action of these regulatory factors is that populations trend toward some sort of an equilibrium. The attainment of an equilibrium by an animal population depends upon relative stability in the plant community containing the animals. Actually, many years are required for vegetation to reach a climax; but in many places the changes of vegetation are so slow that the animal community, or at least some species, may be treated as at equilibrium.

True equilibria never occur in nature for several reasons. The discreteness of individuals prevents attainment, although in large populations an equilibrium may be reached in a statistical sense. For equilibrium to occur, the population at all times would have to be the same in number and composition. Thus when a female dies, another female of the same weight would instantaneously have to take her place. Obviously, mammalian life does not function in this way. Individuals die singly and are eventually replaced by the survivors of a litter. Thus the population fails to reach a steady state.

Furthermore, the factors regulating the population may shift frequently. One year may be dry and another wet; predators may come and go; competitors may be strong or weak. For these reasons, it is no surprise that true equilibria are never attained in nature.

But still another type of complication may appear: a stationary population can be attained by simultaneous changes in two factors that happen to compensate for each other. Actually, this event amounts to a shift of limiting factors without a change in population size. Because only the limiting factors have altered, this situation results merely in an accidental numerical identity, and cannot be regarded as a true equilibrium.

In spite of these numerous practical deficiencies, the concept of equilibrium has usefulness. It helps us to understand the action of various factors in predicting trends in population, and to suggest birth and mortality rates. For these reasons some evidence will be presented that in natural populations the changes may be very small and that statistical equilibria occur in this sense.

Natural Equilibria

Obviously, equilibria are more likely to occur in an environment that has only a few variable factors. This situation can be found in urban areas supporting rat populations, because both food and shelter vary little during the year. The number of Norway rats in urban blocks (Figure 8-1) in Baltimore may remain relatively stationary for many months (Davis, 1953). Some other cases of apparent equilibrium exist.

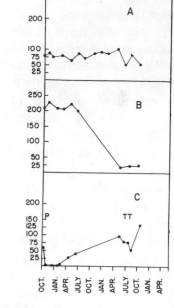

Figure 8-1. Fluctuations in Rat Populations in Certain City Blocks. The number of rats in certain blocks may remain stationary for many months, A; or increase, B; or decrease, C.

The number of opossums, minks, and raccoons caught by the same effort on a farm in Mississippi for five years was 50, 47, 40, 45, and 49. There is no doubt that the data for equilibria of mammalian populations are scanty, but this situation is not surprising, because an equilibrium can only be demonstrated when measurements show that the environmental conditions are constant. Since we lack adequate methods of measurement and the ability to maintain a constant environment in nature, it is to be expected that the concept of equilibrium remains idealistic. Tropical mammals presumably have relatively stationary populations, obeying the principle that environments that contain many species are stable. Studies of populations under such conditions are badly needed.

POPULATION CHANGES

In the process of approaching an equilibrium, the population alters. The growth, fluctuation, and decline of populations may be grouped together under the term "population kinetics" (Lotka, 1925: 57-63), which is the study of velocities of population changes. Data for the changes of natural populations are available for a number of mammals. First, we will discuss the growth of populations and, to simplify the discussion, we will assume that the environmental conditions are constant and that in the beginning there is available a large excess of requirements for the species. Naturally these conditions are never strictly true in nature, but may be approximated by some situations—for example, in certain tropical areas, especially maritime, the climatic changes may be slight. Also, constant conditions are approximated when a species is introduced into a new area. Another way to approximate the conditions of a constant environment is to compare yearly records for a particular time, say April, thereby minimizing seasonal changes. The requirements of this simplification are met when the supply of regulatory factors is so abundant that their variation does not affect the population. For example, if there is twice as much food as the population needs, a decline of one third will have no effect because an excess still remains.

Rate of Increase

In its simplest terms the general theory of population increase assumes that there is a finite rate of increase and that, as the population grows, the growth-rate is slowed down by a factor related to density. This factor merely indicates that as the population increases beyond a certain point, the rate of growth decreases in inverse ratio until it reaches zero and stops. A population in its very *early* stages (for example, just after introduction onto an island) will increase numerically in proportion to its number. This rate at first depends upon hereditary features such as litter size and duration of pregnancy. But as the population increases, the effects of density will begin to be felt, and the rate of change will alter. Eventually the population reaches the capacity of the area and no longer increases.

The study of changing populations can be traced back to Malthus and Verhulst, who were first to examine the conditions affecting population growth. In 1920 Pearl and Reed published a classic paper on the growth of population in the United States, for which census data have been available since 1790. The population data were plotted against the year (Figure 8-2) and fitted to an equation of a sigmoid curve called the "logistic." The literature concerning this curve is immense (see Andrewartha and Birch, 1954)

Growth

A number of mammalian populations show logistic increases. Emlen, Stokes, and Winsor (1948) showed that the rate of increase of a rat popu-

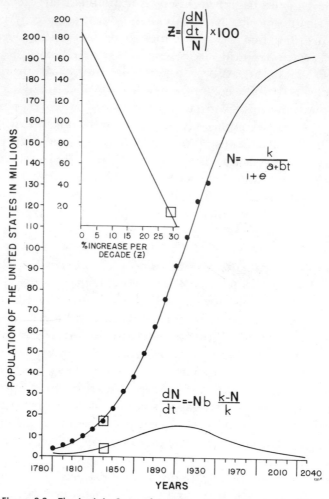

Figure 8-2. The Logistic Curve of Increase of Population in the United States. The insert shows the inverse relation of population gain to population size.

lation (after reduction) was related to the original (prereduction) population as well as to the number surviving after reduction. The details of the relationship are obscured by the variability of the various populations and the crudeness of the census methods, but are in agreement with a sigmoid curve. Since mammalian data, in most cases, represent only one population history, we can say nothing about how often this type of increase occurs in the species. Some good examples are available, how-

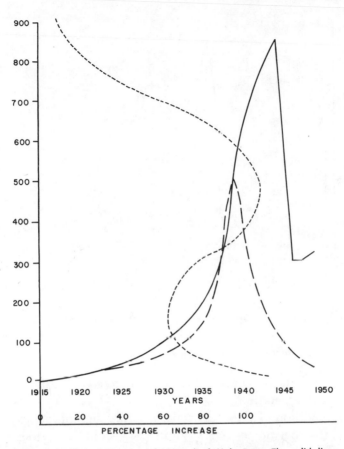

Figure 8-3. Plot of Increase of a Herd of Mule Deer. The solid line represents the population; the long-dash line, the rate of increase; and the short-dash line, the inverse relation. (From Mohler, *et al.*, 1951.)

ever: muskrats; deer at Kaibab; mule deer (Figure 8-3) (Mohler, Wampole and Fichter, 1951); elk (Banfield, 1949); and reindeer (Hanson, 1952). Scheffer (1951) described the increase in reindeer on two islands in the Aleutians. The increase was sigmoid on both islands, but on one rose to a very high level and then collapsed. On the other island the level was not high, and the population has been maintained. Another example is the increase in raccoons (*Procyon lotor*) in Iowa in recent years. The number of pelts harvested increased rapidly (from 20,000 in 1939 to 60,000 in 1942) and then leveled off in spite of a collapse in the market price. The white-tailed deer increased very rap-

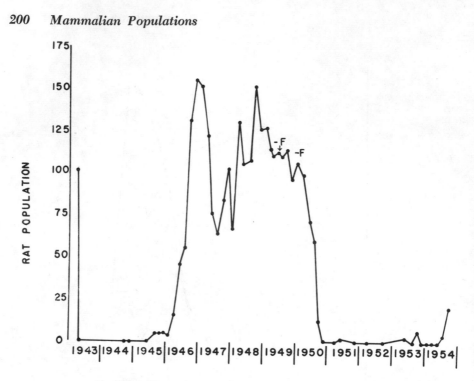

Figure 8-4. Fluctuations in a Rat Population in a City Block.

idly in an area in Wisconsin (Martin and Krefting, 1953) and began to damage the vegetation.

However, although these data are roughly sigmoid, most examples do not fit the logistic in detail. Figure 8-3 shows that the mule deer in Nebraska increased far more rapidly than accounted for by the logistic. The percentage increase (dotted line) is by no means a straight line. The conclusion to be drawn from this situation is that conditions in most mammalian populations are far more complex than the simple postulates of the logistic—hence the need for even more attention to the measurement of population and to postulation of relationships. It will be necessary to consider equations in which the change in population is proportional, say, to the cube of the population, or in which the rate of change varies in some other manner.

Under laboratory conditions, a number of studies have shown that mammalian populations increase in a sigmoid manner. Numerous authors (see Christian, 1961) found a sigmoid increase in house mice raised in large cages or rooms, and in vole populations grown in outdoor cages.

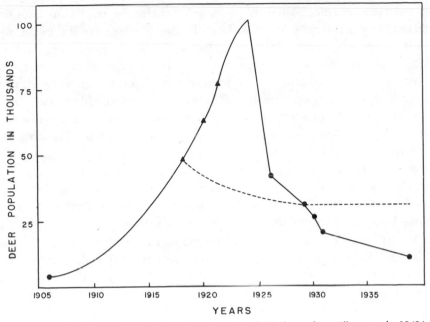

Figure 8-5. The Rise and Fall of a Kaibab Deer Herd. (Redrawn from Allee, et al., 1949.)

Decline

It has been regularly noticed that a population declines when it reaches a high level rather than gradually leveling off at an equilibrium. A rat population fluctuated considerably (Figure 8-4); and reindeer (Hanson, 1952; Scheffer, 1951), and elk (Banfield, 1949) declined. Figure 8-5 is a graph of the famous decline of the Kaibab deer herd. These declines, however, may be expected, because a more elaborate analysis of the logistic predicts that at the asymptote the population will oscillate with decreasing amplitude. This phenomenon is due in part to a lag in time between the production of young and their effective entrance into the population.

Environmental Changes

Populations in nature, however, are not in a constant environment, and hence a major variation arises from seasonal changes in the amount of reproduction, and hence, population. For example, meadow voles increase regularly during the summer and decline in winter. A long-term change can be detected in this situation by plotting the values

for a particular time (April, for example) each year, and thus avoiding
the changes within a year. Another change that occurs during a year
results from migration. Even in subtropical areas, migration and no-
madism are important. Perhaps the most usual type of environmental
change consists of erratic fluctuations of some factor such as food, rain,
etc. For example, populations of lemmings and meadow voles that
depend upon a protective snow cover are abundant during winters of
deep snow. In some cases these fluctuations may be of sufficient magnitude to be classed as calamities. Floods, severe droughts, and earthquakes belong in this group. A major cause of slow changes in environment is the succession of vegetation that occurs on an area. It is well
known that after a fire, a regular and generally predictable series of
changes in plants from fireweed to shrubs, and then to trees, will occur.
Naturally, these changes will be reflected in the populations of the animals, and thus populations themselves are constantly fluctuating due
to changes in the environment. However, it is essential to recognize
that even in a constant environment, population fluctuations may
occur, as for example, in the oscillations about the equilibrium level.

Oscillations

The above examples represent oscillations that may occur when a
growing population reaches the asymptote. Near that point, the lag
in reproductive rate permits the population to go beyond equilibrium.
Then the reverse occurs, and the lag causes it to swing below, setting up
an oscillation (see Chapter 3). Such oscillations are damped, but because of the short series of years, could not be distinguished in nature
from cycles having other causes. This explanation should be considered
in many cases of cyclic populations. However, it seems unlikely that this
type could occur over wide areas. It may, nevertheless, occur in local
areas and be the basis for the oscillations of moose populations on Isle
Royal.

Cycles

The changes in numbers of mammals often occur at more or less
regular periods. Their regularity has stimulated a great interest in
"cycles" of population (Elton, 1942; and Lack, 1954). The periodic
fluctuations in numbers of animals have intrigued mankind for decades,
and masses of data have been accumulated about cyclic species. Re-

cently, however, a considerable advance in understanding has been made and some segments of the problem solved.

First, it is necessary to caution against the premature use of the word "cycle." Tests must be used to determine whether the fluctuations really are cyclic or are indistinguishable from random fluctuations with an average of a particular value. Analysis casts some doubt on the cyclic nature of some conventional examples of "cycles." It is probably desirable to raise our standards for definition of a cycle to include some hypothesis about the mechanism. Thus, a definition would require that the fluctuations be more regular than random expectation (see Cole, 1954a) and that a plausible mechanism for the cause of the fluctuations be apparent. Note that this definition purposefully permits some variation in the length of the cycle and does not require that the cause be completely known. Series of data that do not meet these even vague standards should be called, simply, fluctuations.

Certainly the best known series is the fluctuation of rodents in the Arctic, thoroughly documented by Elton (1942). Some recent papers add more data and hypotheses (see Chitty, 1960). The general outline of the cycle is almost common knowledge. On an average of nearly four years, the rodents reach a high population and then decline precipitously. Several species are involved throughout the northern hemisphere, though the changes are less drastic in the southern parts than in the northern. The mice and lemmings are eaten by foxes, owls (*Nyctea scandiaca*), and shrikes (*Lanius excubitor*), which either starve or emigrate when the rodents disappear. The cause of the fluctuation has been obscure for many years. Elton (1942) rejects disease and sunspots.

Another important group of species fluctuates at about ten-year periods. The varying hare is the major mammal involved (MacLulich, 1937). Various studies (Hickey, 1954; Green and Evans, 1940) describe details of the changes. The major predator is the lynx (*Lynx canadensis*) whose changes in population can be traced by fur reports back to 1735.

MECHANISMS

The irregular fluctuations that frequently occur in populations of mammals may result from a host of factors acting independently or synchronously. For example, a flood may kill mammals; a favorable spring may increase breeding; an ample supply of food may reduce competition. Any factor may vary, and if sufficiently extensive, result in a fluctuation of measurable size. Irregular fluctuations are easily explained if some study can be made of the population and habitat.

Habitat

In a search for mechanisms, habitat (density-independent) factors should be explored first to explain changes. Climate, including its various aspects, may satisfy the problem, through its many local effects. However, many changes occur related to other habitat factors such as soil and nutrition. (These topics are regularly treated in ecological texts and hence are not illustrated here.) Changes in food supply generally depend upon climatic variations and thus would reflect such changes. However, a peculiar condition exists in respect to the bamboos that are the food and cover of many rodents in South America and in Japan. The bamboo requires a specific number of years to flower and fruit, and then dies synchronously over wide areas. The result is an increase and decline of various rodents (Gilmore, 1947) at 6- or 32-year intervals, depending on the kind of bamboo. In this case the cause of the change is known. It depends upon the time required for flowering, and is really the same as an annual cycle of insect populations except that more than one year is required. Unfortunately, little is known about the numerical changes in the rodent populations, but apparently they increase slowly and then decline precipitously upon death of the bamboo.

Even in the presence of a constant food supply, regular oscillations can occur. Insects in the laboratory exhibit periodic changes. Presumably such changes would occur in vertebrates if the food supply could be kept constant. These oscillations are basically the same in mechanism as the oscillations of a population as it reaches the asymptote. The evidence for the relation of food supply to recognized cycles is meager. Thompson (1955) and others report that the lemmings at the peak of the cycle destroyed the vegetation; but others state that lemmings do not destroy their food supply, and MacLulich (1937) considers variations in food supply inadequate to explain the cycle in hares. Actually this explanation is really a predator-prey cycle in which the vertebrate is the predator and the food is the prey.

Predation

Predation is another factor that may explain some changes. Mathematicians long ago (see Lotka, 1925) demonstrated that predator-prey cycles could exist under specific conditions. The parasitic protozoan *Eimeria stiedae* may be responsible for a periodicity in rabbits in New Zealand of about 12 to 14 years. Predation theoretically can produce cycles. In nature, however, fluctuations of mammals do not meet all the requirements of the predator-prey cycle. The natural decline is precipitous (Figure 8-5) rather than symmetrical with the increase. An additional aspect is, that at least in some cases, the predator increases after the prey declines. Foxes (*Vulpes fulva*) in Wisconsin increased after the grouse declined. Furthermore, in a system of vertebrate preying on vertebrate, no evidence exists that a predator can catch up with the prey in order to act as a true governing factor, although this result may occur regularly when pathogens or parasites are involved.

It must be remembered that vertebrate predators tend to prevent their prey from exhausting their food supply. Thus, this mechanism is beneficial and tends to prevent a population from the evils of over-production. In some systems, the various species are well balanced so that no serious exhaustion of food supply occurs, but in other cases the regulation is poor and violent fluctuations take place.

Competition

Competition is the third factor that can explain changes. Hutchinson (1954) indicated a mathematical approach to competition, and entomologists actually demonstrated a cycle under competitive conditions with constant food. Furthermore, it seems likely that competition really is density-dependent among mammals although the data are extremely meager. However, like predation, competition should produce symmetrical cycles.

Competition is an essential feature of the current knowledge (Christian, 1961) of the regulation of birth and mortality rates through an endocrine feedback system. Extensive evidence has accumulated both in natural and laboratory conditions to substantiate the aggressive behavior feedback theory. The original statement by Christian in 1950 focused attention on photoperiod and reproduction as factors in the abrupt decline of populations. Work for a decade has supported the concept but altered the emphasis. The current view is simply that at all times competition among members of a population acts through the nervous centers and the hypothalamus to stimulate the release of adrenocorticotrophic hormone (ACTH), which in turn stimulates the cortex of the adrenal to secrete various other hormones which again in turn act to inhibit reproduction and reduce resistance to infection. This long sequence has a fantastic number of ramifications and details that are properly discussed in physiological texts. Several points, however, are important. Other factors than aggressive behavior can incite the sequence. For example, certain kinds of starvation, burns, toxic substances, and many artificial situations will cause an increase of ACTH and corticoids. These factors are generally individual, that is, the occurrence in one member of a population does not influence the occurrence in another.

Another point is frequently misunderstood. The feedback mechanism always operates, but may be at a low or even unmeasurable intensity. Consider a growing population. At first there are so few mammals that the intensity is trivial; but as the population increases, aggressive behavior becomes more frequent and the mechanism becomes measurable and effective. Still later the mechanism may reduce the birth rate and reduce resistance to disease so that the increase slows down and finally stops. Under special circumstances the mechanism may actually cause a precipitous decline in the population. Consider a somewhat hypothetical example: At a very low population, the resorption of embryos due to this feedback system may be one in 10,000, but at a high population it may be one in ten. At even higher populations, other aspects of reproduction may be affected so that it literally stops (Strecker, 1954). Thus, the feedback is always in action but not always a cause of decline. Other factors of the habitat, such as a flood, reduction of food, or action of predators, may be directly responsible for a decline.

To return to the problem of changes, the explanation should consist of a description of the variety of events that occur in a particular situation. No single cause can be expected to operate at all times and places; a combination of habitat changes, predation, disease, and competition associated with physiological changes will "explain" the increase and decrease of a population. The study of mammalian changes has been seriously retarded by a naïve search for one simple cause.

POPULATION FORCES

The number of mammals in an area is determined by three forces that are usually called **natality, mortality,** and **movements.** Natality is obviously a force for increase and refers strictly to births. It is often replaced by the term "reproduction," or even "production," which generally refers to the number of animals entering the population at some time after birth, such as at weaning. Mortality refers simply to rate of deaths during specified times and is a force for decrease. Movements refers to the entrance or departure of individuals from a given area, and can be a force for either increase or decrease, depending upon the resultant of the two aspects. The term "movements" is somewhat unsatisfactory, but other words have definite connotations that preclude their use. Migration, as used by demographers, is synonymous with movements but is here rejected because it has specialized meanings for birds and fish. A new word, **migrality,** might be coined to give uniformity and avoid certain connotations. This force has two components, usually called **immigration,** or ingress, and **emigration,** or egress. The net resultant of these gives the value of the force of movements (migrality).

The term **force** is used here in the simple physical sense. Forces produce a change in the velocity of the population (rate of growth or decline) and are proportional to the number (or masses) of animals and the rate of change of the velocity. In biological terms, they measure the birth rate or death rate in the population (Lotka, 1925).

This chapter will discuss the biological information concerning these three forces among mammals and will not consider in detail the factors that determine the magnitude of the forces, since the main objective is to discuss the influence of the force on the natural population.

Some comments on methods of obtaining data will help to clarify the discussion of the three forces. In general, methods can be divided into two sequential parts: (1) obtain data from the mammal, (2) calculate values for each of the three forces. The particular techniques used in part (1) obtain data for calculation of the three forces. While details naturally vary with species and place, an essential technique is to mark individuals for determination of age and movement. Innumerable methods for marking mammals are available (Davis, 1956); perhaps the most common is to clip toes according to a numbering scheme (Figure 8-6). When recaptured these mammals provide information on movements and age. Another essential technique is to autopsy specimens for reproduction, growth, age, and physiological or pathological conditions (Figure 8-7). Information on weight and length, as well as date and place, are obtained. Then the reproductive and other organs are weighed and preserved. The information is recorded in code in a ledger ready for transcription to automatic data-processing machines.

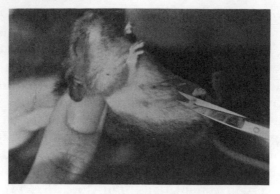

Figure 8-6. Method of Clipping Toes for Individual Identification of a Mouse (*Peromyscus leucopus*). (From Seabrook Farms Co.)

Natality

The first force to be described is, naturally, natality. In actual practice, figures for the number born may have little value in analysis of populations. The practical problem in understanding reproduction is to determine how many individuals survive after birth to enter actively into the population. The simple birth rate has little interest, because the important point is how many reach a size that has some meaning to the maintenance of the species. It is true that data for natality are relatively easy to obtain and are the starting point, but for natural populations the critical aspects occur in the later stages. It should be pointed out that in reality a discussion of "reproduction" consists almost entirely of a description of the rates of mortality of the original group of ova. We should, perhaps, refer to "production" as meaning the number of progeny per head at any specified stage, such as birth, weaning, or opening day of hunting season. This situation suggests the inseparability of births and deaths in any discussion.

Intrinsic Rate

The concept of intrinsic rate of natural increase was developed by Lotka (1925) to indicate the rate of increase that would occur under definite environmental conditions when age distribution is stable and density has no effect. Naturally, the intrinsic rate is equal to birth rate less death rate. Various types of life history have important consequences for the intrinsic rate (Cole, 1954b). For example, the effect of reducing the age at first breeding is much greater on population growth than

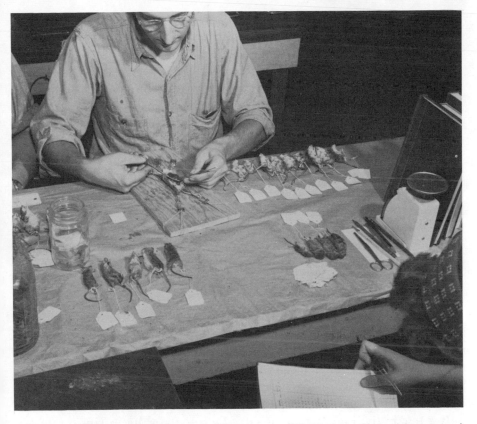

Figure 8-7. Method for Collection of Data. The mice were killed in a jar (lower left), measured (upper left), and autopsied (center). The data were recorded in a ledger book (lower right). The organs were wrapped in gauze and placed in a quart jar. (From Seabrook Farms Co.)

are large increases of litter size. This intrinsic rate has been advanced as an important parameter of populations and reviewed mathematically by Andrewartha and Birch (1954), but it is doubtful that its value for wild mammals matches its claimed value for laboratory populations. In the first place, as indicated above, "births" is not realistic terminology for wild populations because great mortality occurs shortly after birth or hatching, and because it is so difficult to determine births in nature. Furthermore, the intrinsic rate of natural increase can only be determined when the population is low, relative to the carrying capacity, so that there will be no intraspecific predation or competition. It means nothing to state that a pair of mice, *if unhindered*, will take a mere dozen years to produce progeny equal to the weight of the world! Another difficulty is that to determine the rate it is necessary to have an age-specific life table for the species. Such data are rare, to say the least, for wild mammals at the present time.

It is true that the intrinsic rate of natural increase gives the maximum that may be expected under the particular environmental conditions. But this maximum differs under various conditions, and the conditions change so rapidly in nature that it is rarely useful. Indeed, it may be positively misleading by producing undue optimism or alarm. The fantastic figures for increase of rats, such as that one pair in a year will increase to three million or some other absurd number, are based upon the highest possible intrinsic rate. Programs based on these alarming figures are not sound. In some cases, however, the observed rate is close to the intrinsic rate. Kelker (1947) calculated the intrinsic rate of a deer herd and found that it was close to the maximum that could be expected. For the first 6 years after the start of a herd the rate was 1.65, whereas if all mature females had 2 fawns the rate would be 1.66. In other herds the rates were 1.2 and 1.3.

In spite of practical deficiencies, it may be worthwhile to determine approximately the intrinsic rate of increase from a knowledge of the rate of increase of a population in the early stages of growth. Under these circumstances, the environmental conditions are changing very little (because the species has little impact on the habitat), the effects of density are trivial, and the age composition is fairly stable (because only a few individuals are involved). To calculate the intrinsic rate (r) one assumes that it is equivalent to the actual rate of increase when the populations are small. The equation for rate of change can be written:

$$\frac{dN}{dt} = rN,$$

and integrating we get:

$$N_t = N_0 e^{rt}$$

where:

N_t = population at time t,
N_0 = the initial population,
e = the base of Naperian logarithms, and
t = time in suitable units.

The equation can be written, for example, as:

$$N_5 = N_0 e^{5r}, \text{ for a five-year period.}$$

Rates of increase estimated in the above manner may be useful to compare rates of growth in natural populations. Unfortunately, persons dealing with populations are rarely interested in low populations, and census data are hard to obtain for them. Actually the intrinsic rate of increase alone has very limited usefulness, since it is even more idealistic than the birth rate.

Birth Rate

The discussion thus far has described methods of determining the intrinsic rate. Now we must determine the number of young (with various definitions of young) produced per adult female (also several definitions; see below). This value naturally is the number of young multiplied by the number of times young are produced. For example, pocket gophers, having 2.6 young 1.3 times per year produce 3.4 young per "adult" female (Miller, 1947, Chapter 7). The value of 3.4 must be multiplied by an appropriate fraction to change it to a birth rate. It may be assumed that there is an even sex ratio and that all females breed. In this case the birth rate is $\frac{3.4}{2} = 1.7$ young per gopher. But in a real population, young and even some mature females do not breed, and hence, the rate is even lower. For Norway rats (Davis and Hall, 1951) it was found that about 40 per cent of the trappable population was adult females (i.e., had a perforated vaginal orifice). Hence, for a particular population the birth rate is 9.4 embryos per adult female $\times$ 4.8 pregnancies per year $\times$ 40 adult females per 100 rats. The value is 10 embryos per rat per year. The birth rate here mentioned is the finite rate (B), which is the number born per year per rat, and must be distinguished from the rate of increase (r) discussed above. For woodchucks (Davis, 1962) the birth rate was calculated for four different years in two areas. It ranged from 0.93 to 1.77, depending upon sex ratio and proportion of yearlings that bred.

Reproductive Rate

Reproductive rate is the sum of a series of age-specific rates of female births per female in the various age classes, and is often called the **gross reproductive rate** to distinguish it from the **net reproductive rate,** which adjusts for mortality occurring in each age group of females. For wild mammals, crude rates have been about the best that could be obtained, but modern studies of mammalian populations must consider age or size in comparing rates from place to place.

The term **reproductive rate** is suitable for comparative purposes since it bases the measure on mature females and omits males and immatures. The reproductive rate summarizes the information about the number of females born, the frequency of pregnancies, and the duration of breeding season. The sex ratio of young must be known.

Number Born: The first component is the number of young "born" at a time, but the number of live births is hard to determine. Consider, for example, the problems associated with determining the number of young muskrats in a house on a marsh. In contrast, it is simple to accumulate data about the number of embryos per female (Chapter 7). An auxiliary method to counting embryos in pregnant females is to count placental scars. This method is advantageous because scars may be counted in trapping season many months after the breeding season (muskrats, for example). But there are a number of pitfalls, such as loss of scars left from abortions, and so forth. Indeed, there is a poor correlation between the number of scars and the known number of young produced by rats. The relation of the number of scars to the number of embryos should be tested for each species before use. Counts of the number of corpora lutea have been used but, because polyovuly and anovuly may occur, these counts are suspect until tested for each species and even each region.

In attempting to determine from counts of embryos the mammals "born," the first step is to determine mortality *in utero*. This step is necessary because significant loss may occur, especially late in pregnancy. The basic procedure (Brambell, 1942) is to compare the number of corpora lutea with the number of embryos. The method assumes that a single ovum is produced for each corpus, and thus the loss of embryos up to birth may be determined by subtracting the number born (or in the uterus just before birth) from the number of corpora. Another aspect is the loss of entire litters. When the whole litter is lost, the corpora soon disappear and the animal no longer is part of the sample. This entire problem can be approached in three ways:

(1) The loss of some embryos from a litter can be determined as above by the difference between the number of corpora and the number of embryos. The percentage of females showing loss of at least one embryo should increase with age of embryo. A decline in this percentage means that some females lost all embryos and, hence, become

"nonpregnant" and are not used in the sample. So the minimum number that lost all embryos can be determined as in this example: Rabbits with embryos aged 11 to 15 days showed loss in 32 litters (68 per cent) and no loss in 15 litters. Naturally, some embryos will be lost from these litters in later stages. The age group just before parturition had 17 showing loss (27 per cent) and 45 litters showing no loss. Obviously, some entire litters had disappeared, since the proportion of litters showing loss cannot decrease but will be reduced (from 68 to 27 per cent) if litters that have already suffered some loss are completely lost. The maximum number of litters showing some loss after the 11 to 15 day stage will be $\frac{17}{45} = \frac{x}{15}$, or 5.6 The others will be entirely lost. This value is given by $32.0 - 5.6 = 26.4$, or $26.4/47.0 = 56$ per cent of the litters. This method cannot be used unless there is evidence that polyovuly does not occur.

(2) A second method to determine loss compares the number of females with embryos in early stages of growth, with the number in late stages. For example, 96 rabbits in the early stages of gestation were obtained and only 67 during the last stages. Hence, $\frac{96 - 67}{67} = \frac{29}{67} = .42$ of the litters were lost. This method assumes that there is no change in trappability during pregnancy.

(3) A third method compares the number of ova lost at different stages. For example, no rabbits in late stage of pregnancy had lost more than two ova, but 47 per cent of the rabbits in earlier stages had lost three or more ova. Hence, all these rabbits must have lost the entire litter.

Another important aspect is the loss in relation to litter size. With increase in size of the litter, the proportion showing loss increases. The proportion of litters having n ova that suffer no loss is q^n where q is the probability of loss of an ovum as calculated from the entire sample. This formula should be used when comparing intrauterine mortality in different samples to correct for differences in litter sizes.

Brambell continues his analysis to show that there is no significant difference in intrauterine mortality in lactating and nonlactating rabbits, that mortality is greatest in late May, and that there is no difference in loss according to weight of female when litter size is accounted for.

In a later paper Brambell and Mills (1947) discuss loss of ova before implantation by comparing the number of corpora lutea with the number of implantation sites. This type of analysis assumes no poly-ovuly and does not include litters that are completely lost before im-plantation. Also, no information can be obtained about the stage before implantation at which the loss occurs. The method consists of a com-parison of the data from two viewpoints:

(1) The prenatal mortality due to maternal causes will affect the litter as a unit and thus the proportion of ova lost will coincide with the pro-portion of litters showing loss.

(2) In contrast, loss due to embryonic causes will occur among the ova randomly and, hence, the proportion of litters showing loss will be $L = 1 - q^n$, where q is the proportion of ova that are lost and n is the initial size of the litter. The data for each of these relations may be graphed and regression lines drawn or calculated. Suitable calculations (Brambell and Mills, 1947: p. 194) can determine whether the loss of ova is really random (which it was not in this case). The distribution of loss between the two uteri can be determined.

An entirely different approach is to determine the number of pseudo-pregnant animals and, therefore, the loss of entire sets of ova before implantation. The proportion of pseudopregnancies was high in rabbits that ovulated few or many ova, and low in rabbits that ovulated mod-erate numbers. (The numbers were determined by counts of corpora lutea.) Animals with above-average body weight had less loss of entire sets of ova than those with below-average body weight. The total loss of ova before implantation was 10 to 13 per cent, which seems a rather large one.

These methods and results are presented in considerable detail be-cause they show what can be done with pregnancy data to determine a variety of relationships. These analyses should be made whenever a species exhibits high intrauterine loss. However, some species (rats) show so little loss that the analysis is not worthwhile, and, in some species polyovuly is frequent and hence corpora lutea counts are not reliable indicators of the number of ova shed.

Frequency: Given a value for the number produced at some state (born, weaned, etc.), it is now necessary to determine the number of such events per female per year.

For mammals that bear more than one litter a year, the average num-ber of litters per year for the average female may be determined from the prevalence of pregnancy if its duration is known. The prevalence of pregnancy is the proportion pregnant at a particular time, and is obtained by dividing the number pregnant by the total number of mature females in the sample. If 20 out of 50 mature female deer mice are pregnant, then the prevalence is $20/50 = .40$. This crude value can and should be refined by careful definition of "mature" and by stratifying the sample so that the true age and weight characteristics of the total population are appropriately represented. Also, when considering an annual prevalence, each season must be properly represented in the sample. For example, if 20 out of 50 females were pregnant in the breeding season, and 0 out of 200 in the nonbreeding season, the prevalence for both seasons is $20/50 + 0/200$ divided by 2, or $\dfrac{0.4 + 0}{2} = 0.2$ rather than $20/250 = 0.08$. For practical purposes, the annual prevalence can be obtained by averaging the prevalences for the months of the breeding season, thereby overcoming differences in size of sample and seasons.

The incidence of pregnancy is the number of times pregnancy occurs during a time interval (usually a year). It is readily obtained from prevalence by the formula $I_p = \dfrac{P_p t}{d_p}$, where I_p is the incidence of pregnancy, P_p is the prevalence of pregnancy, t is the time unit (usually 365 days), and d_p is the length of time (in the same units as t) that the pregnancy lasts. Care must be exercised in determining d_p. For most mammals, pregnancy is usually determined by observation of the uterus, and the animal is considered pregnant if swellings can be seen. The female is said to be visibly pregnant. But true pregnancy begins earlier and can only be determined by a rather laborious and uncertain procedure of washing the ova from the uterus or making several sections. Hence d will be the number of days of visible pregnancy rather than true pregnancy, unless the laborious method is used. Strictly speaking, then, the formula gives the incidence of visible pregnancies rather than true ones. Furthermore, since there may be loss of entire litters during pregnancy, another restriction is necessary to indicate that the incidence refers to the midpoint in time of visible pregnancies.

For wild rats, pregnancy is considered to last about 25 days and implantation occurs on the seventh day. Hence $d = 18$, and the midpoint is the 16th day of true pregnancy.

These relations may be illustrated by examples from Laurie (1946), who compared the incidence of pregnancies for house mice living in four different environments. The detailed calculations from Laurie for comparing this incidence are as follows: The duration of visible pregnancy in domestic mice is 14.5 days. Employing this figure for wild mice, Laurie uses the above relationship by multiplying the prevalence by $365/14.5 = 25.2$. The results for mice from various places are (figures rounded off): Urban, $I_p = (.22)(25.2) = 5.5$; flour depot, $I_p = (.32)(25.2) = 8.0$; ricks, $I_p = (.41)(25.2) = 10.2$; cold stores, $I_p = (.27)(25.2) = 6.7$. The standard errors can be computed from SE $= \sqrt{\dfrac{pq}{n}}$, where p is the prevalence of pregnancy, $q = 1 - p$, and n is the number in the sample. The standard error of the prevalence is multiplied by t/d (in this case, 25.2) to get the SE of the incidence. For example, the urban mice above had a SE of prevalence of 0.0199, and hence the SE of the incidence is $(0.0199)(25.2) = 0.502$. Two SE's are 1.004, and thus the limits (at 95 per cent confidence level) are 4.5 to 6.5. Similar limits may be determined for the other localities and compared by appropriate statistical tests. These prevalences were standardized for weight and month before calculations.

The same procedure can be applied to determine the number of lactations per year where $I_l = \dfrac{P_l}{d_l} t$, where I_l is incidence of lactation, P_l is prevalence of lactation, t is time interval, and d_l is the duration of lactation. Unfortunately, the value of d_l is hard to obtain even for many common species. However, the importance of the results should encourage accumulation of the data.

An entirely different method to determine the number of pregnancies per year is shown (Figure 7-9). However, this method can only be used for species that have synchronous pregnancies at the start of the season but cannot be used for species with rapidly recurring pregnancies such as occur in most rodents.

Some data were presented (Table 7-1) for the number of embryos and the incidence of pregnancy for several species. The original publications should be consulted for figures on size of sample and variance. These statistical details are omitted here because the data came usually from a miscellaneous assortment of animals from various places and ages, and thus are really very crude. The table merely illustrates some of the range of differences among species and the approximate value of the reproductive rate.

Breeding Season

An aspect that has great influence upon the number of young is the duration of the breeding season. For some species it may be continuous throughout the year, even though a particular female may not breed continuously (see Chapter 7). Most species have a discontinuous breeding season. There may be one particular period as in ground squirrels, some other rodents (Davis, 1945), deer, sheep, and many others. Two definite breeding periods are found in such species as tropical opossums and squirrels. Others, like some rabbits, may have several discrete periods. A large proportion of species, especially rodents, breed throughout most of the year and show a peak in the springtime. Others may have peaks within the season.

Density

The number produced by a population also varies with age of individuals and with a variety of such external factors as food, weather, and breeding sites (see Chapter 7). In addition, many of the above factors are summed into the effect of population density, so that reproductive performance differs from year to year, partly in response to density changes. The number of pregnancies has been found in rats to be inversely related to density. In increasing populations, about 30 per cent of mature females were pregnant, whereas about 20 per cent were pregnant in stationary populations. Some data indicate that a higher proportion of field mice became pregnant at high populations, presumably because of increased likelihood of contact. Malthus long ago called attention to the decline in pregnancy at high density of human populations. Actually, the relation should be curvilinear. At very low densities contacts would be rare, at medium density contacts should be optimal, and at high densities contacts should be influenced by competition (Figure 8-8).

The number of young per litter may also be related to population. In some cases an increase occurs. Muskrats (Errington, 1954) had larger litters at times of high population. However, many authors (see Christian, 1961) studied the relation of density in domestic mouse populations to several measures of reproduction. Reproduction clearly declined as the density increased (Figure 8-9). Voles have a shorter breeding season and less young per female at high densities than during the increase of population. Other species at the population

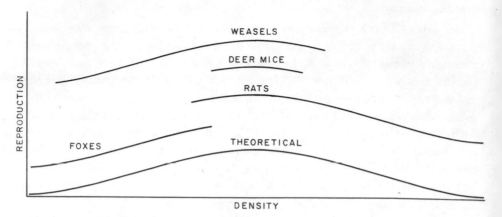

Figure 8-8. Theoretical Relation of Density to Reproductive Processes. The inherent life history may be such that densities at either end of the curve are never attained by some species.

levels studied (rats, Davis, 1953; and hares, Green and Evans, 1940), showed no change in number of young as density changed.

There may be a compensatory change in sex ratio with changes in population density. Data are scarce, but White (1914) reported an amazing increase in proportion of young female rats (*Rattus rattus*) at a time of unusual mortality of adult females. As an experimental test of this old observation, Snyder (1961) removed females from a population of woodchucks and compared the sex ratio of the progeny with that in an area where the sex ratio was not changed. In the experimental area, 40 young males and 89 young females were captured compared to 211 young males and 205 young females in the reference area. The sex ratio of fetuses was 11 to 20 in the experimental area and 129 to 105 in the reference area. Studies of this phenomenon in other species are badly needed.

It is, of course, obvious from the above examples that density affects reproduction. At sufficiently low or high densities, reproduction is hindered, but at moderate densities it is favored. These are quantitative relations whose numerical values differ from species to species and from place to place. Furthermore, the appropriate densities may never be reached in some species. Consider Figure 8-8. The theoretical relation of density is shown with some hypothetical curves for particular species. Foxes, perhaps, never reach the high density that would interfere with reproduction; rats may rarely be low enough; and, possibly, deer mice

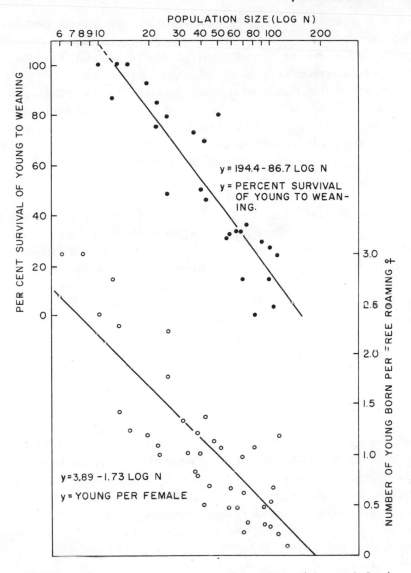

Figure 0-9. Decline in Birth Rate and Survival of Young Mice with Increase in Population Density. The number of young mice born (lower line) and their survival (upper line) declines as the population density increases. (From Christian, 1961.)

are always at optimum. The ordinate in this chart represents any such aspect as proportion pregnant, litter size, etc. At present we can only guess at the location of these curves for a few species.

The problems of natality illustrate clearly the principle that a population of mammals has characteristics different from a mere summation of individuals. The birth rate reflects more than the action of habitat on individual mammals. For example, studies on woodchucks, too complex to be described here in detail, showed that, although for four years the population remained constant numerically, the birth rate rose from 1.3 to 1.6 and then fell to 1.1 and 0.9. Associated with changes in natality there were changes in mortality and migrality. To date, few studies of mammalian populations have determined birth rates, but it is clear that future work will produce many examples.

Mortality

Mortality is clearly a force for decrease of the population. In the preceding section the discussion of reproduction at once raised the question of mortality of the young. Indeed part of the difficulty in determining reproductive rates of mammals is that mortality begins even in the uterus. The present section will discuss mortalities from several viewpoints. For orientation, methods of getting and calculating data will be discussed. Some definitions are needed to clarify certain terms. The discussion of methods refers to populations of wild mammals and thus ignores or minimizes some methods or aspects that would be practical for laboratory or for domestic species.

Rates

A **crude rate** refers to data that have not been restricted into categories. For example, a crude rate might be based on animals of various ages, both sexes, or various weights. A **specific rate** refers to some particular group, such as males, or to some age or weight. An **age-specific table** has each age-group analyzed separately. Actually, all rates are crude if one wishes to consider small enough categories. An age-specific table set up in years is crude in comparison with one on a monthly basis. A table for bacteria on an hourly basis would probably be called crude. Although tables for humans are usually age-specific, age for wild mammals is often hard to determine, and hence crude rates are usually the best that can be arrived at.

There are two kinds of **mortality rates** (Davis, 1960). The probability of dying (q) is the number that died during a time interval divided by the number alive at the beginning of the interval. Thus, if there are 100 rabbits on May 1, and 40 die before the next May 1, the probability of dying (q) is, of course, 0.4. The probability of dying is often expressed as per cent and often called mortality rate. In contrast the death rate (d) is the number that died during the time interval divided by the average population and is an instantaneous rate. If in the above case the population averaged 100 rabbits during the year, then the death rate would be $40/100 = 0.4$. But if the population declined from 100 to 60, then the average was 80 and the death rate is $40/80 = 0.5$ (actually the decline would be exponential and the population would average a little less than 80). Since there is some confusion of terms, it is recommended that mortality rate be left as a general term and **probability of dying** and **death rate** be used with particular meanings. The expectation of life refers to the average number of time intervals (usually years) still to be lived by individuals of a particular age. For new-born individuals it equals the average length of life. The term has limited usefulness in mammals.

Methods

Determination of these values will be described by examples for ease of explanation.

Actual Deaths: If enough dead mammals can be found, it is possible to determine the probability of dying. The simplest case occurs when age is not known. Consider 60 marked rats found dead at known times after marking (Table 8-1). The percentages can be plotted against time

TABLE 8-1. Arrangement of Information About Deaths of Rats to Show Probability of Dying

Time Since Marking (months)	Animals Found Dead	Cumulative Total	Probability of Dying
0 to 1	16	60	—
2 to 3	11	44	.27
4 to 5	13	33	.45
6 to 7	11	20	.67
8 to 9	5	9	.85
10 to 11	4	4	.93
12 to 13	0	0	1.00

units and a smoothed curve drawn through the points. Then the percentage dead at any time can be read from the graph. In this case, since the time represented a year, the smoothed value was 92 per cent, or probability of dying $= 0.92$ per year. This method is very crude because it lumps together both sexes and all ages. Furthermore, it merely gives time since marking, not age. It, of course, assumes that the animals found are a random sample of the deaths. About the best that can be said for this method is that it is better than nothing, and the result should be rounded off to "about 0.9."

A better method is to use animals of known age at death. For example, Banfield (1955) presented data for age at death of caribou (*Rangifer caribou*), based on mandibles found. The data in this case can be organized on an age basis and are hence superior to the above, but sexes cannot be separated, and it is likely that the more fragile mandibles of young individuals are less likely to be preserved and found.

Disappearance: A somewhat similar method can be used to determine how long an individual is under observation. Instead of listing the individuals found dead, the ones captured or observed may be listed (Table 8.2). In this case, 115 adult males were never observed after marking;

TABLE 8-2. Arrangement of Data for Adult Rats Known to Be Alive at Various Times After Marking, Because Each Was Captured

Time Interval (months)	Number Not Captured Again		Known to Be Alive		Percentages	
	Males	Females	Males	Females	Male	Female
0	115	134	344	406	100	100
2	100	100	229	272	67	67
4	62	75	129	172	37	42
6	37	52	67	97	19	24
8	23	28	30	45	9	4
10	5	11	7	17	2	2
12	2	6	2	6	0	0
	344	406				

100 were observed in the first time interval but not again; and so forth. The individuals lived for an unknown length of time after their last capture and hence we know nothing about mortality rates. But we can compare two groups (sexes in this example) if we are willing to assume that the length of time lived after last capture was proportionately the same in both groups. In order to avoid extreme values at the tail-end of the curve, a 50 per cent point or a 95 per cent point can be used. In the above example 95 per cent of the males (read from a graph) had disappeared by 10 months after marking and 95 per cent of the females, by 12.4 months. It was concluded that female rats live longer after marking than do males (Davis, 1948).

Averaging Samples: Both of the above types of data can be treated in another manner that is helpful if ages are not known. The deaths in each year are divided by the number of years lived by the population. To overcome unequal probabilities in different years the following may be used:

$$q = \frac{D_1 + D_2 + D_3 + \ldots + D_n}{D_1 + 2D_2 + 3D_3 + \ldots + nD_n}$$

where D_1 etc. represents the deaths in each year. This method assumes that there is a uniform monthly distribution of deaths and hence that the mean period of death since the beginning of the year is 0.5 years. This point is very significant for species that are hunted or may otherwise have heavy mortality in some months.

Change in Population: Clearly, if the number of mammals is known at two different times, and if there is no emigration and no recruitment into the population from births or immigration, then any difference results from deaths. If a deer yard has 1000 deer on October 1, and 600 on January 31, then the probability of deer dying from October to February is $\frac{400}{1000} = 0.4$. The general formula for changing these data to an annual basis is

$$N_t = N_0 p^{t/i}$$

where:

N_t = population at time t (February) = 600,
N_0 = original population (October) = 1000,
p = annual probability of survival = $1 - q$,
t = time in units = 4 months, and
i = the number of time units in a year = 12 months.

Hence:

$600 = 1000 p^{4/12}$
$0.6 = p^{0.33}$

$$\log_e 0.6 = 0.33 \log_e p$$
$$\frac{-0.51}{0.33} = \log_e p$$
$$-1.545 = \log_e p$$
$$p = 0.213 \text{ and } q = 0.787 \text{ (annual)}$$

The same principle can be used for calculating the population by recapture, although it has all the pitfalls of this census method. It is best illustrated in the following example: Green and Evans (1940: p. 230), in the early winter of 1935-36, marked and released 144 hares. Captured in the late winter were 53, of which 16 had been marked in the early winter. Hence the early winter population was $\frac{144(53)}{16} = 477$ hares. In late winter 156 hares were marked and released. In the spring, 54 hares were caught. Of this number, 31 had been marked in the late winter. Hence the population in late winter was $156(54)/31 = 272$. The number that died from early winter to late winter was $477 - 272 = 205$. Note that this method does not refer to any group of hares but is on a population basis. The value of q is $205/477 = .43$ from early to late winter. These calculations assume no births or immigration.

In contrast, the history of a group of marked individuals can be followed in another manner. Of 253 rats caught in the summer, 52 had been marked in the spring. The population (from another method) in summer was 891. Now if we assume that the same ratio of marked to unmarked occurs in the population as in the trapped sample, then the number of marked rats alive in the population in summer is:

$$\frac{52}{253} = \frac{x}{891} \qquad x = 183$$

Since originally 269 were marked, the probability of dying from spring to summer is $\frac{269 - 183}{269} = 0.32$. This value is crude, refers to both sexes, and to time since marking. Obviously these procedures are merely the determination of mortality from population changes for which general mathematical formulas are available.

As in the case of estimation of populations, a plethora of mathematical methods have been devised to estimate the death rate from recapture data (Jackson, 1948; Bailey, 1952; Leslie *et al.*, 1953; and others). These methods all assume certain conditions such as constant death rate, lack of trap avoidance, random trapping, and so forth, rarely found in practice. Until such conditions are better understood, it is doubtful if these complicated mathematical methods should be used. Another problem is that the computations may be very tedious. Bailey (1952), however, does give a simple procedure, which uses the data from only three trapping periods. Unfortunately, mammal populations regularly fail to meet the assumptions. Leslie, *et al.* (1953) found that the assumptions were not met for a population of meadow voles, but were met for a population of red-backed mice. The differences were dependent on local conditions, and indicate that the validity of the assumptions must be tested for each locality. The conclusion for the future of the recapture method (both for census and mortality results) is that much work needs to be done on the assumptions before the methods are used. (See Chapter 10.)

Life Tables: The conventional method for expressing mortality data for humans is the life table (see any medical statistics text). The application to wild populations has been reviewed by Deevey (1947). Unfortunately, life tables have limited usefulness for wild populations for the following reasons: (1) Age must be known. However, age may be difficult to determine, or ecologically meaningless. Also, for most population problems, mortality rates during short periods (a month) are important; yet age criteria are lacking for such intervals. (2) The number of deaths should change rather systematically from one time unit to the next. This situation holds for mammals on an annual basis but not on a monthly one because of breeding seasons, migration, etc. But monthly mortalities are the crux of the matter for population problems. Cottontail rabbits, for example, are subjected to heavy mortality during breeding and hunting seasons. In spite of these deficiencies in application to wild populations, the life table is often useful.

The table consists of several columns (Table 8-3). The first gives the time units for age; the second, the number dying in each time unit, usually on a percentage or per 1000 basis; the third, the number of survivors out of 100 or 1000 born; and the fourth gives the q_x, or probability of dying, for that time unit (usually multiplied by 1000). A last column is often devoted to the life expectancy. The d_x column is merely the number dying at a particular age, put into a basis of 10,000 for simplicity.

Two basic types of life tables exist. The "cohort" type utilizes data from a particular group of animals from birth till death. Thus their length of life is truly known. In some cases it is permissible to use the date of marking as "birth" if one wants to ignore difference in mortalities with age or if it is known that such differences are trivial.

The other type of life table is based on a sample of animals taken at one time and place. This type is more common because the data are easier to obtain, but an assumption must be made that the population is stationary and that birth rates are constant. The age of the individuals in the sample may be determined by an age character such as tooth wear. In certain cases there is no known discontinuous character for determining age. In these cases, if the species has a short breeding season

TABLE 8-3.   Life Table for Cottontail Rabbits (Lord, 1961)

Of 10,000 Rabbits *in Uteri*

Age Interval in Months	Number Alive at Beginning of Month of Age	Number Dying During Month of Age	Mortality Rate (number dying per 1000 alive at beginning of month)	Complete Expectation of Life (average number of months of life remaining at beginning of month of age)
X	1_x	d_x	$1000q_x$	e_x
0 to 4	10,000	7440	744	6.5
4 to 5	2560	282	110	6.6
5 to 6	2278	228	100	6.5
6 to 7	2050	246	120	6.5
7 to 8	1804	307	170	6.4
8 to 9	1497	150	100	6.4
9 to 10	1347	175	130	6.3
10 to 11	1172	164	140	6.3
11 to 12	1008	212	210	6.3
12 to 13	796	143	180	6.3
13 to 14	653	98	150	6.2
14 to 15	555	55	100	6.0
15 to 16	500	65	130	5.8
16 to 17	435	31	70	5.6
17 to 18	404	24	60	5.3
18 to 19	380	49	130	5.0
19 to 20	331	36	110	4.9
20 to 21	295	47	160	4.6
21 to 22	248	20	80	4.4
22 to 23	228	39	170	4.2
23 to 24	189	32	170	4.0
24 to 25	157	13	80	3.7
25 to 26	144	7	50	3.4
26 to 27	137	30	220	3.1
27 to 28	107	12	110	2.9
28 to 29	95	13	140	2.6
29 to 30	82	32	390	2.4
30 to 31	50	7	140	2.3
31 to 32	43	9	210	2.1
32 to 33	34	11	330	1.9
33 to 34	23	16	700	1.9
34 to 35	7	3	350	2.3
35 to 36	4	. . .	. . .	2.0
36 to 37	4		. . .	1.5
37 to 38	4		. . .	1.0
38 to 39	4	4	1000	0.5

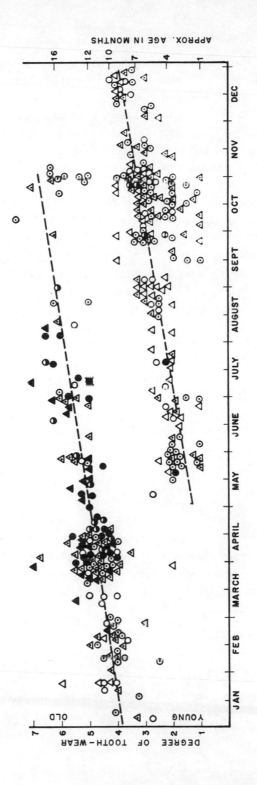

Figure 8-10. Progressive Wear on Teeth as a Longevity Determinant in Mammals. (From Pearson, 1945.)

and has an anatomical character that continuously changes with time, the length of life may be followed by this character. Tooth wear may permit determination of longevity of shrews (Figure 8-10). Other criteria may be used when available. The procedure is to set up standards of condition of the character (degrees of tooth wear, weight classes, etc.) and arrange the individuals according to some time interval (months, seasons, etc.) and the condition of the character. The individuals when plotted will tend to fall on a line, or the percentages in each weight class will indicate the slope of the line. If a character for age can be found, data of this type can be made into a life table. However, the assumption that the birth rates are constant needs examination, for small changes in rates can cause great changes in age distributions. Recently, extensive data for game mammals has become available from hunters' reports and checking-station data. Unfortunately, proof that the above assumptions hold is rarely available, and thus these data can seldom be used to determine mortality, although much other information of value can be obtained from them.

Change in Sex or Age Ratio: A census method requiring knowledge of a ratio (usually sex) before and after a hunting season, and the number killed, has been developed for determining the population. Obviously, the method can be reversed and the number killed can be determined if the sex ratios and the populations at two different times are known. The formula is:

$$\frac{P_1(m_2 - m_1) - K_m}{m_2} = K$$

where:

> $P_1 =$ population (preseason),
> $m_1 =$ number of males (preseason),
> $m_2 =$ number of males (post season),
> $K_m =$ kill of males, and
> $K =$ total kill.

Then:

$$\frac{K}{P_1} = q$$

Thus far, the discussion has considered means of collection of field data and the necessary calculation associated with getting a figure for probability of dying or for death rates. The purely arithmetical devices, which permit one to change monthly rates to annual rates of probabilities of dying to death rates, may be found in Ricker (1958) and Davis (1960).

Results

The methods described above have been used to determine mortality rates of a number of mammals. Some studies give a simple result of observations, even though no particular relationship to a habitat or factor (Table 8-4) is apparent. The table gives data presented in the literature for several species. Earlier studies were generally crude, grouping various ages and sexes. Recent studies are more refined, often showing differences between sexes or among ages. However, for simplicity, some of these studies have been reduced to a generalized crude figure (e.g., roe deer) to give an impression of the order of magnitude of mortality. The refinements are mentioned below.

Factors Affecting Mortality

A variety of circumstances in addition to differences in the actual causes of death can affect mortality. A number of generalizations can now be made about the death rates of mammals. The procedure in the next few pages will be to cite the principle with a few examples, without attempting completeness.

Age: Generally young individuals have higher probabilities of dying than do adults. Very young mammals have very high mortality rates, although few specific data are available. Lord (1961) reports for cottontails that the probability of dying (Table 8-3) in the first four months is 0.74 while for the next four it is 0.30, and that mortality is high for the very old animals, as well as for the very young. Hacker and Pearson (1946) concluded that young and very old mice had a higher mortality, since a greater mortality occurs among small and large mice than among medium-sized ones. Banfield (1949) presents excellent data on age of elk from skulls, showing a high rate for young and old. A high rate also occurs in old wild rats and old Dall sheep.

Sex: Generally, females live longer than do males. This result is found in rats and house mice (Laurie, 1946). However, Hacker and Pearson (1946) found no sex difference in the long-tailed field mouse. Of course, when only one sex is harvested as in deer in many places,

TABLE 8-4.   Some Reported (or Calculated) Mortality Rates of Mammals

Species	Probability of Dying	Age	Sex	Place	Reference (senior author only)
Short-tailed Shrew (*Blarina brevicauda*)	0.97	all	both	U.S.A.	Pearson (1945)
Raccoons (*Procyon lotor*)	0.66	adults	both	Missouri	Sanderson (1951)
Gray Fox (*Urocyon cinereoargenteus*)	0.50	adults	both	Georgia	Wood (1958)
Beechey Ground Squirrel (*Citellus beecheyi*)	0.60	adults	both	California	Evans (1943)
White-footed Mouse (*Peromyscus leucopus*)	0.84 to 0.98	adults	both	Michigan	Snyder (1956)
White-footed Mouse (*Peromyscus leucopus*)	0.98	adults	both	Michigan	Howard (1949)
Long-tailed Field Mouse (*Apodemus sylvaticus*)	0.95	adults	both	England	Hacker (1946)
Black Akodon (*Akodon nigrita*)	0.75	adults	both	Brazil	Davis (1947)
Norway Rat (*Rattus norvegicus*)	0.95	adults	both	Maryland	Davis (1953)
Norway Rat (*Rattus norvegicus*)	0.999	young	both	Maryland	Davis (1953)
Cottontail Rabbit (*Sylvilagus floridanus*)	0.80	adults	both	Illinois	Lord (1961)
Snowshoe Hare (*Lepus americanus*)	0.70	adults	both	Minnesota	Green (1940)
Snowshoe Hare (*Lepus americanus*)	0.53	adults	both	Montana	Adams (1959)
European Rabbit (*Oryctolagus cuniculus*)	0.80	adults	both	New Zealand	Tyndale (1955)
Mule Deer (*Odocoileus hemionus*)	0.42	adults	males	California	Taber (1957)

TABLE 8-4 (*contin.*)

Species	Probability of Dying	Age	Sex	Place	Reference (senior author only)	
Mule Deer (*Odocoileus hemionus*)	0.25	adults	females	California	Taber	(1957)
Roe Deer (*Capreolus capreolus*)	0.40	adults	males	Denmark	Quick	(1960)
Caribou (*Rangifer arcticus*)	0.18	adults	both	Canada	Banfield	(1955)
Dall Mt. Sheep (*Ovis dalli*)	about 0.05	adults	both	Alaska	Murie	(1944)
Fin Whales (*Balaenoptera physalis*)	0.28	adults	females	Antarctic	Wheeler	(1934)
Fin Whales (*Balaenoptera physalis*)	0.34	adults	males	Antarctic	Hylen	(1955)
Fin Whales (*Balaenoptera physalis*)	0.22	adults	females	Antarctic	Hylen	(1955)

the female lives longer than the male. In wild mammals as in man, the female survives longer on the average.

Density: Mortality rates may be greatly affected by the density of population. Actual data for mammals seem to be scarce because so few comparative studies have been made. In a study of wild house mice kept in large cages in the laboratory, when the population was about 20, the mortality from nestling to the free-roaming stage was 5 per cent; at a population of 45, it was 50 per cent; and at a population of 65 it was 75 per cent. Others (see Christian, 1961) have shown an increased mortality of litters of wild house mice as the density of population increased. This has also been shown for voles in seminatural conditions.

Introductions: Animals in a strange environment are generally susceptible to heavy mortality. Alien rats introduced into a population in a city block soon vanished (Calhoun, 1948). Rabbits (*Sylvilagus floridanus*) stocked in an area in Pennsylvania contributed little to the population (McDowell, 1955) since 56 rabbits released in the fall and winter all vanished.

Causes of Mortality

Thus far, little has been said about specific causes of death. The reason for this omission is that the actual cause is relatively unimportant in population problems. In an increasing population the mammals are relatively secure. In a stationary population the animals are susceptible to many causes. The actual cause of death is always complex, and can rarely be assigned without doubt to a particular item. Naturally, an individual may have a number of afflictions. For example, a mouse, starving because of parasites, may be searching for food in a strange place and be caught by a hawk. What causes death? It is best to state that the mouse died under certain conditions or *with* a disease rather than *from* one.

Physical environment rarely directly kills individuals; usually it only

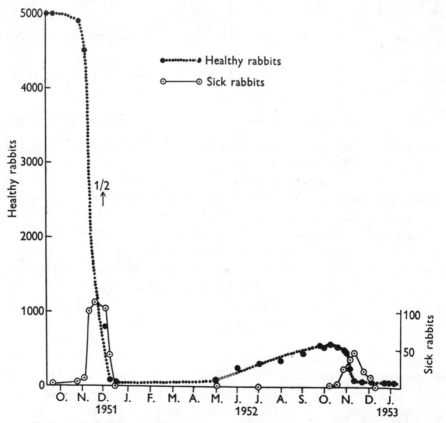

Figure 8-11. Decline in Rabbit Population at the Time of an Epizootic of Myxomatosis.
(From Myers, et al., 1954.)

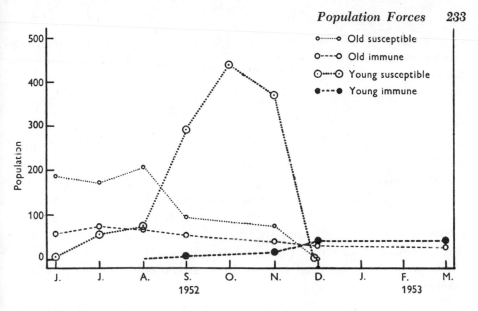

Figure 8-12. Changes in Age Composition and Increase of Immune Rabbits. (From Myers, *et al.*, 1954.)

weakens them. In one study the loss of mule deer was related to the amount of green browse in three areas in winter. In another study of mule deer (Taber and Dasmann, 1957) the relation to vegetation is shown in detail (crudely averaged for Table 8-4). The life expectancy for males was 2.3 years in chaparral, but only 1.3 in shrub; for females it was 4.2 and 2.4, respectively.

Senility is often cited as a cause of death. This statement merely means that the probability of dying increases greatly with age. Several species mentioned above (field mice, rats) have higher rates. Senility itself is no cause of mortality; it is merely a summation of risks.

Diseases may, of course, be an important cause of death. The recent work on myxomatosis in Australia demonstrates the effect of a virus on the population (Myers *et al.*, 1954). The number of healthy and of sick rabbits in an area is shown in Figure 8-11, and the age composition and immunity condition are given in Figure 8-12. It is apparent that the rates of mortality were importantly affected by the myxoma virus.

Movements or Migrality

The force of reproduction produces an increase and the force of mortality produces a decrease in the population. The force of movements or migrality may result in an increase or a decrease depending upon its net value. In fact, in many formulations of population dynamics, movements are included as part of the values of births or deaths. Thus, the natural rate of increase can be written as the sum of births and immigration less the sum of deaths and emigration.

Influences

Movements affect a number of aspects of the population, producing results far greater than their numerical value would predict. These effects are good examples of the principle that the sum is greater than the total of the parts. For example, one infected individual moving into a susceptible population may start an extensive epidemic. Movements influence the following aspects of mammalian populations:

(1) Movements may result in an increase or decrease in a local population, as will be discussed below. True migration may also produce extensive changes in population.

(2) Transmission of disease from animal to animal depends largely upon local movements within an area. When there occurs transmission of disease by insect vectors or through feces, soil, etc., the movement of the vertebrate is less important than it is in strictly contagious diseases.

(3) Spread of disease in a geographical sense depends upon long movements of individuals although, of course, local transmission may gradually spread the disease over small areas. These long, erratic movements are hard to study. For example, a rabid fox was found 60 miles from where it had been marked a few weeks before (when not known to be rabid). Rabies, thus, could be carried a long way. How often either normal or rabid foxes move such distances needs to be known. Many mammals travel long distances after they are driven out of their homes because they are weak; and frequently they are weak because they are diseased. This long series of events means the chances are good that a wandering individual is spreading disease. Unfortunately, it is difficult to obtain quantitative data on this topic. For example, suppose 100 rabbits are driven out of their cover during a bad snowstorm and that some are diseased and capable of transmitting pathogens. A large fraction will die from various causes before capture, but a small fraction will be caught for study. Of these only part will reach the laboratory for examination. Clearly there are not enough animals for statistical study. It is regrettable that observations of this type are so difficult to obtain, but it is wise to recognize the difficulty of obtaining useful data before embarking on an expensive and nonproductive study.

(4) A geographical spread of a species depends upon the successful establishment of individuals in new areas, which in turn depends upon movement of individuals into that area. Since the likelihood of establishment depends upon these and a variety of other circumstances, actually a large number of individuals must enter an area before a successful population can become established.

(5) Genetic interchange by means of interbreeding results from movements. This interchange is important to the maintenance of the species, and, in particular, to the rate of adaptation. This rate is a function of several phenomena, and includes the genetic interchange resulting from movement.

Methods

Several general methods for obtaining data about movements have been developed. The simplest method consists of observing an individual's movements and plotting them on a map. This procedure is practical for conspicuous, diurnal species such as armadillos, woodchucks, and squirrels. Usually, it is not feasible to map all the movements; to give the location at suitable intervals (perhaps 5 minutes) is satisfactory. Maps are essential for analysis of movements by observation. A map need not be extremely accurate, but it should have prominent features (creeks, dead trees, contours) clearly marked for reference points.

Instead of observing the animal directly, one may follow tracks or other signs. Tracks of many species may be observed in snow or in sand. It is possible to dye the feces of some species by feeding methylene blue at a particular place or by injecting radioactive phosphorus and picking up the traces in feces. Also, the individual can be banded by a device containing radioactive materials and followed underground by using a Geiger counter. The chief difficulty with tracking is the problem of confusing several individuals, but sometimes instruments help to obtain more accurate observations.

Dispersal

The emphasis on home range (see Chapter 10) has amassed a fund of information about localization of activity, but from the population viewpoint, studies of emigration or dispersal are more important. It is essential to know how many individuals enter or leave an area and when these movements occur. To be of use in population dynamics, these studies must be related to population size. For further progress, rates of emigration and immigration must be determined for various species, but the accumulation of such data is difficult.

Pressure: The major inciting cause for emigration is population pressure, although some species (lemmings?) or age groups may have an inherent disposition to wander. As the population approaches the capacity of the area, fewer environmental necessities are available, and individuals begin to search for more favorable areas. Thus, as a population reaches capacity, the rate of emigration should increase. Unfortunately, few studies are available about the relation of the rate of emigration to birth rates, death rates, or capacity. For example, does emigration increase proportionately to the death rate as the population increases? Does emigration begin before actual deaths? To answer such questions the various factors would have to be held constant at several levels to determine the value of emigration.

Habitat Changes: In nature a number of environmental conditions can cause dispersal. Even in a constant environment, dispersal may occur because of population pressure. But environmental changes are routine, and unfavorable ones may also induce dispersal. Examples will readily come to mind from the reader's own experience: rats invaded a town when a dump was cleaned up, and they crossed a road in numbers at the time of a flood.

Seasonal changes are also environmental, and cause dispersal, but are considered "normal" rather than catastrophic. Lemmings (Thompson, 1955) move when the snow melts in the spring and when their food supply is exhausted. At these times many appear in strange places (such as buildings). Rats regularly leave fields in the fall. For many mammals, changes in sex ratios (of trapped individuals) have been found to occur in spring and fall, apparently the result of more movement by males than by females. A fall shuffle occurs in squirrels and a number of other species, and is often reflected in increased highway mortality.

Age: The emigration rate is often higher in young mammals than in adults, presumably because they are weaker, less experienced, and poorly established. Young raccoons were recaptured at considerably greater distances from the place of marking than were adults. In a study of European rabbits, all of the 29 rabbits dispersed from warrens were young. A carefully planned study showed young deer mice (*Peromyscus maniculatus*) dispersed more than did adults, but males and females showed no difference. Coyotes (*Canis latrans*), especially the young, spread from Yellowstone Park in considerable numbers.

Sex: Emigration may differ according to sex. The males in a number of species show greater movements, which may mean a greater home range or a wider dispersal. Sex ratio changes are suggestive evidence of dispersal. Males are commonly more frequently caught than are females as a result of their greater dispersal and more extensive home range (Stickel, 1946). However, if the sex ratio in a particular season changes to favor males, it is concluded that movements of males are greater than those of females.

Homing

The problem of homing has been studied in a number of cases. Homing implies that the individual can return to an area from beyond the area of his acquaintance. Thus, a study in England found that several mice (*Apodemus sylvaticus*) had returned to their homes after being released on the opposite side of a lake, far beyond the normal range. Other authors report similar instances. Unfortunately, to prove that these returns are not random requires an immense amount of work. It is necessary to trap in all directions from the point of release and to correct in some manner for the differential between mortality rates of animals in strange and in familiar surroundings. It is not easy to find proof, even in bats, that homing ability occurs in mammals.

Geographic Spread

The discussions in this chapter concern individual movements because these are the major concern in population studies. However, the geographical spread of a species needs to be mentioned briefly, for it is merely local movements on a grand scale. Although detailed evidence is usually lacking, from a general series of observations over the years it is known that many species have extended their range. A notable study, however, by Ecke (1954) shows in detail how the Norway rat extended its range from 1946 to 1950 in parts of Georgia and drove out the roof rat.

Population Change

The extent of movement is related to population change. Immigration may be negligible or appreciable, depending upon the population level. For example, the immigration of rats into city blocks is negligible when the population is saturated (Calhoun, 1948) and trivial even in growing populations. The widespread failures of stocking programs for game species are a reflection of the fact that immigration is often impossible because the area has already reached capacity. But immigration may be appreciable. The success of rats in South Pacific islands and mongooses in the Western hemisphere shows what may result. Of course, in these cases, breeding began after the first invaders became established and was largely responsible for the present population. In a small area Stickel (1946) showed that nearly all immigrants came from nearby. Emigration, likewise, may be trivial or important, depending upon the circumstances. Strecker (1954) found that emigra-

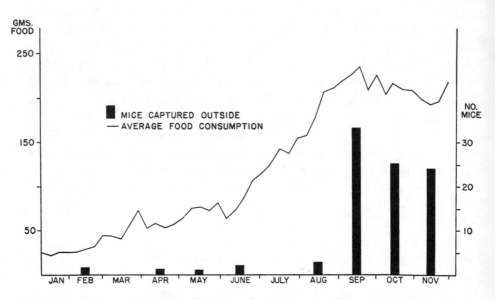

Figure 8-13. Increase of the Number of Emigrants from a Mouse Population with Population Growth. (From Strecker, 1954.)

tion occurred in a colony of house mice at a very low level until the population approached the capacity. Then the number leaving the area increased greatly (Figure 8-13).

True migrations, of course, produce significant changes in the populations. The spectacular increases and decreases of bats in certain areas are a constant reminder of their magnitude. These phenomena are temporary, and occur when food is generally abundant but the demands for breeding space are not met. Hence, the population is far below saturation at the time.

In the discussion of mortality, some mention was made of the increased vulnerability to predators and other causes of death of animals in strange places. Dispersing animals are, of course, in unfamiliar surroundings. Indeed, a major explanation for the tendency of animals to remain within a home range is the increased protection afforded by familiarity of surroundings. For example, Errington (1946) noticed the severity of losses of muskrats traveling from one pond to another.

Movement, then, is another quantitative aspect of population forces. The problem is not whether it occurs, but how much. Is it trivial or important? Unfortunately, there is no "yes" or "no" answer. The reply is always, "That depends upon other factors." As an example, suppose we have a suitable island with no rabbits. We introduce a pair every year for several years. The first pair is very important, the second less so, and the subsequent ones even less so, until at the end of perhaps ten years it makes no difference whether we introduce a pair or not.

Summary

The three population forces discussed (natality, mortality, and migrality) determine the population at a given time and place. These forces in turn are determined by a host of environmental factors, some physical and some biological. Suffice it to say that the three forces, through the mechanism of their effect on environmental factors, react on each other in a compensatory manner and thus tend to stabilize the population. For example, consider the reciprocal relation of reproduction and mortality. When the reproductive rate goes up, conditions resulting in an increase of mortality are often created. Data showing this type of relation may be found in almost every study in which the conditions were sufficiently constant to permit comparisons. Movements, of course, fit into the picture, since when reproduction is low, immigration occurs; and when reproduction is high, emigration occurs. However, full stability is almost never attained because the environment is constantly changing and because the animals are discrete units and so cannot compensate exactly for each change. Thus, both over and under compensation regularly occur.

REFERENCES

Adams, Lowell. 1959. An analysis of a population of snowshoe hares in northwestern Montana. Ecol. Monog. 29. 141-170.

Allee, W. C., Alfred E. Emerson, Orlando Park, Thomas Park, and Karl P. Schmidt. 1949. Principles of Animal Ecology. Philadelphia, W. B. Saunders Co. 837 pp.

Andrewartha, H. G., and L. C. Birch. 1954. The Distribution and Abundance of Animals. Univ. of Chicago Press. 782 pp.

Bailey, N. T. J. 1952. Improvements in the interpretation of recapture data. J. Anim. Ecol. 21(1): 120-127.

Banfield, A. W. F. 1949. An irruption of elk in Riding Mountain National Park, Manitoba. J. Wildl. Manag. 13(1): 127-134.

Banfield, A. W. F. 1955. A provisional life table for the barren ground caribou. Canad. J. Zool. 33(3): 143-147.

Brambell, F. W. R. 1942. Intra-uterine mortality of the wild rabbit, *Oryctolagus cuniculus* (L.) Proc. Roy. Soc., London B, 130: 462-479.

Brambell, F. W. R., and I. H. Mills. 1947. Studies on sterility and prenatal mortality in wild rabbits. III. The loss of ova before implantation. J. Exp. Biol. 24(1-2): 192-210.

Calhoun, J. B. 1948. Mortality and movement of brown rats in artificially supersaturated populations. J. Wildl. Manag. 12(2): 167-172.

Chitty, Dennis. 1960. Population processes in the vole and their relevance to general theory. Canad. J. Zool. 38(1): 99-113.

Christian, John J. 1961. Phenomena associated with population density. Proc. Nat. Acad. Sci. 47(4): 428-449.

Cole, LaMont C. 1954a. Some features of random population cycles. J. Wildl. Manag. 18(1): 2-24.

Cole, LaMont C. 1954b. The population consequences of life history phenomena. Quart. Rev. Biol. 29(2): 103-137.

Davis, David E. 1945. The annual cycle of plants, mosquitos, birds, and mammals in two Brazilian forests. Ecol. Monog. 15: 243-295.

Davis, David E. 1947. Notes on the life histories of some Brazilian mammals. Bol. Mus. National (Zool.) 76: 1-8.

Davis, David E. 1948. The survival of wild brown rats on a Maryland farm. Ecol. 29(4): 437-448.

Davis, David E. 1953. The characteristics of rat populations. Quart. Rev. Biol. 28(4): 373-401.

Davis, David E. 1956. Manual for analysis of rodent populations. Edwards Bros. 82 pp.

Davis, David E. 1960. A chart for estimation of life expectancy. J. Wildl. Manag. 24(3): 344-348.

Davis, David E. 1962. The potential harvest of woodchucks. J. Wildl. Manag. 26(2): 144-149.

Davis, David E., and Octavia Hall. 1951. The seasonal reproductive condition of female Norway (brown) rats in Baltimore, Maryland. Phys. Zool. 24(1): 9-20.

Deevey, E. S. 1947. Life tables for natural populations of animals. Quart. Rev. Biol. 22(4): 283-314.

Ecke, Dean. 1954. An invasion of rats in southwest Georgia. J. Mamm. 35(4): 521-525.

Elton, Charles. 1942. Voles, Mice and Lemmings. Oxford Univ. Press. 496 pp.

Emlen, John T., Jr., A. W. Stokes, and C. P. Winsor. 1948. The rate of recovery of decimated populations of brown rats in nature. Ecol. 29(2): 133-145.

Errington, P. L. 1946. Predation and vertebrate populations. Quart. Rev. Biol. 21(2): 144-177.

Errington, P. L. 1954. On the hazards of overemphasizing numerical fluctuations in studies of "cyclic" phenomena in muskrat populations. J. Wildl. Manag. 18(1): 66-90.

Evans, F. C., and R. Holdenried. 1943. A population study of the beechey ground squirrel in central California. J. Mamm. 24(2): 231-260.

Gilmore, R. M. 1947. Cyclic behavior and economic importance of the Rata-Muca (*Oryzomys*) in Peru. J. Mamm. 28(3): 231-240.

Godfrey, Gillian K. 1955. Observations on the nature of the decline in number of two *Microtus* populations. J. Mamm. 36(2): 209-214.

Green, R. G., and C. A. Evans. 1940. Studies on a population cycle of snowshoe hares on the Lake Alexander area. I. Gross annual censuses, 1932-39. J. Wildl. Manag. 4(2): 220-238. II. Mortality according to age groups and seasons. J. Wildl. Manag. 4(3): 267-278. III. Effect of reproduction and mortality of young hares on the cycle. J. Wildl. Manag. 4(4): 347-358.

Hacker, H. P., and H. S. Pearson. 1946. The growth, survival, wandering, and variation of the long-tailed mouse, *Apodemus sylvaticus*. Biometrika 33: 333-361.

Hanson, Herbert C. 1952. Importance and development of the reindeer industry in Alaska. J. Range Manag. 5(4): 243-251.

Hickey, Joseph J. 1954. Mean intervals in indices of wildlife populations. J. Wildl. Manag. 18(1): 90-106.

Howard, Walter E. 1949. Dispersal, amount of inbreeding, and longevity in a local population of prairie deermice on the George Reserve, southern Michigan. Contr. Lab. Vert. Biol., U. of Michigan, No. 43. 50 pp.

Hutchinson, G. E. 1954. Theoretical notes on oscillatory populations. J. Wildl. Manag. 18(1): 107-108.

Hylen, Arvid, Age Jonsgard, Gordon C. Pike, and Johan T. Rudd. 1955. A preliminary report on the age composition of Antarctic fin whale catches 1945-46 to 1952-53, and: Some reflections on total mortality rates of fin whales. Norwegian Whaling Gaz. 10: 577-589.

Jackson, C. H. N. 1948. The analysis of a tsetse-fly population. III. Ann. Eug. 14(2): 91-108.

Kelker, George H. 1947. Computing the rate of increase for deer. J. Wildl. Manag. 11(2): 177-183.

Lack, David. 1954. The Natural Regulation of Animal Numbers. Oxford Univ. Press. 343 pp.

Laurie, E. M. O. 1946. The reproduction of the house mouse (*Mus musculus*) living in different environments. Proc. Roy. Soc., London B133(872): 248-281.

Leslie, P. H., Dennis Chitty, and H. Chitty. 1953. The estimation of population parameters from data obtained by means of the capture-recapture method. Biometrika 40(1-2): 137-169.

Lord, Rexford D. 1961. Mortality rates of cottontail rabbits. J. Wildl. Manag. 25(1): 33-40.

Lotka, A. J. 1925. Elements of Physical Biology. Williams & Wilkins. 460 pp.

MacLulich, D. A. 1937. Fluctuations in the numbers of the varying hare (*Lepus americanus*). Biol. Ser., U. Toronto Press 43: 136 pp.

McDowell, Robert A. 1955. Restocking with "native" cottontails. J. Wildl. Manag. 19(1): 61-65.

Martin, F. R., and L. W. Krefting. 1953. The Necedah Refuge deer irruption. J. Wildl. Manag. 17(2): 166-176.

Mohler, L. L., J. H. Wampole, and E. Fichter. 1951. Mule deer in Nebraska National Forest. J. Wildl. Manag. 15(2): 129-157.

Murie, Adolph. 1944. The Wolves of Mount McKinley. Fauna of the National Parks 5, Washington. 238 pp.

Myers, K. I. D. Marshall, and Frank Fenner. 1954. Observations of two succeeding epizootics in Australian wild rabbits on the Riverine plain of southeastern Australia, 1951-1953. J. Hyg. 52(3): 337-360.

Pearson, O. P. 1945. Longevity of the short-tailed shrew. Am. Mid. Nat. 34(2): 531-546.

Quick, Horace F. 1960. Animal population analysis. Manual Game Invest. Techniques 7.1-7.35.

Ricker, W. E. 1958. Handbook of computations for biological statistics of fish populations. Fish Res. Board Canada Bull. 119: 1-300.

Sanderson, Glen C. 1951. Breeding habits and history of the Missouri raccoon population from 1941-1948. Trans. N. A. Wildl. Conf. 16: 445-461.

Scheffer, Victor B. 1951. The rise and fall of a reindeer herd. Sci. Month. 75(6): 362-365.

Snyder, Dana P. 1956. Survival rates, longevity and population fluctuations in the white-footed mouse (*Peromyscus leucopus*) in southern Michigan. Misc. Publ. Mus. Zool. 95: 1-32.

Snyder, Robert L. 1961. Evolution and integration of mechanisms that regulate population growth. Proc. Nat. Acad. Sci. 47(4): 449-455.

Stickel, Lucille F. 1946. The source of animals moving into a depopulated area. J. Mamm. 27(4): 301-307.

Strecker, Robert L. 1954. Regulatory mechanics in house mouse populations: The effect of limited food supply on unconfined population. Ecol. 35(2): 249-253.

Taber, Richard D., and Raymond F. Dasmann. 1957. The dynamics of three natural populations of the deer *Odocoileus hemionus columbianus*. Ecol. 38(2): 233-246.

Thompson, Daniel Q. 1955. The 1953 lemming emigration at Point Barrow, Alaska. Arctic 8(1): 37-45.

Tyndale-Biscoe, C. H., and R. M. Williams. 1955. A study of natural mortality in a wild population of the rabbit, *Oryctolagus cuniculus* (L.) New Zealand J. Sci. and Tech. Section B, 36(6): 561-580.

Wheeler, J. F. G. 1934. On the stock of whales at South Georgia. Cambridge Univ. Press Discovery Reports 19: 351-372.

White, F. N. 1914. Variations in the sex ratio of *Mus rattus* associated with an unusual mortality of adult females. Proc. Roy. Soc., London B47: 335-344.

Wood, John E. 1958. Age structure and productivity of a gray fox population. J. Mamm. 39(1): 74-86.

chapter nine

METABOLISM OF POPULATIONS

To ACHIEVE our goal of understanding how populations function in nature we must go beyond an analysis of the dynamics of numbers of organisms to the study of population metabolism. Information on numbers, rates of increase and decrease, and biomass is essential to an understanding of the changing organization of populations, and is preliminary to an understanding of their metabolism. The study of population function might be termed population physiology, and be considered analogous to the study of the physiology of individuals. Similarly, the study of population structure would be analogous to the study of the structure of individuals. These are rather weak analogies, yet they are productive since they help us to apply concepts developed at the level of the cell, organ, or individual to higher levels of biological organization. At present, population physiology is largely concerned with metabolism, and deals with two separate processes: bioenergetics or energy flow, and mineral cycling.

It would be desirable to study a population as a single unit, but for mammals this approach is nearly impossible to achieve. Instead, in large animals, such as the majority of mammals, the metabolism of a population is assumed to be the sum of the metabolism of the individuals comprising it. A great deal is known about the metabolism of individual mammals, mainly from studies of human beings, domestic animals, and, increasingly, from mammals in the wild state. However, this knowledge has only recently been applied to populations, and, of the work that has been done, most has been involved with energy flow. Very little attention has been directed to the role of mammals in cycling nutrients and minerals through ecosystems. In the following discussion, we will be concerned mainly with energy flow; the section will be concluded with a brief introduction to mineral cycling.

It should be emphasized that population metabolism is a new topic of interest to mammalogists. Data for populations are very few and generalizations drawn from these data are necessarily tentative. Nevertheless, we introduce considerable material on this topic because it provides a much needed focal point around which to organize information which has had relatively special application and interest. For instance, such subjects as food habits, behavior, metabolism, and growth are all fundamental to estimates of bioenergetics yet have little direct application to one another. For this reason we anticipate that the study of population metabolism will become increasingly important in the immediate future.

ENERGY DYNAMICS OF POPULATIONS

All living systems—individuals, populations, and ecosystems—are highly improbable aggregations of energy (and matter, since $e = mc^2$) which are inherently ordered, comprising many physical and chemical gradients (Patten, 1959). Energy enters these systems and is stored or degraded; that is, energy flows through the system in one direction and is not cycled. If the flow of energy through the system ceases, there is almost immediate breakdown of the system's components, and death.

Thermodynamic Aspects of Systems

Energy systems conform to the laws of thermodynamics. These laws provide us with an expression of the limits of energy flow or storage we would expect in natural systems. The First Law states that in a given time:

Energy contained in a system = energy taken into or
received by the system — energy lost from the system   (1)

or symbolically by the conventional symbols:

$$\Delta H = q - w \tag{2}$$

where ΔH is the change in heat energy content of the system, q is the heat absorbed from the surroundings, and w is the work done by the system upon the surroundings. The First Law also states that energy can neither be created nor destroyed. For our purposes the First Law means that we should be able to account for all the energy entering or leaving the population; that is, we should be able to construct an energy-flow balance sheet.

The Second Law is concerned with the losses of energy from the system and the limitations on the conversion of heat into work. In order to do work energy must be at a higher level than the environment, and in doing work energy changes from a higher to a lower state; that is, the energy "runs down." For example, steam can do work in a steam engine because the temperature of the steam is higher than that of the environment. When an engine does work, it also gets hot, and heat is lost to the environment. The energy lost to the environment has reached a lower state and is no longer available for further work. Thus, we can see that energy is in two forms: (1) the energy available for work, or free energy, and (2) the energy unavailable for work. Unavailable energy is also referred to as "entropy." The Second Law states that as energy is transformed from one state to another there is loss of free energy and an increase in the entropy of the system. Stated symbolically this is:

$$\Delta F = \Delta H - T\Delta S \tag{3}$$

where ΔF is the free energy change of the reaction, ΔH the change in heat content, and $T\Delta S$ the quantity of energy degraded from a free or high-grade form to a low-grade form during the reaction (T is the absolute temperature and ΔS is the increase in entropy). In ecological systems this means that when energy is transferred through the population, some of it will become unavailable and, therefore, the energy flow through populations can never be expected to reach 100 per cent efficiency.

Although it is useful to speak in terms of energy flow, in natural systems it is actually a gradient of separate particles of potential energy in food and organisms, rather than a smooth gradient such as that encountered in classical physical systems. There may be a time-lag in the rate of utilization of the "packages" of potential energy. The potential energy in food or organisms is determined by burning samples of the materials in a calorimeter. The energy content of the sample equals the calories released by combustion, measured as heat.

Energy Flow in Natural Populations

Let us consider energy flow for a mammal population. Energy flow is defined as the total assimilation of energy by the population; that is, the amount of consumed energy (I) which is digested and absorbed through the gut wall (Ia). For mammals, $I > Ia$. The energy that is not assimilated is collected as feces. Energy flow may go to two processes: maintenance or production. Maintenance includes energy used in nutritive processes, muscular work, maintenance of homeostasis, and replacement of protoplasm; while production energy is that used in the

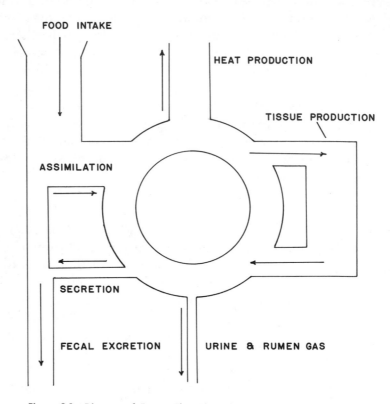

Figure 9-1. Diagram of Energy Flow Through an Individual Mammal or a Population. The balloon symbolizes production, but at any instant of time it would also indicate the standing crop of tissue.

addition of new tissue such as bone and muscle in growing animals, fat tissue in adults, and new individuals growing in the uterus of pregnant females. A small proportion of the assimilated energy is also lost from the body as amino acids, sugars, lactic acid, and other materials in the urine. These relationships are shown diagrammatically in Figure 9-1, where the sphere represents an individual or a population.

Considered symbolically, energy flow is:

$$E_t = R_t + P_t \tag{4}$$

where E_t is the rate of total energy flow, R_t is the total cost of maintenance and P_t is the total production for a given time interval, or:

$$E_t = I_t - F_t \tag{5}$$

where I_t is the energy consumed and F_t is the energy lost in the feces. Fecal energy includes some excretions from the gut and cells from the gut wall which would be lost from the assimilated pool. Since, at present, we can determine R_t, I_t and F_t only in the laboratory on individual animals, it is necessary to extrapolate from laboratory estimates of these parameters to the representative age or size classes in a population. Thus, for mammals:

$$R_t = \Sigma(RB)_{wt} \cdot 4.8 \cdot 24 \tag{6}$$

where R is the average oxygen consumption per gram per hour, B is the biomass, w is the particular weight or age class, t is the temperature of the environment when the animal is active and of the nest when the animal is not active; 4.8 is a caloric equivalent to convert liters of oxygen to calories (assuming an RQ of 0.8), and 24 is the hours per day. In addition:

$$P_t = \Sigma(PN)_w \cdot 1.4 \tag{7}$$

where P is the average production in grams of live tissue, N is the number of individuals, w weight or age class, and 1.4 a caloric equivalent for a gram of live mammal tissue.

Therefore:

$$E_t = \Sigma 115.2(RB)_{wt} + 1.4(PN)_w \tag{8}$$

or, considering food consumption:

$$E_t = \Sigma K_c(CB)_{wt} - K_f(FB)_w \tag{9}$$

where K_c and K_f are the caloric equivalents of the food and feces for a particular diet.

Efficiencies

In addition to knowing the rates of energy capture and assimilation, it is important to know the efficiency with which the population uses energy. Efficiency refers to the ratio, useful output/intake, and since the useful output of energy is subject to various interpretations, several different kinds of efficiencies are recognized (Patten, 1959; Odum, 1959; and Slobodkin, 1960). First are those efficiencies concerned with processes occurring within a population. These include:

$$\text{Tissue growth efficiency} = \frac{\text{potential energy used in growth}}{\text{assimilated potential energy}}$$

$$\text{Ecological growth efficiency} = \frac{\text{potential energy used in growth}}{\text{ingested potential energy}}$$

$$\text{Assimilation efficiency} = \frac{\text{potential energy ingested, minus feces energy}}{\text{ingested potential energy}}$$

$$\text{Individual growth efficiency} = \frac{\text{standing crop of potential energy}}{\text{potential energy used in birth and growth}}$$

Other efficiencies are concerned with the transfer of energy between populations. Some populations are often grouped with others having similar food habits, thus we can recognize herbivores, and carnivores, as trophic levels of a community. Efficiencies may include ratios of a process at one trophic level to the same process at the preceding level as, for example:

$$\text{Trophic level assimilation efficiency} = \frac{\text{energy assimilated at level of carnivore}}{\text{energy assimilated at level of herbivore}}$$

These may also include ratios which compare process, such as:

$$\text{Utilization efficiency} = \frac{\text{energy consumed by carnivore}}{\text{energy produced by herbivore}}$$

Many other efficiency ratios have proved useful, some of these will be described later.

Measurement of Energy Flow

In this section we will consider the problems of measuring energy flow in mammals and the nature of the processes involved. Let us consider each component of the energy flow formulas separately.

Food Consumption

The usual method of measuring food consumption is to offer a known amount of food to a penned animal at time 1, remove the uneaten food at time 2, and determine the difference. The weight of food consumed is converted to energy by burning samples in a calorimeter; or the energy may be determined by using a table of caloric equivalents. Caloric values are available for most human and livestock foods and for many wild-plant species (Golley, 1961a). Fewer values are available for animal tissues (Golley, 1961a; Slobodkin and Richman, 1961). Aside from the usual problems of collecting uneaten food and determining weights of food accurately, there are more difficult problems associated with determining the type of food to offer and extrapolating from laboratory conditions to the populations in the field.

Most mammals can subsist on a varied collection of food items. For this reason, general knowledge of the food habits of a wild species may not be of much value when devising a laboratory ration. We really require knowledge of the food habits of the species at a particular season and in a particular habitat. With this information we can offer food in the actual proportions present in nature, or in those observed in the stomachs of individuals from the population. This information may be obtained by actually watching the feeding of individuals throughout a period (Brown, 1961), examining stomach contents (Williams, 1959) or the fecal material (Murie, 1946) of a sample of animals from the population.

The approximate food consumption of free-living mammals may also be estimated if the weight of the stomach contents and the number of times the stomach is filled daily is known. The number of activity periods per day has been determined for many mammals, and since activity is usually concerned with food collecting, the number of these periods is an estimate of times the stomach is filled daily. Using this technique, Golley (1960) found that the amount of food eaten by the meadow mouse (*Microtus pennsylvanicus*) was close to that determined in the laboratory (0.86 g wet wt/g/day versus 0.61 to 0.86 g wet wt/g/day) assuming 10 activity periods per day and a filling of the stomach to twice the mean observed contents at each period. This method of estimating food intake in free-living mammals also gave close agreement with the quantity of food consumed in the laboratory by the cotton rat (*Sigmodon hispidus*). This technique may have wide application.

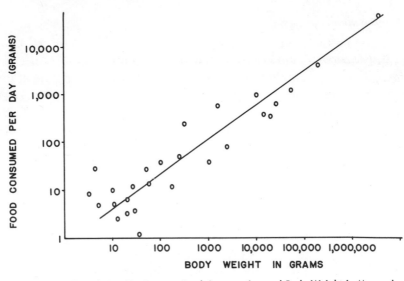

Figure 9-2. The Relationship Between Food Consumption and Body Weight in Mammals. The data on which the graph is based were obtained from a variety of published sources.

Food consumption of the individual varies with weight and with the physiological condition of the animal. Figure 9-2 shows the linear relationship between food consumption and body weight of mammals held in the laboratory but in many cases fed diets chosen to simulate their natural diet. Growing mammals require more food per gram than do mature adults, and although they require larger quantities of energy, a smaller proportion is used in maintenance. As the animal grows, the successive increments in body weight decrease per unit food intake until growth ceases and food intake is used for maintenance alone. Pregnancy does not usually result in increased food intake (Figure 9-3) because there is a decline in muscular activity during gestation. The weight gains during pregnancy are considerable; the energy saved by decreased activity is used for this growth. Actually it is the period of lactation and not gestation which imposes a drain on the mother. Depending on the rate of milk flow, lactation may triple the food consumption over that of the nonlactating state (Figure 9-3).

Food consumption may also be influenced by environmental factors such as type of food, temperature, and so forth. The food intake of herbivores appears to be slightly higher than that of carnivores of the same body weight. However, the relationship is not especially clear where data from a variety of sources are used (Figure 4-3). Where one

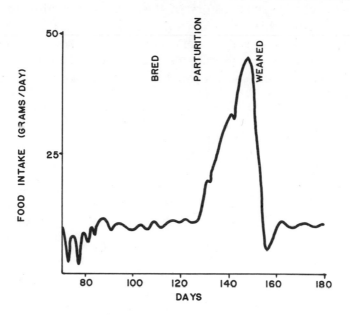

Figure 9-3. The Influence of Pregnancy and Lactation on Food Intake in the White Rat. Note the increased food intake after parturition. (Redrawn from Brody, 1945.)

species is presented with different diets, the results can be quite marked. For instance, Morrison, *et al.* (1957) fed masked shrews (*Sorex cinereus*) on three different diets at a temperature of 25°C. The pooled averages for these experiments show the influence of diet on food consumption:

Worms	3.12 g/g/day
Newborn rats	2.02 g/g/day
Liver	1.56 g/g/day

Worms, which contain 37 per cent earth in the digestive tract, and whose bodies are only 12 per cent solid matter, and rats, which contain undigestible bones, represent a less concentrated energy source than liver.

It has been reported by many workers that the rate of food consumption varies inversely with the environmental temperature; however, the response to temperature is not immediate. Sealander (1952) has shown for the white-footed mouse (*Peromyscus leucopus*) and the deer mouse (*P. maniculatus*) that this adjustment period was from 8 to 12 days at temperatures of 6.0° to 10.5°C, and 15 days at 29.5° to 32.5°C

(Figure 9-4). The thermal history of the animals was also important, since animals with a history of warmth had thinner coats and compensated for their reduced insulative efficiency by increased food consumption. The food consumption may also be influenced by the supply of drinking water for those species which do not obtain their water metabolically or from food.

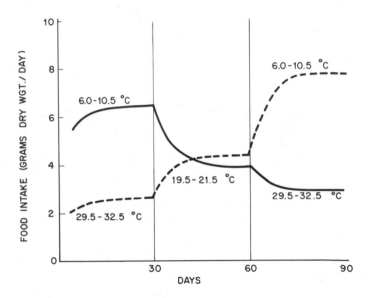

Figure 9-4. The Influence of Temperature on Food Intake in *Peromyscus*. Adjustment is not abrupt, but rather, requires several days before equilibrium is achieved. (After Sealander, 1952.)

Unassimilated Materials

The proportion of the ingested energy which is assimilated is determined by subtracting the energy voided in the feces from that consumed. Actually the feces contain undigestible material plus excretions from the body proper into the digestive tract, secretions from the digestive glands, abrasions from the walls of the gut, and bacteria and protozoa from the stomach and caecum. The proportion of "extra" materials in the feces is highly variable and depends on the type of diet and plane of nutrition. The result of not correcting for these materials in the feces is a slight underestimate of the assimilated energy.

The digestibility or rate of assimilation of food depends on the diet and the food intake. For animals which have not developed special adaptations for handling roughage, a diet of plant food may be highly undigestible. Similarly, animal diets containing large quantities of bone and hair may be undigestible. Beside this dietary influence, digestibility may be affected by the quantity of food consumed. For instance, in steers, as the dry matter consumption increases, the fecal energy loss increases (Figure 9-5).

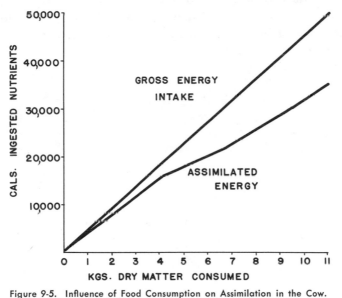

Figure 9-5. Influence of Food Consumption on Assimilation in the Cow. As food intake increases, assimilation declines. (After Brody, 1945.)

In the laboratory, on artificial diets, many small wild mammals, including carnivores, appear to be able to assimilate about 90 per cent of the ingested energy. But not to know the efficiency of assimilation of free-living mammals on natural diets creates a very serious gap in our knowledge.

Maintenance

The energy requirements for maintenance of the body include the basal metabolism, the energy cost of utilizing food and excreting wastes (termed the calorigenic effect of food, Kleiber, 1961), the energy cost of activity and the energy cost of maintaining body temperature in hot or cold environments.

Basal metabolism: Basal metabolism is the heat production during complete rest in a thermoneutral environment, or while in a postabsorptive condition (that is, uncomplicated by the energy-cost of feeding). According to Brody (1945) about 5 to 15 per cent of the basal energy is expended for the work of blood circulation, 5 per cent for the work of the kidneys, and 5 to 15 per cent for the work of respiration. The remaining basal cost represents the energy used in maintaining the living state and body temperature. Basal metabolism is a convenient base line for measuring the energy expense of various processes in the individual, but since the wild mammal is seldom, if ever, under basal conditions, it is of limited usefulness to the mammalogist interested in energy flow.

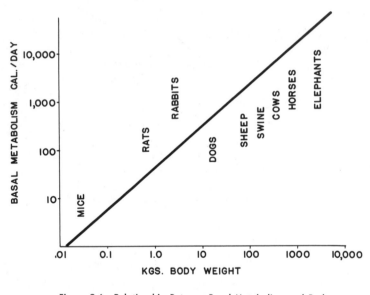

Figure 9-6. Relationship Between Basal Metabolism and Body Weight of Mature Mammals of Different Species, from Mice to Elephants.

Basal heat production is correlated with body size in mature mammals. There is no direct correlation with body weight or surface area, but a correlation with what has been called the metabolically effective body weight. For mammals from mice to elephants this value is approximately the 0.7 power of the body weight (Figure 9-6). This means that an increase in the body weight of 100 per cent is associated with a 70 per cent increase in the metabolic rate. The reason for this relationship appears to be that the neuroendocrine system, which controls the level of metabolism, increases in size approximately in proportion to the surface area rather than to the weight of the body. Thus, the size of the neuroendocrine system, the surfaces, heat dissipation, and heat production all vary in parallel with about the 0.7 power of weight. The shrews have been reported to deviate from this general trend (Pearson, 1948), but recent work of Morrison, Ryser, and Dawe (1959) shows that the observed very high metabolic rate of shrews (*Sorex cinereus*—9.0 cc $O_2/g/hr$) is probably due to the calorigenic effect of their meat diet. It is difficult to measure the basal value of metabolism in shrews since these mammals will die if not regularly provided with food. When reasonable estimates of the calorigenic effect are subtracted from the minimal rate of metabolism, the calculated basal rate falls on the curve for other mammals.

The Calorigenic Effect of Food: When an animal is fed, its heat production increases above the basal level. This increase is called the calorigenic effect of food or, more commonly, the specific dynamic action (SDA), and is due to the energy requirements of the biochemical functions of the nutritive processes. The SDA is variable, depending on the balance of nutrients in the diet and those assimilated. When the digested nutrients exceed the amount which can be utilized for production and activity, the calorigenic effect per unit of digested nutrient is increased. In general, the calorigenic effect is greater for protein than for fats or carbohydrates.

Energy Cost of Activity: The influence of activity on metabolism has not been studied intensively. Brody (1945) has compared the resting and working metabolism of domestic livestock, and Benedict and Lee (1938) have studied the effect of running in activity wheels on marmot metabolism. Recently, Catlett (1961) reported on the oxygen consumption of house mice (*Mus musculus*) during various types of activity. A summary of his results are:

Type of Activity	cc $O_2/g^{.7}/hr$
Aggressive	18.3
Investigative	15.0
Ingestive	9.5
Sedentary	8.0
Huddling	8.0

All of these data suggest that the energy cost of normal activity (that is, when the animal is not forced to be active in a device such as a spinning wheel) is about twice the resting metabolism (basal metabolism plus energy cost of feeding).

Influence of Temperature on Metabolism: A summary of the influence of temperature on metabolism is shown diagrammatically in Figure 9-7. The thermoneutral zone between B and B' is that region where the

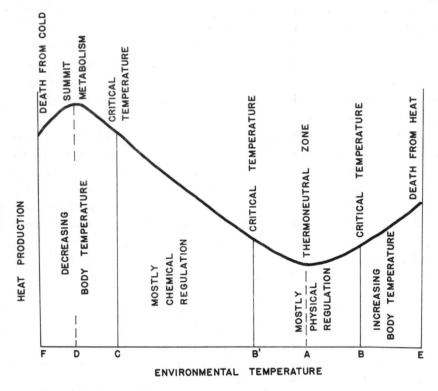

Figure 9-7. Diagram of the Influence of Temperature on Heat Production. (Redrawn from Brody, 1945.)

animal does not expend energy above the basal level to maintain the temperature of the body. At B', thermogenesis begins to increase to balance thermolysis, while at C the temperature-regulating mechanisms cannot cope with decreasing environmental temperature and the body temperature begins to decline. At D heat production is maximum, after this point heat production and body temperature decline. At the other end of the curve, the metabolism begins to rise at B, and body temperature increases. High environmental temperatures may depress food intake and utilization as well as reduce growth and reproduction.

To maintain stable body temperatures when the environmental temperature increases or decreases, mammals must resort to chemical temperature-regulating mechanisms as well as to the physical ones (insulation, moisture, vaporization from the skin, moving blood to the surface of skin, huddling, and building shelters), discussed in Chapter 4. These chemical mechanisms include altering the metabolic rate by such devices as shivering, changing muscle tension, increasing the production of adrenaline and thyroxine, and building up the SDA by greater food intake. The ability to regulate body temperature chemically varies with age, size, and previous thermal history. The young of many mammals are imperfectly homeothermic for a period after birth. For instance, the body temperature of children stabilizes between one and two years of age, while that of young white rats stabilizes in about three weeks. Body size is also an important influence since, considering equal conditions, the larger the animal the flatter the heat-production curve with decreasing environmental temperature. Previous thermal history or acclimatization also plays a role, since mammals can be acclimated to either hot or cold environments and thus be better able to adjust to further heating or cooling.

The effect of temperature on population metabolism is considered to be very significant (Pearson (1960)). The effect is certainly important in unusually hot or cold environments; however, in temperate regions many mammals, especially the small forms, adjust their activity patterns to the temperature and remain in insulated shelters when adverse temperatures occur. Under these conditions the mammals may remain near the thermoneutral zone during much of the day.

Methods of Measuring Maintenance Energy: To determine the heat cost of maintenance, the animal may be confined in a calorimeter and the heat production measured directly. Alternately, an indirect method may be employed in which the volume of oxygen consumed or carbon dioxide produced by an animal in a respirometer is determined and converted to energy with proper caloric equivalents. There are many indirect methods of measuring maintenance metabolism. One method is to confine the animal in a closed chamber of known volume containing a suitable carbon dioxide absorber such as potassium hydroxide (KOH). As the animal uses O_2 and produces CO_2, the latter is absorbed by the alkali and the volume of gas in the system drops—the decrease in volume being measured by a manometer or some other device. Many variants of this technique have been used successfully. In other systems carbon dioxide production is measured separately, or is measured together with oxygen.

In order to convert the oxygen used or carbon dioxide produced to calories of heat in the indirect methods, it is necessary to know the respiratory quotient (RQ). The RQ is the ratio of the volumes of carbon dioxide produced to oxygen consumed. The RQ is of special interest because it varies with the type of nutrient catabolized in the body; for instance, for carbohydrates the RQ is 1.0, for fats about 0.7, and for proteins about 0.8. Once the RQ is known, the caloric value of the volume of gas can be read from a table of caloric equivalents and heat production calculated. If both the oxygen and carbon dioxide are not measured in the respirometer, the RQ may still be determined if the chemical composition of the diet is known. Where only one gas is measured and the composition of the diet is not known, an RQ of 0.8 is usually assumed. At an RQ of 0.8, the caloric equivalent for oxygen is 4.8 cal/l O_2.

To estimate accurately the total heat production of a population from laboratory determinations, it is necessary to know: (1) the type of food consumed, in order to calculate the RQ; (2) the weight distribution of the population; (3) the daily activity periods; and (4) the temperature in each portion of the animal's habitat. To obtain a reasonable estimate of this important component of energy flow, we should be able to partition accurately the heat production of the species in each particular habitat. An alternative approach would be to measure metabolism directly in the field, but this is a difficult technical problem. At present, certain workers (see Odum and Golley, 1962) are trying to correlate excretion rates of radioactive isotopes with metabolism to break this bottleneck in measuring energy flow.

Production

The production of tissue or growth is often measured in the field by weighing animals each successive time they are captured. However, it is seldom possible to capture all the age groups within a population, and the young animals which are least susceptible to capture are those storing the most energy as tissue production. Therefore, an alternative method of estimating production is often useful. This method utilizes information on the age distributions of the population, the growth curve for the species, and the caloric equivalent of animal tissue.

In all mammals the normal growth curve has an early phase of growth with a rising slope and a later phase with a lower rate of increase (Figure 9-8). The junction between these two phases often corresponds

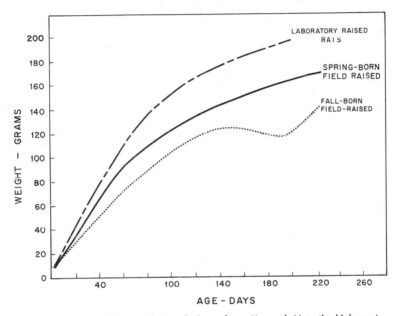

Figure 9-8. A Typical Postnatal Growth Curve for a Mammal. Note the higher rate of growth of *Sigmodon* in the laboratory, and the depression in growth occurring in winter of cotton rats born in the fall. (Drawn from data of Dunaway (1959) and Meyer and Meyer (1944).)

with puberty. Although the average size of the animal at maturity and the slope of the growth curve are genetic characteristics of the species, the actual values of these parameters under a given set of environmental conditions may vary considerably. The prenatal and postnatal states of nutrition, which may be influenced by environmental and social factors, are especially important. For these reasons, growth curves used in predicting production should be obtained for the population under investigation and for each season during the study. Growth curves determined in the laboratory, because of optimal nutritional conditions, often exceed growth in the field (Figure 9-8).

If an appropriate growth curve is available, and the age of the individuals in the population is known, the weight of tissue produced in a given number of days can be estimated from the curve for each age. The gain in weight is then converted into energy with the proper caloric constant. If the time interval between measurements is sufficiently small, a reasonable estimate of production may be obtained. In this method the weight increase of pregnant females is an important complication. Logically, the weight gained during gestation can be considered as production. However it is questionable if this gain can be converted to energy with the caloric constants given below. The reason for this is that a large proportion is water (75 per cent of the fetus, 85 per cent of the placenta, and 95 per cent of the amniotic fluid (see Brody, 1945, for dairy cattle)), while the dry matter itself may have a higher fuel value than mature tissue.

The caloric value of mammal tissue has been determined for only a few species. The available records for wild mammal tissue are:

	kg cal/gm dry	kg cal/gm live	
Microtus pennsylvanicus	4.65	1.4	Golley (1960a)
Mus musculus	5.67	1.7	Golley (1958)
Oryzomys palustris	5.84	1.9	Sharp (1962)

In general, the caloric value of dried mammal tissue is 5 kg cal/g. However, extremely fat animals may be considerably higher, since fats have combustion values as high as 9.5 kg cal/g.

The proportion of the assimilated energy (ΔH) which is converted to growth may be considered to correspond to the free energy (ΔF) of the thermodynamic equation.

Additional Energy Losses

Not all of the protein which is assimilated is completely oxidized in the body. The heat of combustion of each gram of protein catabolized is 5.7 kg cal, but of this, 0.9 kg cal is excreted in the urine in the form of urea. In addition, energy is lost by passage of other organic materials, such as lactic acid and sugars, in the urine. The percentage loss of energy in the urine depends on the nitrogen intake. For herbivores, this loss may be about 5 per cent of the energy consumed.

Some mammals, such as ruminants, produce large quantities of gas by fermentation in the digestive tract. The major gases produced in the rumen of cattle are CH_4 and CO_2, but H_2, H_2S, and CO are also formed. Brody (1945) has calculated that the fermentation energy loss for a 1200-lb cow is about one third of the resting metabolism; methane production alone may amount to 9 per cent of the gross energy intake.

Actually these losses may not be as significant as they appear, since they arise from the breakdown of the undigestible portion of the diet which has become digestible because of the fermentation process.

Intrapopulation Energy Flow

The limited information on the energy flow in mammal populations is shown in Table 9-1. The estimates for *Sigmodon* and *Odocoileus* are synthetic; that is, estimates of the energy flow components have been

TABLE 9-1. Intrapopulation Energy Consumption and Utilization of Mammals (kg cal/m²/yr)

	Microtus pennsylvanicus	*Sigmodon hispidus*	*Odocoileus virginianus* *	*Peromyscus polionotus*	*Reithrodontomys megalotis*	*Mustela frenata*
Authority	Golley, 1960	Golley, 1961b		Davenport, 1960	Pearson, 1960	Golley, 1960
Population density, No./ha	48.9	12	.15	10.0	30.0	2.9
Standing crop of energy	0.190	0.146	1.27	0.017	0.042	0.011
Available food	1580	1620		73.0	1788	1.9
Food consumption	25	17.2	52.6	3.6		0.6
Maintenance	17	8.83	39.5	3.3	8.3	0.5
Production	0.5	0.53	0.64	0.08		0.01
Rumen gas	0.0	0.0	2.96	0.0		0.0
Energy flow	17.5	9.36	43.1	3.38		0.51

* Synthetic data are based on population estimate by Chase (1962) for George Reserve Deer Herd of 74 deer per 1200 acres, average weight 130 lb per deer; food intake of 72 cal/lb/day, 82 per cent of diet of alfalfa and corn digestible (French, *et al.*, 1956); production of 37 adult deer per 1200 acres per year (Chase, 1962); rumen gas .33 per cent of basal energy expense (Brody and Proctor, 1933), and basal metabolic rate of 27 cal/kg/day (Silver, *et al.*, 1959); maintenance cost calculated by difference.

multiplied by typical population estimates to obtain the flow. The *Sigmodon* data were all obtained in the ecology laboratories at the University of Georgia by one investigator, while the *Odocoileus* estimates were based on studies of the George Reserve deer herd, Michigan, by Chase (1962). The estimates of food intake of deer were made by French, *et al.* (1956) and of metabolism by Silver, *et al.* (1959). Temperature corrections for metabolism were made for *Reithrodontomys* (Pearson, 1960) and for *Sigmodon*. Metabolism was not corrected for activity. Since these latter records are based on laboratory determinations, each probably underestimates true energy flow. It must be emphasized that the data summarized here are preliminary and approximate. Therefore, the conclusions and comparisons which we will draw should be considered as suggestive rather than final.

TABLE 9-2.   Efficiency Ratios for Mammal Populations in Per Cent

Ratio	*Microtus pennsylvanicus* (Golley, 1960)	*Sigmodon hispidus* (Golley, 1961b)	*Odocoileus virginianus* (Table 9-1)	*Peromyscus polionotus* (Davenport, 1960)	*Mustela frenata* (Golley, 1960)
Food assimilated / Food ingested	70.0	54.4	82.0	93.9	85.0
Growth / Assimilation	2.9	5.66	0.015	2.4	2.0
Growth & reprod. / Assimilation	3.9				
Growth / Respiration	2.9	6.0	0.016	2.4	2.0
Growth & reprod. / Respiration	4.0				
Growth / Ingestion	2.0	3.1	0.012	2.2	1.7
Growth & reprod. / Ingestion	2.7				
Standing crop / Energy flow	1.1	1.6	0.03	0.5	2.2
Standing crop / Growth	38.0	27.5	1.98	21.3	110.0
Standing crop / Growth & reprod.	27.9				
Standing crop / Respiration	1.1	1.7	0.03	0.5	2.2
Ingestion / Avail. food	1.6	1.1		4.9	31.6
Assimilation / Avail. food	1.1	0.6		4.5	26.8

The efficiency ratios (Table 9-2) show similar relationships in each population. A relatively large proportion of the food consumed is assimilated. The tissue growth efficiency (growth energy/assimilated energy) ranges from 0.02 to 5.66 per cent, and the low efficiencies probably reflect the relatively long life and large size of mammals. As shown by the above ratio and the ratios of growth/respiration, standing crop/growth, and standing crop/respiration, most of the assimilated energy in mammal populations is used in maintenance rather than in tissue production.

Influence of Herbivory and Carnivory

We would expect energy flow to be influenced by the food habits of the population. Carnivores should have a higher assimilation efficiency since meat is more easily digested than plant food, but the maintenance energy costs should also be higher since energy must be expended in capturing the prey. The limited data in Table 9-1, based on laboratory estimates of food intake and metabolism, do not show these expected differences. Herbivores appear to have as high an assimilation efficiency on the artificial diets as carnivores (Table 9-2). Laboratory data introduce a definite bias into our comparison; we anticipate that the differences between herbivores and carnivores will be resolved when the energy flow components can be measured directly in the field. The ratio of utilization efficiency (assimilation/available food) illustrates another difference between herbivores and carnivores. Herbivore populations appear to utilize a very small proportion of the energy available to them.

Influence of Body Size

The influence of body size on energy flow limits the size of the population maintained on a given area (Figure 9-9). We have already presented reasons for this relationship. Since heat production varies as the 0.7 power of body weight, a small mammal uses proportionally more energy per gram than does a large mammal. For the same amount of energy the population of small mammals must use a greater percentage in maintenance, and therefore, sustains a lower biomass. It will also be noted that carnivores sustain a lower population biomass than herbivores; the reason for this effect will be discussed in a later section.

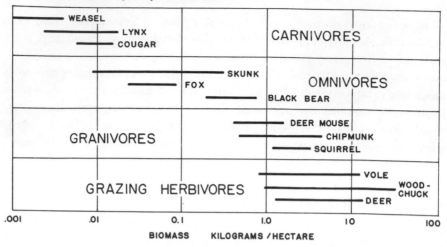

Figure 9-9. Relationship Between Food Habits, Size of Body, and Population Biomass. (Redrawn from Odum, 1959.)

Seasonal Fluctuations in Energy Flow

Up to now we have been considering energy flow from an annual point of view; in addition there are seasonal fluctuations in energy flow. Climatic changes may influence the animals indirectly through the food, or directly by temperature and precipitation. In northern climates the decline in quantity and quality of the forage in winter is well known. Weathered, mature forage, particularly grasses, is very low in protein and phosphorus, has almost no carotene, is lacking in palatability, and is low in digestibility (Morrison, 1949). Badly weathered forage may not even supply enough nutrients for maintenance. This decline in the value of plant foods in winter may result in a decrease or cessation of growth and reproduction.

Seasonal fluctuations in temperature affect energy flow through an influence on metabolism. Pearson (1960) has calculated the energy flow of *Reithrodontomys* in summer and winter. During the winter (December) the energy expended in metabolism increased 30 per cent over that in July. Pearson did not measure growth in the harvest mouse population, so we do not know if the increased requirement for heat production was taken from the growth component or represented an increase in the total energy flow. However, growth did cease in winter in a population of meadow mice (Golley, 1960), and in cotton rats (Dunaway, 1959).

The potential energy in the body of many mammals varies seasonally since the proportion of fat changes throughout the year. Mammals entering a period of inactivity (hibernation, aestivation) or a period with an abundance of food, regularly show an increase in the amount of fat on the body. A study by Connell (1959) of the fat cycle in the old-field mouse (*Peromyscus polionotus*) showed that this species has two peaks of fat deposition (Figure 9-10). One peak occurred in summer when high temperatures limited the activity of this small rodent, and the other occurred in winter when seeds were abundant. During these periods of fat deposition the energy content of the body would increase above the average values given earlier.

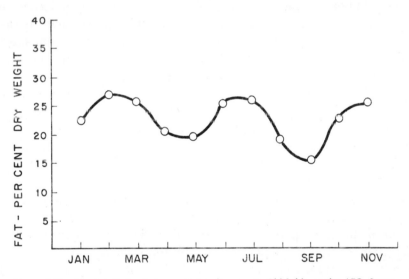

Figure 9-10. The Fat Cycle of *Peromyscus polionotus* in Old-fields on the AEC, Savannah River Project, Aiken, South Carolina. Note the winter and summer peak in per cent body fat in this species. (As determined by Connell (1959).)

Interpopulation Energy Flow

Populations do not exist as separate entities but are part of the food chains and food webs of ecosystems. Energy enters the ecosystem as light energy from the sun, and is converted by green plants through the process of photosynthesis into chemical potential energy. Green plants under natural conditions can convert about 1 to 5 per cent of the total solar energy available to them. The energy available in the plant bodies is then consumed by the populations on the herbivore trophic level, then transferred to the carnivore level, and so on.

The most simple example of interpopulation energy relationships is the food chain. Golley (1960) studied a food chain in Michigan, which included the vegetation of an old field, meadow mice (*Microtus pennsylvanicus*), and least weasels (*Mustela frenata*). This food chain was unusually unidirectional, since the meadow mice were almost completely herbivorous, while the weasels preyed almost exclusively on the mice. In this system the vegetation converted about 1 per cent of the solar energy into plant tissue; the mice consumed about 2 per cent of the plant food available to them; and the weasels consumed about 31 per cent of the available mice (Figure 9-11). Of the energy ingested, the plants used about 15 per cent in respiration, the mice 68 per cent, and the weasels 93 per cent. Although these data are approximate because estimates of ingestion and metabolism were extrapolated from laboratory determinations, they suggest that there is an increase in the utilization of energy from plant to carnivore levels, and an increase in the maintenance cost. In this example, so little energy was converted into weasel flesh that a carnivore preying exclusively on weasels could not be supported. These relationships between utilization efficiency and maintenance cost appear to act as limiting factors on the number of steps in a food chain.

We might also briefly consider energy flow through the trophic levels of whole ecosystems. Information is mainly available for aquatic ecosystems and, in general, these show that about 10 per cent of the production of the green plants is transferred to the herbivores, 1 per cent to the carnivores, and 0.1 per cent to the top carnivores present in the system. As mentioned earlier, there is a tendency in these systems for the higher trophic levels (the carnivores) to use a greater proportion of ingested energy in maintenance. Terrestrial systems will probably show similar relationships. In many terrestrial systems the proportion of the energy flow passing through the mammal populations will probably be only a small proportion of the total. The reason for this is that a relatively small amount of energy stored in vegetation enters the grazing herbivore trophic level; the major portion of the vegetation falls to the ground and is used by reducer food chains living on the soil surface or in the uppermost layer of the soil. For instance, in the old field ecosystem studied by Golley (1960), meadow mice, the major vertebrate herbivore, consumed only 2 per cent of the available energy. Herbiv-

Energy Flow Diagram of a Food Chain in an Old-field Community in Southern Michigan.

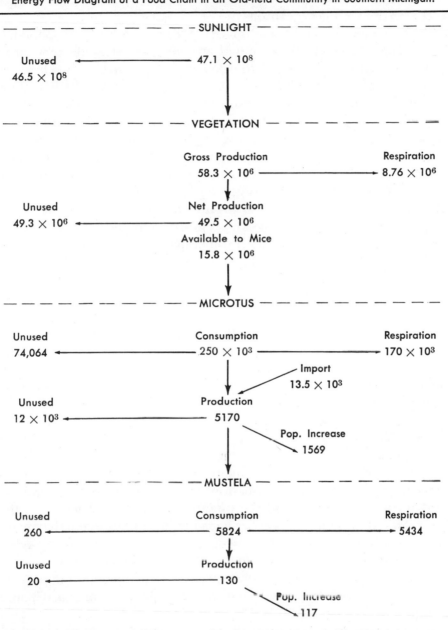

After Golley, 1960

Figure 9-11

orous insects may have consumed another 10 to 20 per cent of the potential energy in the vegetation.

Although the reasons for the relatively insignificant role of mammals in the energy flow of the ecosystem are not completely clear, we may consider the following: First, the density of mammals is much lower than that of invertebrates, while their biomass is much higher. This means that the metabolizing tissue of the mammal population is organized into fewer, large units. As we have noted earlier, large units consume less and require less energy for maintenance. Second, the energy which is consumed is used in different proportions in mammals and invertebrates. Mammals live a relatively long time and therefore a greater proportion of their energy flow is used to maintain the "standing crop" rather than being used in production. The combination of the slower rate of metabolism of large animals and the longer life-span result in a slower flow of energy through mammal populations.

These conclusions about the bioenergetic role of mammals should not be interpreted as implying that mammals are insignificant members of the ecosystem. Their large size, long life, activity, and mental development often permit them to assume a dominant position in other respects. These same qualities may also allow them to influence strongly the growth and development of vegetation and, through the vegetation, other animals. This effect is most clearly expressed in severe environments, simple systems, or where the natural checks on population growth have been removed by management.

MINERAL CYCLING

The biogeochemical role of mammals in the ecosystem is poorly known. A great deal of information is available on the mineral requirements of mammals and the quantity of mineral elements in the body. Most of this information has been obtained for the cell, the organ, or the individual, and has not been extended to populations living under natural conditions. In this section we will endeavor to summarize information on mineral cycling at the individual level to provide a preliminary basis for considering mineral cycling in mammal populations.

At one time or another, nearly every element has been found in living tissue. Underwood (1956) lists the major elements: C, H, O, N,

S, P, Ca, K, Na, Cl, and Mg, which occur in fairly high concentrations, with Fe, Cu, Mn, Zn, I, Co, Mo, Ni, Al, Cr, Sn, Ti, Si, Pb, Rb, Li, As, F, Br, Se, B, Ba, and Sr as constantly present in tissues and fluids of higher animals and plants, and with V, Ag, Au and Ce as occasionally present. In addition to the major elements, Fe, Cu, Mn, Zn, I, Co and Mo are the only elements conclusively shown to be essential for higher animals. The presence of many of the minor elements in living tissues is probably due to their constant occurrence in soil, food, water, and the atmosphere with which the animal is associated.

The mineral elements which remain as ash, after the organic material of the body has been burned away, make up about 5 per cent of the body, calculated on a fat-free empty weight. A majority of the ash is derived from the skeleton (about 80 per cent), while a minor, but very important, amount is derived from the body fluids and tissues. In general, calcium and phosphorus are the most important mineral constituents in bone, while in the soft tissues potassium, phosphorus, sulfur, and chlorine are most abundant.

The mineral elements can be classified into (1) the energy elements, (2) the macronutrient elements, and (3) the micronutrient elements (Gilbert, 1957). The energy elements are: carbon, oxygen, hydrogen, and nitrogen. Mammals obtain oxygen from the air, and the remainder of the required elements from the food and water they consume. Except under desert conditions, where water is limiting, carbon, hydrogen, and oxygen are usually abundant. Nitrogen is exceedingly important, and animals on a low protein diet may exhibit stunting of growth, lower reproduction, and lowered resistance to disease. The macro- and micronutrient elements constitute a very small proportion of the structural makeup of animals. They have a capacity to function in very small quantities, indicating that they act as catalysts in hormone or enzyme systems, either as constituent parts of the hormones, enzymes, vitamins, or co-enzymes or as enzyme activators.

The Macronutrients

The macronutrient elements, including phosphorus, calcium, magnesium, potassium, sulfur, chlorine, and sodium, are necessary in somewhat greater amounts than the minor elements.

Phosphorus is essential in every living cell, and its compounds have more functions than any other single mineral nutrient. The daily re-

TABLE 9-3.   The Mineral Requirements, the Mineral Pool and Turnover Rate per Day for Representative Mammals.* (Values, mg/kg)

Wt Class, kg → Mineral ↓	.01 to .1		.1 to 1.0		1.0 to 10.0		10 to 100		100 to 1000		Body Pool, mg/kg
	Required, mg	% of Pool	Required, mg	% of Pool	Required, mg	% of Pool	Required, mg	% of Pool	Required, mg	% of Pool	
Calcium	900	6.0	180	1.2	280	1.9	34–109 ***	0.2–0.7	47	0.3	15,000
Chlorine	800	53.3	20	1.3	230	15.3	160	10.7	38	2.5	1500
Cobalt	0.4				0.2		0.06		2		
Copper	0.7	35.0	1	50.0	0.5	25.0	0.73	36.5	R **		2
Fluorine	0.6	0.6			0.04	0.04	0.08	0.08			96
Iodine	1.3	325	0.008	2.0	0.6	150.0	0.02	5.0			0.4
Iron	30	75.0	5	12.5	5	12.5	0.74	1.9	R **		40.0
Magnesium	60	12.0	5	1.0	10	2.0	10	2.0	R **		500.0
Manganese	5.6	186.7	2	66.7	1.6	53.3	0.11	3.7	0.3	10	3.0
Phosphorus	900	9.0	160	1.6	340	3.4	31–86 ***	0.3–0.9	38	0.4	10,000
Potassium	600	17.1	60	1.7	188	5.4	80–220 ***	2.3–6.3	55–110	1.6–3.1	3500
Sodium	500	33.3	200	13.3	130	8.7	103	6.9	25	1.7	1500
Sulfur			R **		14	0.6			R **		2500
Zinc	0.3	3.6	R **		0.9	10.7	0.11	1.3	R **		8.4
Species:	Mouse		Rat		Monkey Fox Cat Mink		Dog Man Sheep		Swine Horse Cattle		

* Data abstracted from Spector (1956).
** R = mineral required.
*** Variation due to varied data for dogs.

quirement for phosphorus is quite high in mature animals (Table 9-3), and increases with growth, pregnancy, or lactation. About 80 per cent of the phosphorus in the body is in the skeleton, about 10 per cent in the muscles, and 1 per cent in the nervous system.

Calcium is the most abundant mineral element in the body. About 99 per cent is contained in the bones and teeth; however, the small fraction in the fluids and tissues is extremely important in maintaining normal excitability of muscles and nerves, and proper acid-base equilibrium. Daily requirements are difficult to determine since the utilization of calcium depends on the physiological state of the animal, the ratio of calcium to phosphorus, and the presence of Vitamin D in the diet. The Vitamin D requirement is at a minimum when the ratio of calcium intake to phosphorus intake is between 1:2 to 2:1. Carnivores appear to have a higher requirement for calcium than do herbivores.

Magnesium is closely related to calcium and phosphorus in its distribution and metabolism in the body. About 70 per cent of the body magnesium is in the skeleton. This element is required for life, and is important as an activator of phosphates.

Potassium is quite abundant in the mammal body, and is found mainly in muscle tissue. This element is necessary for growth, and is important in carbohydrate metabolism and muscle function, and in nerve excitability.

Sulfur occurs mainly in proteins containing the amino acids cystine and methionine; only a very small amount occurs as sulfates. Sulfur, in cystine, is principally found in hooves, horn, and hair, and in certain compounds such as biotin, Vitamin B, and insulin. Mammals can use inorganic sulfur compounds in the diet, but can also reutilize sulfur-containing amino acids resulting from protein breakdown in the body.

Chlorine and Sodium mainly enter the body from the outside, are used, and are then excreted as sodium chloride. The body contains about 0.16 per cent sodium and 0.11 per cent chlorine. These elements are found almost entirely in the soft tissues and fluids. They help maintain the acid-base balance of the body, the total osmotic pressure of the extra cellular fluids, and the formation and flow of gastric and intestinal secretions. Herbivores and some carnivores often require extra salt in the diet, while other carnivores obtain a sufficient amount from flesh and blood. The body can adjust to a low salt diet by reducing the output of salt through the kidney.

The Micronutrients

Iron is found in the body mainly in complex forms bound to two kinds of protein—those containing iron as part of a heme or porphyrin unit, and those in which iron is not chelated in a porphyrin ring. In man, about 73 per cent of the iron is in hemoglobin, 3.3 per cent in myoglobin, and 16.5 per cent in nohemin iron protein complexes. In the average adult mammal, iron represents about 0.006 per cent of the whole body—differences between adults of different species are small. There appears, however, to be considerable variation in the amount of iron in bodies of the newborn of different species. These differences are probably due to variations in the amounts of iron stored in the liver and in levels of hemoglobin in the blood. The absorption of dietary iron is regulated by the cells of the intestinal mucosa. The absorbed iron is retained with great tenacity.

Copper: The normal adult mammalian body contains about 1.5 to 2.0 ppm of copper. Newborn and very young animals usually contain two to three times more copper per unit of body weight than adults—largely due to high copper storage in the liver. Copper is important in blood formation, for the proper utilization and absorption of iron, for correct bone development, and for adequate growth of hair or fur. Continued ingestion of copper in excess of nutritional requirements leads to accumulation in the tissues and eventually to copper poisoning.

Manganese is found in mammal tissues at very low concentrations—at levels substantially below those of copper. The variation in manganese content between species and between organs is quite small. Manganese is necessary for proper growth, for sufficient mineralization of the bones, and for reproduction.

Zinc occurs in the body of adult mammals at concentrations of about 30 ppm, which is approximately one-half the amount of total body iron and 10 to 15 times that of body copper. Zinc is concentrated in the bones, hair, and pigmented tissues of the eyes. Newborn animals are more variable in zinc content than adults; and those with high values, such as the cat and guinea pig, can be accounted for by the fact that they are born with hair. Zinc may also accumulate in the reproductive organs of the male. Zinc is necessary for the proper functioning of several enzyme systems of the body and is essential for normal growth.

Iodine is found throughout the body tissues and secretions, and probably occurs in every cell in the body. In man the body contains about .4 mg/kg, and of this, from 20 to 40 per cent is concentrated in the thyroid gland. Concentrations also occur in the ovaries, bile, and hair. Iodine is an essential component of thyroid hormone, which exercises control over the rate of energy metabolism, physical and mental growth, neuromuscular function, circulatory dynamics, metabolism of food nutrients, and so forth. The requirement for iodine is related to heat production, and in normal adults is increased by activity, disturbances, pregnancy, and lactation.

Cobalt is distributed throughout the body at extremely low concentrations, with highest concentrations in the liver, kidneys, and pancreas. Cobalt exists in tissues as a part of Vitamin B_{12}. It is required by ruminants in about the same amount as iodine, and its main action is to promote the growth of the rumen microorganisms which synthesize Vitamin B_{12} for the host animal. Nonruminants also require cobalt if their diet does not contain preformed Vitamin B_{12}.

Molybdenum has also shown to be essential in the nutrition of mammals. The concentration in the tissues is very low, being similar to that of manganese, and much lower than copper. Mammalian muscle tissue usually contains 0.05 to 0.10 ppm on a dry basis, with higher concentrations in the liver. Molybdenum is a constituent of essential enzymes and interacts reciprocally with copper.

Other Trace Elements: Several other trace elements have important influences in mammalian physiology. *Fluorine,* while not an essential element, occurs universally in soils and plants and is present at low equilibria in the tissues. Soft tissues contain about 2 to 4 ppm on a dry basis, while bones and teeth concentrate fluorine at levels of about 100 ppm on the dry fat-free basis. Fluorine prevents dental caries, but at high levels may be toxic. *Selenium* is consumed by mammals in vegetation growing on soils with high concentrations of this element. The interest in selenium is due to its toxic effects, which cause loss of vitality, emaciation, erosion of the joints, soreness of hooves, loss of hair, atrophy of the heart, cirrhosis of the liver, and eventually death. Edible herbage on seleniferous soil may contain 10 to 20 ppm of selenium; however, certain species of plants of the genera *Astragalus, Stanleya, Oonopsis* and *Xylorrhiza* concentrate the element and may contain several thousand ppm.

The macro- and micronutrients are obtained by the animal through the intake of food, with subsequent absorption through the intestinal wall. Not all elements are absorbed equally; for instance, iron, manganese, and zinc are poorly absorbed, while iodine and molybdenum are absorbed more easily. The elements are lost from the body through excretion into the intestinal tract and deposition in the feces, through the urine, body secretions, and exhalation. Of the trace elements, iodine and molybdenum are largely excreted by the kidneys; manganese, copper, and zinc largely in the feces; iron in the urine and feces; and cobalt in the feces, bile, and urine. Macronutrients may be lost in part through the feces, when there is an exchange of minerals in the intestinal lumen with the body pool or when there is fecal excretion of elements, and in part through the kidneys. Table 9-4 is a summary of normal values of fecal excretion for several species (Berger, 1960), and illustrates the difference in rate of excretion for different minerals.

Mineral Turnover

In Table 9-3 the mineral requirements for maintenance and normal vigorous activity for different male mammals are presented as a function of body weight. The data were abstracted from Spector (1956) and represent values for adult males on maintenance diets, with one exception. The mouse data were from young animals, which would mean that the values are somewhat higher than the values for adult mice. In Table 9-3 the mineral pool for all species is based on the values for man. Actually, this is probably an appropriate generalization since the concentration of elements in most organs of different species of mammals (Spector, 1956), and in the whole body of such diverse mammals as the cow and man, are similar. In contrast to this constancy of the mineral pool, the mineral requirements for different species appear to vary widely. Mineral requirements are inversely correlated to body weight, in a manner similar to food intake or to the caloric requirements. This is a reasonable correlation when we remember that the trace elements function as catalysts in enzyme or hormone systems, or as enzyme activators.

With information on the daily requirements for minerals and the body mineral pool, we can calculate the percentage daily turnover of the mineral pool, assuming intake and excretion are at equilibrium. Although the values given in Table 9-3 are approximate since they are based on limited and in some cases preliminary information, they clearly indicate that turnover time varies with the size of the species.

TABLE 9-4. Normal Values for Dietary Intake and Fecal Excretion of Electrolytes *
(Values, mg/day)

Species	Sodium		Potassium		Calcium		Magnesium	
	Intake	Excretion	Intake	Excretion	Intake	Excretion	Intake	Excretion
Rat	11.5 to 115	2.3 to 6.9	39 to 195	15.6 to 27.3	20 to 100	10 to 60	12 to 24	9.6 to 18.0
Dog	230 to 1725	23 to 230	780 to 2340	19.5 to 156	20 to 3000	60 to 2800	12 to 180	12 to 120
Man	1150 to 3450	11.5 to 115	1950 to 2925	195 to 585	500 to 1500	300 to 1300	240 to 480	120 to 360

Species	Chloride		Phosphorus	
	Intake	Excretion	Intake	Excretion
Rat	17.8 to 177.5	3.6 to 10.7	62 to 186	15.5 to 62
Dog	355 to 2663	18 to 180	620 to 1240	465 to 620
Man	1800 to 5325	18 to 107	775 to 1550	310 to 775

* Calculated from Berger, 1960.

For large mammals it is approximately several months, while for small ones it may be only a few days.

Mineral Cycling at the Population and Ecosystem Levels

The general outlines of many biogeochemical cycles are well known. The nitrogen cycle, for instance, appears in most elementary textbooks in biology. The general pattern of these cycles is that minerals, under the influence of gravity, move from high to low altitudes. The transporting agent is usually the water of streams and rivers, and ultimately the minerals are deposited in the ocean depths. However, at any position on the way to the ocean, living organisms can capture the elements, concentrate, and transport them. Mammal populations may or may not play a significant role in these processes —information is not available. One recent study suggests that a mammalian carnivore, the dolphin (*Tursiops truncatus*), fills a minor role in phosphorus regeneration in an esturine ecosystem (Table 9-5). A mammalian herbivore population may be considerably more important in this connection.

TABLE 9-5. Phosphorus Utilization of Esterine Organisms in Doboy Sound, Georgia *

Population	Biomass, 10^9/g dry wt	Biomass P, 10^6/g	P Utilization, 10^6 g/day
Marsh Grass			3.7
Phytoplankton			1.3
Total plants			5.0
Benthic invertebrates	0.9	5.0	0.5
Marsh crabs	1.8	10.4	0.4
Snail	0.2	0.8	0.25
Clam	0.4	2.6	0.1
Shrimp	0.03	0.3	0.1
Dolphin			0.005 **

* From Pomeroy and Bush (1959).
** Based on 50 dolphins eating 23 kg of fish per day.

REFERENCES

Benedict, F. G., and R. C. Lee. 1938. Hibernation and mammot physiology. Carnegie Inst. Wash., Publ. 497: 1-239.

Berger, E. Y. 1960. Intestinal absorption and excretion. In, Mineral Metabolism, an Advanced Treatise, Vol. 1, Part A, pp. 249-286, New York, Academic Press, Inc.

Brody, S. 1945. Bioenergetics and Growth. New York, Reinhold Publ. Corp. 1023 pp.

Brody, S., and R. C. Proctor. 1933. Growth and development, with special reference to domestic animals. 31. Influence of the plane of nutrition on the utilizability of feeding stuffs. Review of literature and graphic analysis of published data on the net energy and specific dynamic action problems. Univ. Missouri Agric. Exp. Sta. Res. Bull. 193.

Brown, E. R. 1961. The black-tailed deer of western Washington. Wash. State Dept. Game, Biol. Bull. No. 13. 124 p.

Catlett, R. A. 1961. Social behavior and bioenergetics in relation to density of house mice. (MS, presented before 41st annual meeting of Amer. Soc. Mammalogists.)

Chase, W. W. 1962. Productivity of the George Reserve deer herd. Proc. First Natl. White-tailed Deer Symp., Univ. Georgia Center for Contin. Ed.

Connell, C. E. 1959. Seasonal lipid levels in three population groups on an old-field ecosystem. Ph.D. Thesis, Univ. Georgia.

Davenport, L. B. 1960. Structure and energy requirements of *Peromyscus polionotus* populations in the old-field ecosystem. Ph.D. Thesis, Univ. Georgia.

Dunaway, P. B. 1959. In, Ecological Research, Health Physics Div. Annual Progress Rpt., Oak Ridge Natl. Lab., for period ending July 31, 1959: pp. 33-37.

French, C. E., L. C. McEwen, N. D. Magruder, R. H. Ingram, and R. W. Swift. 1956. Nutrient requirements for growth and antler development in the white-tailed deer. J. Wildl. Manag. 20: 221-232.

Gilbert, F. A. 1957. Mineral nutrition and the balance of life. Manag. Norman, Univ. Oklahoma Press: 350 pp.

Golley, F. B. 1958. Energy dynamics of a food chain of the old-field community. Ph.D. Thesis, Michigan State Univ. 102 pp.

Golley, F. B. 1960. Energy dynamics of a food chain of an old-field community. Ecol. Monogr. 30: 187-206.

Golley, F. B. 1961a. Energy values of ecological materials. Ecol. 42: 581-584.

Golley, F. B. 1961b. Studies of energy flow in *Sigmodon hispidus*. (MS, presented before 41st annual meeting, American Soc. Mammalogists).

Kleiber, M. 1961. The fire of life, an introduction to animal energetics. New York, John Wiley & Sons, Inc.: 454 pp.

Meyer, B. J. and R. K. Meyer. 1944. Growth and reproduction of the cotton rat, *Sigmodon hispidus hispidus,* under laboratory conditions. J. Mamm. 25(2): 107-129.

Morrison, F. B. 1949. Feeds and Feeding. Ithaca, N.Y., Morrison Publ. Co. 1207 pp.

Morrison, P. R., M. Pierce, and F. A. Ryser. 1957. Food consumption and body weight in the masked and short-tail shrews. Amer. Midl. Nat. 57: 493-501.

Morrison, P. R., F. A. Ryser, and A. R. Dawe. 1959. Studies on the physiology of the masked shrew, *Sorex cinereus.* Physiol. Zool. 32: 256-271.

Murie, O. J. 1946. Evaluating duplications in analysis of Coyote scats. J. Wildl. Manag. 10: 275-276.

Odum, E. P. 1959. Fundamentals of Ecology. Philadelphia, W. B. Saunders Co. 546 pp.

Odum, E. P., and F. B. Golley. 1963. Radioactive tracers as an aid to the measurement of energy flow at the population level in nature. In, Radioecology (Proc.

First Symposium on), Vincent Schultz and Alfred W. Klement, Jr. (editors). New York, Reinhold Publ. Corp. (In press.)

Patten, B. C. 1959. An introduction to the cybernetics of the ecosystem: the trophic — dynamic aspect. Ecology 40: 221-231.

Pearson, O. P. 1948. Metabolism of small mammals, with remarks on the lower limit of mammalian size. Science 108: 44.

Pearson, O. P. 1960. The oxygen consumption and bioenergetics of harvest mice. Physiological Zoology 33: 152-160.

Pomeroy, L. R., and F. M. Bush. 1959. Regeneration of phosphorus by marine animals. First Int. Oceanographic Congress: pp. 893-895.

Sealander, J. A., Jr. 1952. Food consumption in *Peromyscus* in relation to air temperature and previous thermal experience. J. Mamm. 33: 206-218.

Sharp, H. F. 1962. Trophic relationships of the rice rat, *Oryzomys palustris,* living in Georgia salt marshes. MS Thesis, Univ. Georgia.

Silver, H., N. F. Colovos, and H. H. Hayes. 1959. Basal metabolism of white-tailed deer—a pilot study. J. Wildl. Manag. 23: 434-438.

Slobodkin, L. B. 1960. Ecological energy relationships at the population level. Amer. Nat. 94: 213-236.

Slobodkin, L. B., and S. Richman. 1961. Calories/gm in species of animals. Nature 191: 299.

Spector, W. S. 1956. Handbook of biological data. Philadelphia, W. B. Saunders Co.

Underwood, E. J. 1956. Trace elements in human and animal nutrition. New York, Academic Press, Inc. 430 pp.

Williams, O. 1959. Food habits of the deer mouse. J. Mamm. 40: 415-419.

chapter ten

ACTIVITY AND BEHAVIOR

THE DAILY ACTIVITIES of mammals may be classified in several ways. One would be according to function, and concern maintenance, social organization, sexual actions, protection, and home range. Another would be based on seasonal fluctuations, and consider migration, hibernation, reproductive period, and social changes. For the present chapter the first method is more convenient, and hence will be followed. First, we will have a discussion of daily activities for maintenance, and comments on home range, dispersal, and migration. Then the senses and sexual and social behavior will be described, followed by consideration of communication, care of the young, protection, and learning. The available information is so extensive that only a few examples can be cited to illustrate each point. The immense variety of behavior among mammals is a reflection of adaptation to a variety of habitats. Several aspects of behavior are hardly noticed here. Such topics as maturation, learning, and instinct are more fully covered in books on psychology or on behavior (Scott, 1957).

Most of an animal's activities are devoted to obtaining food. Except during the breeding season, as much as 90 per cent of the waking hours may be involved in obtaining nutrients for the build-up of energy. Only trivial amounts of time each day are required to dig burrows or repair nests, satisfy physiological functions, and avoid enemies. Even in the breeding season provision of food is a major activity, and is facilitated by the fact that breeding generally occurs at a time when food is easily found. Of course, rest and sleep occupy the other portion of the day.

Direct observation is the chief method for study of behavior. In general, the investigator goes to a spot where he can watch the animal and follow its activities. One investigator camped on the trail of elk and followed them on their migrations in the spring to high altitudes. Another spent many cold hours watching squirrels during the February breeding season. For nocturnal, fossorial, and secretive species, other methods are required. Trapping, marking, and releasing supply information on movements and interactions. Self-recording devices (Pearson, 1959) provide voluminous information. The use of machines to record behavior has been neglected and offers a fertile field.

GENERAL ACTIVITIES

The maintenance of life in a mammal requires a variety of activities associated with the procurement of food, shelter, and protection. An obvious principle is that the extent of activity must be adequate to maintain the kind of life permitted by the mammal's anatomic and physiologic adaptations. While in general the members of a taxonomic group are active at similar times, some conspicuous exceptions occur. For example, flying squirrels are strictly nocturnal in contrast to other squirrels.

Night-and-Day Activities

Many species are active at irregular intervals throughout both day and night. Shrews, to maintain an active life, require food at regular, frequent intervals. The animal actively searches for food, then rests for an hour or so. Studies of moles (Godfrey, 1955) showed that individuals were active both day and night in short-term rhythms. An individual would sleep for about three and a half hours, and then become active for about two and a half. Certain rodents, especially the meadow vole (Pearson, 1959) show activity at any hour of the day or night (Figure 10-1). The fisher, a very large weasel, is active at all times of day.

Daytime

In contrast, other species are strictly diurnal. Ground squirrels and most tree squirrels are active only while there is light, and actually are unable to get around in the dark. Many rodents, for example the mountain viscachas of Peru, are active only during the daytime.

Also many of the carnivores—some members of the weasel family, for example—are active only during the day. As is well known, most of the ungulates, such as bison, are active chiefly in the daylight hours, although under certain conditions they may graze at night.

Nighttime

Other forms prefer, or are strictly limited to activity at night. The harvest mouse (*Reithrodontomys megalotis*) (Figure 10-1) shows a clear preference for nocturnal activity (Pearson, 1959). Some of the carnivores, raccoons, for example, may occasionally be active during the day but usually restrict their operations till darkness. A detailed study of the frequency of activity (Sharp and Sharp, 1956) showed that a few raccoons came out around 5:00 P.M., and that the peak of activity occurred about 8:00 P.M. Most of them had completed their actions by 5:00 A.M. A study of the dusky shrew (Ingles, 1960) showed that two major peaks of activity occurred during the night. An experimental reversal of day and night caused a reversal of the pattern. An experimental study of certain mice (Miller, 1955) indicated that the animals were active primarily at night. When the length of darkness was 16 hours the animals were present during the entire period, but when the length was reduced to 12 or 8 hours, the rodents showed a greater burst of activity during the darkness. Observations on the European rabbit in Australia showed that individuals grazed all night long, and in Tasmania neither rain nor shine nor temperature seemed to affect the start of the evening activity. Some animals, such as wolves, may be active during the daytime, but perform certain activities such as traveling long distances, at night.

Seasonal Changes

In many species a seasonal change in activity may occur. In the winter the red squirrel (Layne, 1954) has a short day for its activities, which show practically no difference at any time between morning and evening. In contrast, during the summer when the day is long, these animals have peaks of activity in the morning and evening, and rest during the middle of the day. This change is equally noticeable in woodchucks. Some species have special problems in their activity due to climatic situations. Beavers (*Castor castor*) in the far north of Russia are nocturnal, but live under the ice for about six months

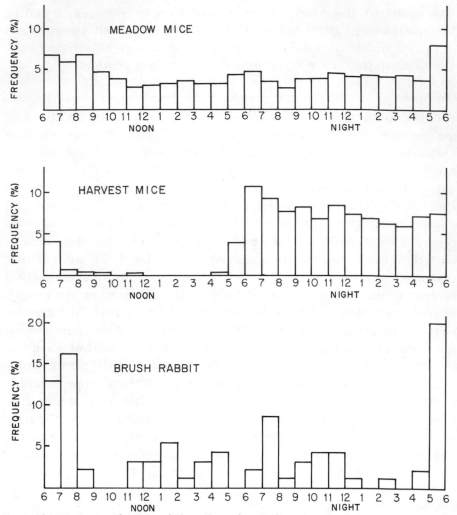

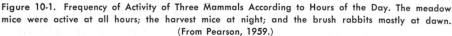

Figure 10-1. Frequency of Activity of Three Mammals According to Hours of the Day. The meadow mice were active at all hours; the harvest mice at night; and the brush rabbits mostly at dawn. (From Pearson, 1959.)

of the year. In the darkness of the long nights, they find no great difficulty in conducting their major activities. Other species in unfavorable desert climates become inactive (estivate) during the summertime. Not all individuals may estivate, but only the adults. Certain opossums in Tasmania (Hickman and Hickman, 1960), have periods of activity throughout the year, alternating with periods of dormancy.

The longest spell of dormancy observed was twelve days. During this time the temperature of the individual dropped considerably.

Weather

Weather conditions may affect activity, although data are scarce or anecdotal. During rain or snow, mammals may seek shelter for a short time. Low temperature may stimulate activity except, of course, in hibernators. Wind often deters activity, at least temporarily; perhaps the cause is partly the uncomfortable effect on fur and partly uneasiness resulting from the noise. Careful quantitative studies are badly needed here.

The effect of weather on the activity of desert mammals has been examined by physiologists interested in problems of heat resistance and water loss. Mammals in deserts avoid high temperatures and low humidities by remaining underground or by restricting their activities to the nighttime. In addition, they may estivate or hibernate during as much as half of the year. Several kinds of small ground squirrels live in the California deserts where the temperature may reach 110 F. Individuals retire frequently during the day to lose heat in their burrows. They start estivation in August and remain underground till March.

FOOD

A major activity, of course, is obtaining food. Some individuals feed rather constantly, whereas others feed in bursts of activity. The European rabbit in Australia, during the nonbreeding season, will spend about 90 per cent of its active period in feeding. On the other hand, during the mating period, it will feed for only 70 per cent of the time (Myers and Poole, 1961). In winter pronghorns spend about 77 per cent of their time in feeding, and in summer, only 63 per cent. Conversely, in winter only 15 per cent of the time is spent lying down, but in the spring, 27 per cent is so spent (Buechner, 1950). Carnivores may at one moment catch an individual prey and thus have a large quantity of food upon which to gorge themselves. Four coyotes are known to have consumed 75 pounds of meat from a doe in one half hour. Presumably, under such circumstances, they could then live for a long period without feeding. The cape fur seal (*Arctocephalus capensis*) in Africa goes to sea for about ten days to feed, and then rests on land for several days. Other species such as ruminants bolt large quantities of vegetation and then retire to a secluded spot to chew their cud. Omnivores may spend a much smaller amount of time feeding. Howling monkeys (Altman, 1959) feed about 25 per cent of the time during the day, sleep or play 52 per cent, and travel 23 per cent. In contrast rabbits, as herbivores, must spend many hours more in feeding than do omnivores.

Water

Water for drinking is also obtained under a wide variety of conditions. Some forms such as the ungulates may travel long distances daily or weekly to obtain a relatively large quantity of water from a stream or pond. Other forms such as rodents and carnivores may drink only occasionally, usually getting enough water from their food. Indeed, some forms never drink water at all, but survive on water produced physiologically. Some mammals lap up their water, whereas others suck in large quantities at one time. Water may be stored either physiologically as in fat, or in the large stomach as in the camel.

Storage

The storage of food occurs in some species. It is well known that some rodents such as squirrels place quantities of nuts in secure spots for eventual use. A more notable type of storage occurs by moles that store live earthworms, and by shrews (Ingram, 1942) that collect live snails in underground storage chambers, utilizing them from time to time. Some mammals store food in quantity internally in the form of fat. Many hibernators, such as woodchucks (*Marmota* sp.) and jumping mice (*Zapus*), accumulate large quantities for use after the animal wakes up at a time of scarcity. For example, a 10-pound woodchuck may add 2 pounds of fat in September and October, utilize a little during sleep, but most of it in February after emerging from hibernation.

From the above it is clear that mammals obtain food and water under a wide variety of circumstances and in an infinite number of ways. The general principle can only be stated in very wide terms, i.e., that activity is adjusted to permit obtaining a supply of food adequate for the animal's needs. The details of activity and food collection are not known in many species, and provide a fertile field for study.

REST AND SLEEP

During the nonactive periods, mammals rest or sleep. Usually these times are spent in some sort of a hole or burrow, but many forms rest in the open. In some species certain members of the herd will lie down for rest, while others continue grazing and thus remain alert to any danger. Many of the ungulates bed down after feeding in a place where they can watch the surrounding area for danger. Thus some individuals can sleep while others are merely resting. The individuals can select a spot where there is a mat of vegetation and may actually clear rocks away before bedding down. Aquatic forms such as manatees (Moore, 1956) may rest and sleep on the surface. The sea otter (*Enhydra lutris*) wraps long weeds of kelp around its body and sleeps on the surface, prevented from drifting by the kelp leaves. Some species that sleep either during the day or during the night in a particular burrow or nest, may return to the same spot time after time. Others, however, such as the gorilla, make a new nest almost every night for sleeping.

HOMES

The homes of mammals are extremely diversified as might be expected. Some forms dig a burrow in the ground and line it with leaves or grass. Others, that dig underground tunnels, simply widen out a spot to form a chamber, or use a side tunnel for their home.

Burrows

Many rodents have extensive burrow systems consisting of many feet of tunnels with a variety of branches. Diagrams of these burrows show great variation, depending upon local types of soil and the presence of rocks or tree roots. The shrew mole (Dalquest and Orcutt, 1942) makes ventilation holes from its burrows to the exterior. The star-nosed mole (*Condylura cristata*) builds up mounds of mud in marshy areas and constructs a nest within. Other kinds of mammals, such as certain carnivores, also make homes underground. A study of the winter dens of skunks (Allen and Shapton, 1942) showed that a den system averaged more than two openings, more than one nest, and more than one blind pocket. The depth was about 40 inches and the total length about 20 feet. Ground squirrels (*Citellus* sp.) of the western states and Siberia make similar burrow systems. European rabbits live in groups and associate around a system of extensive diggings. Indeed their economic damage is due largely to their conspicuous destruction of vegetation around the burrow system. Some aquatic forms such as the muskrat and beaver, construct their own homes, which presumably develop from burrows in the banks of streams or other inland waters, and eventually become independent structures. Many species do not make a burrow system, but merely build a simple structure on the ground. Jackrabbits for example, make a form of shelter in which they rest and sleep.

Nests

Still other kinds of mammals, squirrels for example, construct nests in trees or use an available hole in the trunk. Nesting material is often brought in for lining. Among mammals, raccoons are perhaps the most versatile, since they will live in a hollow tree, in a burrow on a river-bank, or even in a nest out in open, marshy areas. Mammals have appropriated a wide variety of locations for their homes, including the structures built by man. Many species are commensal, living and feeding in man's habitations. While the rats and mice are well known in farm buildings and houses, many other forms in other parts of the world also live close to man. In Europe the dormouse (*Glis* sp.) is common in houses (Thompson, 1953) and in many parts of Asia a shrew (*Suncus* sp.) is a regular inhabitant. These mammals often become pests by causing damage and carrying disease.

WALKING AND TRAVEL

An integral part of behavior is the means of travel. Terrestrial forms walk, run, or trot, while aquatic forms swim—using a variety of motions of the legs and tail; others fly or glide. Some forms habitually run, sometimes at high speeds. The large ungulates generally travel at a slow pace, using a trail to get from one place to another. However, when pressed, they may run at a gallop—attaining a speed of 25 to 35 miles per hour. Wolves can run 35 to 40 miles per hour for at least four miles (Stenlund, 1955). Dolphins (*Delphinus delphis*) can swim at speeds of 16 to 21 mph, and the Blackfish (*Globiocephala* sp.) (a whale) can travel through water at 25 mph. Most species use all four legs in running or walking. However, many species have accentuated the use of hind legs, resulting eventually in the jumping forms such as the rabbit, kangaroo mouse, and of course, kangaroos themselves. Individual species show great variation in the actual gait or sequence of the muscular motions in movement. Some forms have long, slow strides, whereas others take short, quick steps. (See Chapter 4 for more details on this topic.)

SANITATION

Cleanliness and care of the fur are important activities in all mammals. In nature mammals are surprisingly clean, even when living underground. Indeed, the only dirty mammals are those found with man. The fur is groomed by licking or by scratching, thus keeping its condition clean and untangled. Some species, such as many carnivores, devote most of their resting time to cleaning and licking their fur. Others, such as the bison, have regular trees and rocks for rubbing. Small mammals use both claws and teeth for cleaning burrs or other material from their fur. Aquatic forms naturally keep clean through the action of the water.

HOME RANGE

In the course of their activities, mammals move around an area called a "home range." The term "range" is now generally defined as the area utilized by the animal in its normal activities. The word "normal" is sufficiently vague to permit each author to include his pet ideas in the term! Actually, there seems little reason to formulate a rigid term for all species and places, and all seasons, since there is so much variation everywhere. Territory is a special type of home range—one whose boundaries are defended against members of the same species. Some mammals may have a true territory, but may not manifest it in their overt behavior because of low population density, or of nocturnal or fossorial habits.

Measurements of Home Range

Methods of obtaining information about home ranges vary from simple observation to relatively complicated devices, including automatic recording and even calculating. The simple observations, of course, are useful only for species that can be readily observed. Many diurnal mammals, such as squirrels and large ungulates, can easily be followed, and a map of their activities over a period of time will indicate the size of the home range. Unfortunately, relatively little work of this type has been done, apparently because it is tedious and requires many hours of field work. Another method for obtaining information is to recapture large numbers of individuals and measure the distances between captures. The animals may be marked by any appropriate means, such as tags that can be read when the animals are recaptured, or in less specific ways such as trimming the fur in patches or painting it. A minor variation of both methods is to mark the animal and then follow it by simple observation. Luminiscent paint, special bells, radioactive compounds, or broadcasting equipment, for example, may be attached to the animal and its travels followed in this way. Still another method relies on signs left by the animals, such as tracks in the sand or snow, or in a special powder spread for the purpose, which may provide excellent information about the travels of individuals. A recent innovation is to place smoked kymograph paper in strategic places and record the footprints of toe-clipped mice. A further method is to permit the mammals to feed upon food containing dye that will color the feces. Under these circumstances the movement of one or more individuals, depending upon the number so fed, can be determined.

Methods of Calculation of Home Range

No matter how the information about home range is collected, the methods of calculation are relatively similar. Thus, whether the distances between points were obtained by simple observation, by recaptures, or by complicated electronic devices, the estimate of the range is carried out by the same general procedure. The calculations may be divided into two basic categories:

(1) *Area:* A simple process for indicating the home range is to draw on a map a circle that includes all the observations made on the movements of an individual. The area included within the line may then be readily measured. However, a number of complications occur when this procedure is examined in detail. For example, if the locations have been obtained by trapping, one must assume that the animal could have gone at least half way toward an adjacent trap. Thus the area must be enlarged peripherally by half the distance between traps. This technique is particularly necessary where traps

have been set in a regular grid (Dice, 1952). A further modification of this method, not discussed here, has been proposed by MacLulick (1951) but has rarely been tried, presumably because the calculations seem rather complicated.

Still another version of this general procedure is to determine the center of activity (Hayne, 1949). The arithmetic is a little tedious,

EXAMPLE OF HOME RANGE

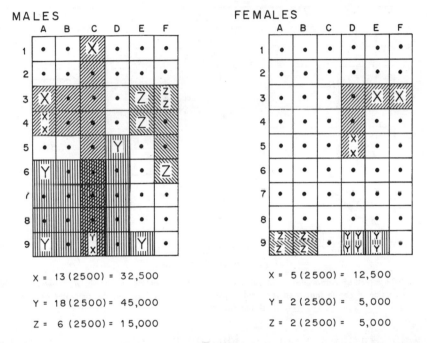

X = 13 (2500) = 32,500

Y = 18 (2500) = 45,000

Z = 6 (2500) = 15,000

X = 5 (2500) = 12,500

Y = 2 (2500) = 5,000

Z = 2 (2500) = 5,000

Figure 10-2. Examples of Home-range Calculations of Individuals Trapped on the Grid System.

but consists simply of arranging the recaptures on a grid and determining their values on the XY axis. Then an average of these locations will give the center of activity (Figure 10-2). For example, the center for male X is a point 1.8 units from the left side and 4.2 from the top; for male Y it is 2.8 units from the left and 7.6 from the top; for male Z it is 5.6 from the left and 3.8 from the top.

A number of advantages exist in this general procedure. Whether the traps are set in the grid or at random, the information is relatively easy to summarize, and the calculations are not very complicated, unless one is using the border-strip method suggested by (Dice, 1952). A map of the area must be made, however, and where many locations are trapped only once or twice, the time involved in map-making becomes excessive. There are some further disadvantages. Many recaptures of the same individual are required before the extent of home range can be obtained: It has been demonstrated for many species that as the number of recaptures increases, the area of known range will gradually increase (Figure 10-3). Indeed, it seems that at

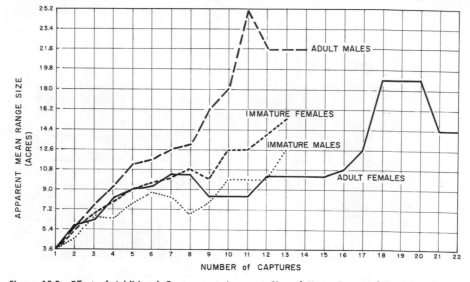

Figure 10-3. Effect of Additional Captures on Apparent Size of Home Range of Snowshoe Hares. The extreme size of range indicated for adult males results primarily from the activities of one male. (From Adams, 1959.)

least 15 recaptures of an individual mouse are necessary before the full extent of its home range is revealed (Stickel, 1954). Another disadvantage is that the method is entirely unsuited for mammals that follow paths or tunnels underground. These individuals rarely leave their normal routes, and thus do not fit into the trapping scheme. A further disadvantage applies to the traps set in a grid. The considerable work involved in laying out the grid is not worthwhile unless it is to be used for many months. In addition, the spacing of the traps is important. It is clear that if they are placed very close together, individuals will be captured more often, will spend a longer time in the traps, and thus will not travel as far or as frequently as they normally would. On the other hand, if the traps are too widely spaced, the mammal will rarely get captured beyond the first trap in its area, and therefore no indication of the extent of the home range will be obtained. Thus the spacing of traps, especially in the grid procedure, requires careful experimental work before definitive measurements can be taken.

(2) *Frequency of Recapture Distances:* A measurement of home range is frequently obtained by simply recording the *distances* between captures. The information can be obtained from traps set in a grid or from traps set randomly. The procedure is merely to record the number of captures as a frequency distribution according to the distance between them. An example is available from the work on woodchucks (Table 10-1). Distances between captures were tallied and

TABLE 10-1. Proportions of Movements (Distances Between Successive Recaptures) Occurring at 500-ft Intervals for 1957-1960

Woodchucks	Number of Movements	0 to 500	501 to 1000	1001 to 1500	1501 to 2000	2001 to 2500	2501 to 3000	Over 3000
Adult Male	176	.66	.26	.03	.02	.02	.00	.01
Adult Female	236	.77	.18	.02	.01	.00	.01	.01
Yearling Male	24	.25	.17	.29	.00	.08	.00	.21
Yearling Female	25	.64	.28	.04	.04	.00	.00	.00
Young Male	76	.51	.28	.04	.01	.01	.04	.11
Young Female	85	.57	.15	.08	.02	.01	.00	.17

then the proportions were calculated for each distance by sex or age categories. The percentages can be readily compared by simple statistical procedures. The distances can be measured in two ways: They can be taken from the place where the animal was first marked or observed, or from each successive location. Whether the distances are measured from the original location or from successive ones makes no difference in the result (Young, Strecker, and Emlen, 1950).

The frequency-of-recapture procedure has some advantages. The traps can be set randomly, thereby avoiding the labor of setting traps in a grid. An additional advantage is that recaptures of all individuals can be used; thus the procedure is suitable for such forms as foxes that can be recaptured a few times. Furthermore, information during short periods of time can be obtained since the data from animals captured only two or three times can be employed. Some disadvantages are apparent. Short movements seem to be favored; it is difficult without considerable effort to arrange the traps sufficiently far apart. Another disadvantage of the frequency-of-recapture method is that no definite boundary of home range is given, merely a description of the frequency of distances observed. The arithmetic is perhaps a little more extensive than for the area method, but the determination of significance of differences is much more satisfactory. For the area method it is necessary to determine a mean size of home range and the standard deviations. Since many observations must be obtained to determine a significance of difference, only very great differences can be detected. In contrast, the frequency-of-recapture uses all of the information and the differences can more readily be determined.

Extent of Home Range

Information about the size of home range has been collected for a wide variety of mammals, utilizing many different techniques. Many of the studies were summarized by Blair (1953) but since that time additional information has been obtained. A persistent problem in home range observations is to separate out the transient individuals. This difficulty is especially frequent in the recapture method. The following examples will indicate some studies that illustrate different aspects or are especially complete. The data on woodchucks (Table 10-1) shows several features: The adult males and adult females both remain within restricted areas, but the females keep within a smaller range. The yearling males seem to disperse great distances, although for short periods of time they remain within the home range. In contrast, the yearling females are sedentary. The young males may remain for short periods of time in a restricted area and then travel. To a considerable extent the season of the year influences the actual measurements that can be obtained. The information on woodchucks was procured simply by recaptures. The home range of gray squirrels (Flyger, 1960) may be interpreted by a comparison calculated from sight records which averaged 132 feet, whereas distances between captures averaged 187 feet. These differences depended on the fact that some squirrels became habitual visitors to certain traps, while others frequented spots where they were particularly likely to be seen, thus giving many low values.

Numerous studies of small rodents give different values for different ecological situations or geographical areas. In general, such animals as the deer mouse have a home range of about half an acre or less. In some very poor habitats in New Mexican deserts the home range was as large as five acres. The microtine rodents often seem to have a small range, most measurements being in the neighborhood of a quarter of an acre even in winter. However, their fossorial habits may bias the results. In one study, muskrats, representative of the larger rodents, appeared to have a wider range: about seventy per cent were recaptured within 160 feet of the previous capture. Extensive studies have been made on the commensal rats following the pioneer work of Petrie and Todd (1923) in Egypt. These authors found that roof rats rarely left the small houses in the cities. Further studies in the United States and England show that the Norway rat generally lives within an area of about 150 feet.

Obviously the habitat situation is very important in determining the variation. A detailed study of house mice (Young, Strecker, and Emlen, 1950) showed that in a very favorable situation 70 per cent of 1330 recaptures were obtained within 5 feet. In contrast, in a different location in Maryland, only 44 per cent of 129 recaptures were obtained within 5 feet. This information illustrates the influence that ecological conditions may have on the size of home range. A study of the home range of the snowshoe rabbit (Adams, 1959) showed several interesting points. The adult males have a home range (25.2 acres) larger than that of the adult females (18.9 acres). The size of the home range increased gradually with the number of recaptures up to about seven (Figure 10-2). However, there was another sudden increase at a later time presumably due to seasonal differences. Also the size of the home range of the immature females increased more rapidly, perhaps due to sampling vagaries. The data were analyzed by the distances between recaptures, and it was found that the value (353 feet) for adult males was significantly greater than that for adult females (229 feet).

Studies of some carnivores, such as bobcats (*Lynx rufus*) and marten (*Martes americana*) show that they have large ranges—measured sometimes in terms of square miles. A study of foxes (Lord, 1961) showed that a family lived for many months in the spring and summer in an area of one square mile (Figure 10-4). Several studies of deer have also been made, using either direct observation or some device such as bells. Depending on the local situation, the home range seems to be restricted to within a few miles. Some studies have been made on primates as well. In Brazil the white-faced monkey (*Cebus* sp.) was trapped, marked, and released (Causey, *et al.*, 1948). Individuals remained in a small area, and similar results have been obtained for howling monkeys, gibbons, and rhesus monkeys in nature.

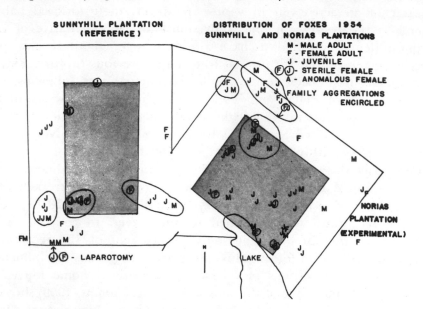

Figure 10-4. Home Range and Social Groups of Gray Foxes. Note that the groups usually contained an adult male and female and several juveniles. (From Lord, 1961.)

From numerous studies of movements, several generalizations can be made. The males usually have a wider range than do females. Adults have larger ranges than the very young, but subadult individuals often disperse widely. Larger mammals, as would be expected, have larger home ranges. Carnivores have wider ranges than do herbivores. Mammals in dense populations have smaller ranges than those in sparse populations.

These studies of movements are very helpful in delimiting the amount of movement that does occur. Apparently, very few species really lack some sort of a home range. However, local conditions exert a great influence, and thus it is difficult to compare results from various places or years.

The function of a home range for a mammal is presumably to provide the necessities of life. Familiarity with the details of the home area permit greater efficiency on obtaining food, water, and other needs and also greater protection. A mammal that knows its surroundings can find food promptly and escape readily. The behavior of a mammal in a strange place contrasts spectacularly with that in a familiar one. The mammal in a strange area appears lost, bumping into objects and making wrong turns. The animal at home is confident: it ranges freely, or hides at once at the first sign of danger.

In studies of movements it is essential that the animal be observed in a place that it knows. Release of animals in a strange place may lead to erroneous conclusions. For example, the notion that rats wander widely has been held for a generation because of a misinterpretation of facts. Long ago an investigator captured a number of rats in various places in New Orleans and released them in two central locations. The rats were recaptured at considerable distances, some as far as four miles away. But the conclusion that "rats travel widely" applies only to rats liberated in strange places.

DISPERSAL

While most mammals remain for the major part of their lives within a small area, some individuals disperse early in their life in search of a new range. In most cases the dispersal is forced by pressure of the surrounding individuals who actively drive out the young. For example, young white-footed mice shortly before they attain sexual maturity may leave their home nests and travel great distances—some as far as half a mile. Similarly, woodchucks in Pennsylvania remain near the home burrow until approximately July 1, when large numbers move into new areas. Naturally, if the individual finds a suitable home near its birth area it will settle there. But in many cases it may have to travel a long distance and survive numerous hazards before finally finding a suitable place. Dispersal serves a number of very important functions in the maintenance of the species. For one thing, it reduces the population in the local area so that the remaining individuals will have more resources. Equally important, dispersal spreads the species into habitats that for one reason or another may be vacant. It may even result in the establishment of a new geographic race. Thus, while the hazards of traveling long distances are great, the benefits accruing to the species may not only be useful, but essential.

A surprising exception occurs in the prairie dog (King, 1955). These rodents live in colonies closely associated and highly integrated in behavior. Curiously, the adults rather than the young, after weaning spread out to colonize order areas. While this behavior might appear "unselfish," it is more likely, perhaps, that the habitat within the colony has deteriorated, or that the adults wish to avoid solicitation by the young.

Migrations

In addition to the dispersal movements of individuals, there may be extensive migrations of large groups. In a few cases the migration is essentially the same as that found among birds. For example, certain bats breed in the New England states during the summertime and migrate in the fall to the West Indies, where they spend the winter before returning again in the spring. The most spectacular migrations are found among bats. In general, bats breed in the summer in particular areas and then migrate to caves for the winter season. This type of migration, of course, is quite different from the conventional type performed by birds. For example, many of the little brown bats (*Myotis lucifugus*) of New England spend the summer producing young on Cape Cod and then migrate to caves in New Hampshire, New York, or Pennsylvania for the winter. A more usual type, perhaps, is found in many tropical bats that migrate north or south out of the tropics for the summertime. The Mexican free-tailed bat (*Tadarida braziliensis*) spends the summer producing young in caves in the southern United States, and then in August migrates down into Mexico where it spends the winter roosting in caves. This species does not hibernate. Other types of bats in tropical areas, such as the large "flying foxes" of Australia, range over tremendous areas in search of food. These migrations are irregular and do not seem to be associated with breeding.

The more usual type of migration is simply a wandering in a general north-south direction according to the season. The bison formerly wandered north through the plains region in the spring and then moved southward in the fall. Other examples may be found in the herbivores of Africa that move in great numbers to and fro in relation to the rainfall and vegetation. A similar type of migration occurs in mountain areas where individuals move in groups up and down the mountainsides. Bighorn sheep (*Ovis canadensis*) in Idaho, for example, may migrate as far as forty miles between winter and summer, and even in the summer may wander considerable distances. The bighorns move slowly in herds, usually of five or more individuals but sometimes in groups up to fifty. Species may differ very greatly in the extent of their migration. In many areas of California the mule deer migrates up and down the mountainsides, but in the dry areas of southern California this same species remains in the chaparral forest throughout the year.

Spectacular migrations are found also among many of the aquatic ocean mammals. For example, whales migrate extensively throughout the oceans. Whale-bone whales (*Balænidae*) live in high latitudes in summer while food is abundant, but move into temperate regions in winter, where food is scarce, to breed. The humpback whale (*Megaptera novængliae*) migrates from polar ice to the equator for the winter. The northern fur seal spends the year in the open Pacific Ocean, but returns to the off-shore islands of Alaska for breeding. Seals from various rookeries mingle during migration but sort themselves out in the spring to return to their own breeding grounds. They remain on land until October or later and then wander all over the Pacific. Some seals have been marked on the Pribilof Islands near Alaska and have been found later in the vicinity of Japan. Apparently adult males do not travel as far as females or young.

SENSES

The behavior of a mammal is naturally oriented to its environment through the senses that indicate the nature of the surroundings. In general the senses of smell, sight, and hearing are the most important, although touch may be vital in certain species.

Vision

Sight is overwhelmingly important in primates, and hence man tends to use this situation as a standard. Most of the better-known primates are diurnal and use sight to determine the characteristics of the environment. However, some of the more primitive primates are nocturnal—but have large eyes as adaptations for vision at night. Many diurnal rodents such as ground squirrels and viscachas use vision to detect danger; indeed it is extremely difficult to approach these mammals undetected. Grazing ungulates such as the prong-horn detect danger at great distances. Most other mammals have relatively weak sight, some being essentially blind or at least only distinguishing light from dark. Most mammals lack color vision and thus live in a world of various shades of gray. An essential part of vision is the detection of movement, and in many cases this feature is far more critical than the actual characteristics seen in the environment. However, in some cases sight may be important for special purposes. According to McHugh (1958) the bison calf locates its mother visually by looking throughout the herd under circumstances that prevent it from using smell. In general, however, bison have very poor sight—especially at a distance.

The location of the eyes varies among mammals. In some, such as rabbits, the eyes are placed on the side of the head and the individual can see backward almost as well as forward, thereby greatly improving its chances of escape. In contrast, the eyes of primates are placed in front thereby permitting binocular vision. Another variation is their location on top of the head as in the hippopotamus and prong-horn antelope.

Smell

The sense of smell is highly developed among mammals and perhaps provides the most information about the environment. For example, carnivores and herbivores regularly detect prey or danger through the sense of smell. The need for a hunter to stay on the lee side of game is common knowledge. Small mammals detect insects in logs or under the ground in part by smell. Apparently mice and shrews can determine the presence of a live insect in a cocoon by smell (Holling, 1958). Smell largely governs reproductive behavior of mammals. A variety of odor-producing glands occurs in mammals: preputial in deer and beaver; anal in mustelids; perineal in rabbits, squirrels, and guinea pigs; sebaceous in hamsters, shrews, and male goats; suborbital in deer; and interdigital in sheep. The functions of these and other glands are not completely known, but their influence on reproductive behavior or home-range activities has, in most cases, been well established. In some instances certain glands function as protective devices.

Hearing

Hearing is highly acute in many species as indicated by the large size and flexibility of ears. For example, deer can turn their external ears in a semicircle when attempting to get the maximum sound. The ultimate in the use of the ears is found in bats, which have a highly developed system of echolocation (Moehres, 1960). The individual produces sounds that bounce back from the surroundings, thereby indicating the bat's position or the location of prey. Many bats have extremely large and complicated external ears.

The actual wavelengths heard by different mammals vary greatly. Some species have a relatively narrow range and others (especially bats) have a very wide range. Echolocation has recently been recognized in the porpoise (Norris *et al.*, 1961). Certain whales also may have echolocation. Although lacking vocal chords (Jonsgard, 1959), they are still able to produce sounds.

Taste

Taste is important for mammals in the choice of food. Many forms however, have a very weak sense of taste, and often simply bolt their food. Actually relatively little is known about the gustation ability of different mammals.

Touch

The last sense, touch, is used for detection of nearby objects and has been developed principally in connection with burrowing or tunneling. Many species have developed long whiskers which project from the sides of the face to approximately the width of the animal's body and touch the sides of the burrow or trail when it is narrow. Thus the animal knows when it is getting too close to a wall or into too narrow a passage. In some forms tactile hairs have developed on the tail that assist the animal when it moves backward. The use of touch as developed among humans to determine specific characteristics of the surroundings is relatively rare among the lower mammalian forms. Most species do not use their front paws to detect heat or cold or danger.

REPRODUCTIVE BEHAVIOR

The sexual and courtship activities of mammals are less spectacular than those of birds or even of some reptiles and fish. However, it is certain that further study of mammals will show that courtship activities occur extensively throughout the group. Perhaps the fact that vision is relatively unimportant among most mammals dictates that the sense of smell should be most widely used. Up to the present, however, studies concerned with the details of reproductive behavior patterns have been so grossly neglected and so little studied, that a systematic account is difficult to provide. Only rarely is information available about more than one or two species in a group, and thus comparisons are not easy. Trends within orders or classes are not yet discernible except for the obvious point that closely related species behave similarly. Comparative studies of sexual behavior may not only enlarge our understanding of behavior in general but also clarify other features of mammalian life.

Courtship

Recently research on some forms such as the European rabbit (Southern, 1948) show that intricate behavior may occur. For example, the courtship in rabbits consists of flagging the tail, and later a complicated jumping display with emission of urine while the rabbit is in the air. These detailed patterns differ greatly from the aggressive behavior shown against other males at this time. Copulation itself in rabbits may be prolonged, lasting as much as two hours. In some species of rodents, copulation may consist of numerous intromissions during a period of an hour or more. Among the bighorn sheep and other bovids, the males behave in a specific way when approaching a ewe that is in estrous. They approach with a particular gait and sniff the genitals of the female. A bizarre behavior occurs among giraffes (Innis, 1958). The male tests the urine of the female by taking quantities in its mouth and eventually spitting it out. Apparently by this test the male determines when the female is in heat. Several males may test one female and eventually chase her. The male will attempt to drive other males away from the female that is in heat.

Behavior of the Male

The importance of the male's behavior is shown by the fact that in several species thus far studied the females will come into heat shortly after males are placed with them. In goats (Shelton, 1960) the female ovulates about ten days after it is placed with a male. In mice (*Mus musculus*) the females come into estrous about three days after they are placed with the males. Various tests among mice have shown that the olfactory sense is important for these physiological reactions. If the olfactory nerves of a female are cut, there is no response when placed with a male.

Duration of Sexual Behavior

The existence of a specific period in the female (estrus) for copulation is responsible for the brief duration of courtship and reproductive activities. In other vertebrates (birds for example) there is a long period of behavior in which the animals respond visually. Mammals, however, must find the female in the appropriate stage of the reproductive cycle and generally copulate after a very brief period. Apparently, with some exceptions, there is little maintenance of a pair bond between the members of the sexes. Nevertheless, in spite of the relatively small amount of sexual behavior, many features need much greater analysis. The fact that so many mammals are nocturnal and live underground has greatly hindered this study.

Raising the Young

A further feature in the sexual behavior of mammals is that the female generally performs the major share of work in raising the young. Rarely does the male take part in these activities. For example, in most rodents the male is present only for the very brief time of courtship and copulation, and then leaves the female to raise the young alone in the nest. Among European rabbits the female drives the male away at the time the young are born and raises them herself.

SOCIAL BEHAVIOR

The social behavior of mammals has been observed more frequently than has the sexual, perhaps because social behavior occurs at all times of the year and thus is more readily studied. While it is true that sexual behavior is "social" in the sense that it involves several mammals, nevertheless social behavior usually implies relations among groups of individuals irrespective of sex. Thus such features as dominance orders, herds, and communication are considered part of social behavior.

Rank

A social order exists in nearly all species that live together in groups. Generally, the position of individuals is determined by fighting behavior that is performed in stereotypic patterns. For example, as is well known, rodents fight aggressively until one individual admits defeat and hence avoids the other. Deer mice arrange themselves in a straight-line order of dominance. In this manner the social organization is developed so that each individual knows its particular place. This type of dominance occurs very widely among mammals. The European rabbit has been studied extensively, and it has been found that both males and females arrange themselves in a rank order. Fighting among them may be very bitter, and occasionally one individual will kill another by tearing out its entrails with a kick in the abdomen. Several deer have been observed (Cowan and Geist, 1961) to have a distinct series of elements in their aggressive behavior. When two individuals confront each other, first they crouch, then they approach, lick each other's noses, and flick their tails. Next, the two animals circle each other much in the manner of dogs and begin to snort. The final stage is a rush at each other that continues until one individual admits defeat. Giraffes (Innis, 1958) may fight very aggressively by trading blows with their heads. The individuals swing the head sidewise with such force that occasionally the opponent is knocked out for as long as 20 minutes. Bighorn sheep go through a series of preliminary patterns of licking before rushing headlong at each other. The blows delivered by a ram against another ram may be heard for long distances. However, the victor does not evict the vanquished. Shrews (Crowcroft, 1955) have elaborate patterns of aggressive behavior including squeaks and screams and, in certain situations, tail vibrations. Actual fighting consists of biting the opponent's tail or of boxing matches. A South American rodent, the viscacha, rarely fights an invader, but bluffs, squeaks, chases, and finally squirts urine at the aggressor.

Territory

While most species of mammals merely organize themselves into social rank, other species may develop territorial behavior. Often it is difficult to distinguish between the two, although the mammals themselves rarely seem to be confused. For example, numerous rodents such as squirrels have been said to be territorial, but careful analysis shows that the organization consists of social rank. Nevertheless, some species are clearly territorial in the sense of defending a particular area. One spectacular form is the northern fur seal, in which the male comes out on land, defends a chosen breeding area against other bulls, and collects a harem there. The female is not territorial in any way. Another example of territorial behavior is found in the llama, a species of camel living in South America. Individual males defend a particular area against interlopers for long periods of time. The most spectacular territorial behavior, however, occurs among the primates. This pattern has been studied best among howling monkeys, but also has been observed in red spider monkeys (*Ateles geoffroyi*), gibbons, and several other species. The individuals join together in bands within which there is a rather strict social and territorial organization. In addition, the band itself defends its territory against other bands of the same species. The territorial defense is first performed by an intricate series of displays, including threats and vocalization; then, if necessary, actual fierce fighting occurs. In principle, the defense of territory by mammals follows closely the procedures found in birds, some reptiles, and some fish.

Groups and Herds

During a great part of their lives many mammals associate in groups. Within the group there may be a social organization developed through fighting; however, since each individual learns its place, there is at any one moment little or no fighting in the herd. Herds or groups of mammals may be extremely large and hence conspicuous. Herds of ungulates, such as bison or South African antelope, have been known to number in the millions. These animals probably have smaller groups within the large mass, but nevertheless show relatively little social organization. Other species, such as the bighorn sheep, go in small groups that may be led by a ewe. Certain primates, in contrast, are usually led by a dominant male. Booth (1957) reports that the colobus monkeys in African forests live in small groups. In some cases, such as those of the giraffe and llama, the herd composition may change seasonally. At times of breeding the dominant males no longer associate with other males, but join groups of females. Generally speaking, in such species the young males that are not yet sexually dominant continue to associate together in groups. At maturity these individuals break away from the group and join a female herd.

Colonies

Many species, especially rodents, live in colonies containing numerous individuals. Strictly speaking the colony is not a herd, since the term herd is usually restricted to groups that wander about. In contrast, a colony is a group that remains in a particular area. The individuals in the aggregation may develop a rather definite social organization including even subgroups within the colony. The prairie dog (King, 1955) may live in groups of several hundred individuals, divided into smaller groups each of which has its own social organization. In some cases the group will defend its territory against other groups. Some species of rodents, such as the white-footed mouse and the Norway rat, may form temporary aggregations in the wintertime, presumably for the maintenance of heat by living close together in the same burrow system. Manatees (Moore, 1956) aggregate when the temperature drops below 50 degrees. Just how these aquatic mammals can benefit from an aggregation under these circumstances is a puzzle. Generally, the major benefit derived from the herd is protection against predators through a mutual warning system. However, some groups of carnivores such as wolves have developed cooperative hunting (Stenlund, 1955). A pack of timber wolves may surround an island to drive the deer out onto the ice, where a part of the group may attack them. Baldwin and Schwartz (1952) report that two mongooses worked together on the beach to catch crabs. Cooperative activities are generally rare among mammals, however.

Social Feeding

The feeding activities of mammals are often social, presumably because the food is located in restricted areas. It is common in tropical regions to find numerous mammals assembling at particular trees, such as the fig, to feed. Monkeys, rodents, opossums, coatis, and many others will be found feeding together throughout the day.

It is a logical outcome that members of the same species will associate in an area where the food supply is abundant. Under such circumstances the social organization may be readily apparent. For example, Sharp, *et al.* (1956) found that raccoons congregated at a garbage dump showed a clearly defined social organization. Cattle, at least under domesticated conditions, show a very subtle type of rank while feeding. The dominant individual will travel in a straight line while grazing, whereas the subordinate individuals will tend to shift away from the path of the dominant cow. A similar situation occurs among sheep and many wild herbivores.

Leadership

Determining the leadership of a herd or aggregation presents many problems. It is often difficult to discover which one of them is the leader, since the animal in front is not necessarily the one that determines the course of events. In some groups of ungulates it seems that a female will lead the herd and organize its activities. In bison (Mc-Hugh, 1958) a particular individual was observed to lead the group about two thirds of the time. Studies of leadership among mammals are greatly needed to replace the numerous and current, but less reliable anecdotal material about mammalian behavior.

COMMUNICATION

An integral part of social behavior is the means of communication. Without ability to convey information from one individual to another, social behavior could not exist. Among mammals sounds are perhaps the most important means. Warning signals are frequently found among species—even those that associate only loosely. Many rodents such as ground squirrels have distinct warning calls, often one special type for a predator on the ground, and another for a danger from overhead. Many species of ungulates have various snorts or bellows, and the South American vicuña (Koford, 1957) has a number of vocalizations to warn of danger.

Vocalizations are also used in territorial fights as threats that may be sufficient to warn away an interloper. It is apparent that sound has the ability to transmit information across areas where vision is impossible. Thus a colony of ground squirrels, through the use of sound, can warn members that are hidden in burrows; and a group of primates in a jungle forest may warn individuals that are unable to see the source of danger. The behavior of gray squirrels (*Sciurus carolinensis*) has been intensively analyzed (Bakken, 1959) and is given in Table 10-2. It is clear that a variety of calls and movements serve to communicate information from one squirrel to another.

In addition to sound, vision plays a very important role in communication. Perhaps the most common element is the visible sign employed to indicate the location of other individuals. The white tail of the deer serves first as a warning but secondly as a direction finder, showing where other members of a herd have gone. Similarly, various tail-flagging movements and other visually perceptible devices call attention to the behavior of other individuals. Sound and vision naturally give contemporaneous information. These methods of communication indicate the presence of some particular situation, and are of an instantaneous nature. On the other hand, mammals have also developed communication

TABLE 10-2.   Calls, Signals, and Postures of Gray Squirrels *

Calls, Associated with	Sex	Age	Description	Associated with
Mating Chases:				
Buzzing	male	yearling and adult	stridulating insect or partly stifled sneeze	hunting for or chasing the female during mating chase
Warning or Alarm:				
Intense alarm chuck	both	all	rapid kuk, kuk, kuk	imminent danger
General alarm chuck	both	all	drawn out ku-u-uk ca, one per two seconds	danger
Warning chuck	both	all	slower, short kuk, kuk, kuk, kuk; or kuk, kuk, kuk, qua-a-a-a	immediate past danger; usually follows general alarm call
Attention chuck	female	adult	low chucking, barely audible at 30 ft	given to young as warning (?) call
Juvenile scream	both	juvenile	soprano scream; mouth at maximum gape	handling in cone or removal from nest; probably signifies fear
Female scream	female	yearling and adult	lower harsh scream, like combined scream and snarl	at males around her while cornered in mating chase (warning?)
Groups:				
Mew	both	adult and (?)	resembles meow of a cat	(?)
Rapid chucking	both	all (?)	kuk, kuks rolled together	sometimes given before entering nest
Whistling	(?)	(?)	resembles ground squirrel whistling	sometimes given by occupants after nest is entered
Purr	both	young	low purring like a cat	play

TABLE 10-2. Calls, Signals, and Postures of Gray Squirrels * (Continued)

Description of Signals	Sex	Age	Given to	Associated Situation	Associated Behavior
Tail Signals, associated with intimidation or warning:					
Rapid, stiff fore-and-aft jerks	both	all	all sex, age and species groups	feeding encounters and mating chases; directed toward other squirrels	may be followed by short ground chase
Rapid, flexible fore-and-aft waving	both	all	surrounding area	disturbance; not directed toward other squirrels	warning call may or may not be given (warning?)
Mating Chase or Intersex Signals:					
Short, rapid fore-and-aft flips	male	yearling and adult	yearling or adult female	given by male when first seeing female, during the breeding season	male moves to feeding female
Slow waving, 1 to 4 in a series	male	yearling and adult	yearling or adult female	follows preceding signal and movement	male follows female in slow ground chase
Slow fore-and-aft waves through wide arc	male	yearling and adult	yearling or adult female	female cornered during mating chase	lead male faces female
Circular waving	male	yearling and adult	yearling or adult female	same as above	same as above

Postures	Sex	Age	Given to	Associated Situation	Associated Behavior
Tail pressed over back and at one side of head	both	juvenile	strange objects	variable	may jump away several times during approach
Tail pressed over back	both	yearling and adult		danger or disturbance gone	posture while on limb giving warning call
Foot stamping	both	all		variable	variable

* From Bakken, 1959.

methods that can persist for a long period of time by the use of glandular materials. These odoriferous substances may be deposited on particular sites and remain there for weeks. Many of the larger carnivores leave scent as well as markings to indicate their hunting region. Glands may also be used, especially in sexual behavior, to indicate the condition of an individual at the moment. The males in many species determine through smell the breeding condition of the female. Furthermore, individuals presumably determine whether another individual is a stranger or not by the sense of smell. Unfortunately, our knowledge of these types of behavior is largely anecdotal, and should be more extensively studied.

Subterranean mammals have special problems in communication. Naturally vision atrophies under these conditions to the point that many species, such as moles, can do little more than distinguish day from night. Some rodents, the South American *Ctenomys* for instance, have poor vision, but can distinguish objects at 50 feet. However, warning calls are given underground by these animals, so that as one walks over the pampas in Argentina one may hear a muffled "tuco-tuco" that gives rise to their local name. In addition, scent is presumably highly developed for short-distance communication.

CARE OF YOUNG

The care of the young by mammals needs to be considered directly under the topic of social behavior as well as under that of communication, since such a large part of development depends on adequate transferral of behavior from one generation to the next. Many mammals live in burrows or nests, thus keeping the young in close association for at least a couple of weeks. Other species, especially ungulates, may have only one young apiece, but bring their young together promptly as members of the herd. Under these circumstances the young soon learn the social behavior of other individuals both young and adult. The time of parental care may vary from extremely short to extremely long. In some rodents the young are forced to shift for themselves after a matter of weeks in the nest, and are literally driven away. In contrast, the young sea otter (Kenyon, 1959) associates with its parents for a year. The female diligently cares for the young, helping it feed and letting it rest on her chest while she swims along on her back.

The period of suckling in mammals provides extensive opportunity of the young to become adjusted in behavior with each other and with their parents. The suckling may be relatively frequent, as occurs in many rodents and in some carnivores, or may be relatively infrequent. The Alaska fur seal (Bartholomew, 1959) feeds her pup only once a week. The pups are very precocious and gregarious, getting together in groups of several hundred and wandering about extensively. Generally the female knows her own pup and the pup knows its mother; thus the pup always suckles its own mother, even at the end of a week.

Play is an integral part of socialization, and consists of "make believe" fighting and sexual behavior that serves to develop the coordination and postures necessary in adult life. Play is widespread among mammals, occurring in carnivores of many types, manatees, numerous ungulates, and even many rodents.

Family Life

Family grouping occurs in some mammals. Gray foxes are monogamous for life, and the pups stay with the parents through the summer (Figure 10-4) but disperse in the fall. Beaver may permit even yearlings to remain in the lodge. Many primates allow the young to remain with the clan for several years before sexual maturity. Even then, only the males that contest for dominance may be chased away. A variation of family grouping is the merger of several families. Female wolves may use the same den and raise two litters of pups simultaneously.

PROTECTION

The reaction of mammals to danger is extremely varied. In addition to the avoidance of danger whenever possible, two general kinds of behavior are indicated: First, the danger must be detected; and second, some action must follow. Many species rely on secrecy or deception—at least at first. The cottontail crouches in its form till the danger is very close, and then bursts out, usually startling the predator. In contrast, jackrabbits (Lechleitner, 1958) usually sneak or run away at once. The difference in behavior presumably represents a difference in the amount of cover in the habitat. Many large forms such as the pronghorn depend upon the principles of disruptive coloration (the striking neck marks) and countershadings (dark upperparts, light underparts) to avoid predators.

Detection of Danger

The senses of sight and smell are major devices to determine the presence of danger. Usually species that live in open habitats depend primarily on sight. Ground squirrels and woodchucks watch for enemies or intruders of their own species by sitting upright or raising the head. Bison and muskoxen (*Ovibos moschatus*) survey the surroundings systematically. In contrast, species living in forested areas or underground regularly use smell. Deer and many rodents have highly developed olfactory senses. In addition such species may use hearing to detect danger.

Escape

When danger becomes imminent the mammal attempts to flee. Rabbits, as mentioned above, burst out of their resting places relying on surprise and speed to escape. Other mammals, such as rodents, dash into a hole or protective bush. Squirrels may hide on the opposite side of a tree. Large mammals generally flee while the danger is still far away.

Weapons

Many misconceptions occur about the function of various weapons. Devices may be divided into several categories. Some, such as the claws and fangs of cats, are primarily to capture prey and only incidentally used for protection. Others, such as the antlers of deer, are primarily employed for settling problems of social rank and only incidentally for defense. These species usually have a separate means (blows by hooves in deer) for protection against predators. Lastly, only a few weapons are specifically designed to repel predators. The spines of porcupines and other rodents, and the anal glands of skunks are examples. When a mammal is captured it defends itself as best it can with available weapons, such as teeth, claws, or feet.

Death-Feigning

A physiological trick is practiced by the opossum (*Didelphis* sp.) under certain circumstances. When approached, the animal throws some physiological "switches" that permit it to appear dead. It lies on its side, the mouth opens, the eyes become glassy, respiration ceases, and the animal becomes limp. The predator is supposedly deceived and goes elsewhere. The mechanism for this behavior is essentially unknown, and should be a rewarding area of research.

In summarizing the reaction of animals to danger, it is noteworthy that several stages occur: First, the mammal avoids dangerous areas; second, it detects danger and flees; and third, as a last resort it fights.

* * *   * * *   * * *

A summarization of the social behavior of mammals indicates that they follow the general principles found among all the vertebrates. The opportunities for social behavior are highly dependent on the methods of communication, which in mammals are primarily by means of smell and sight—followed to some small degree by hearing and touch. For reasons that are not altogether clear, the social behavior of mammals is rather poorly known. Perhaps their nocturnal and burrowing habits have greatly restricted the opportunities for study. Equally important, perhaps, is the retarding effect of anecdotes and anthropomorphic interpretations of behavior. Numerous opportunities exist for objective study of mammals that will determine the causes and consequences of specific activities.

LEARNING

The role of learning in the life of wild mammals must be extensive but, surprisingly, little is known about it. While the topic of learning in general has received intensive attention from psychologists, and a mass of experimental and theoretical work is available (see any elementary psychology text), mammals have been tested only in captivity to confirm or deny an hypothesis suggested by human problems. Most of the work has been done on a mammalian abstraction, the white rat, which has little resemblance to a wild mammal. Thus it is relevant here only to summarize some of the main aspects of learning and comment on their pertinence to wild species.

Learning is usually considered to be a process whereby an animal associates particular responses with particular stimuli. The response involves the entire animal, although only certain parts may visibly react. The stimulus includes both internal and external aspects. Thus, by means of learning, mammals improve their efficiency of living; they reduce the number of responses that may be fatal and the number of trial-and-error episodes in the habitat. A mammal that has learned many responses is efficient.

Many types of behavior are not learned but are inborn or innate, for example, various reflexes and responses to external stimuli. However, it is likely, following the lead of ethological research in birds, that many behavioral sequences are an alternating chain of innate and learned responses. Another aspect that must be noted is that maturation through physiological or anatomical growth may permit a behavior pattern to begin, thereby mimicking learning.

The conditioned response is probably a major process of learning in wild mammals. Presumably both respondent (classical) and operant conditioning occur. Studies of these processes in wild species are rare, but observations indicate that mammals readily learn to associate one experience with another in nature. Young and adult mammals surely learn that particular marks (the stripes of a skunk, for example) are associated with an unpleasant experience. Also mammals must learn that opening a nut will be rewarded by a tasty morsel.

The basic principles governing all learning apparently apply here. Practice is important and normally would be distributed over a period of time. Motivation, perhaps, is even more vital in wild mammals than in captive ones. Reinforcement occurs daily in the lives of mammals: finding food, discovering a cool spot to rest, sexual activities. Indeed, in contrast to the protected life of humans, reinforcement of learning must occur universally among mammals. Extinction of learning, and forgetting, would naturally occur in wild mammals.

This summary of the presumptive role of learning in mammals calls attention to the lack of information about the learning process in the wild. However, there is no doubt that mammals can learn, and do acquire extensive knowledge.

REFERENCES

Adams, Lowell. 1959. An analysis of a population of snowshoe hares in northwestern Montana. Ecol. Monog. 29: 141-170.

Allen, Durward L., and Warren W. Shapton. 1942. An ecological study of winter dens, with special reference to eastern skunks. Ecol. 23(1): 59-68.

Altman, Stuart A. 1959. Field observation on a howling monkey society. J. Mamm. 40(3): 317-330.

Bakken, Arnold. 1959. Behavior of gray squirrels. Symp. on the Gray Squirrel (V. Flyger, Ed.), Cont. 162. Maryland Dept. Res. Ed.: 393-407.

Baldwin, Paul H., C. W. Schwartz, and E. R. Schwartz. 1952. Life history and economic status of the mongoose in Hawaii. J. Mamm. 33(3): 335-356.

Bartholomew, George A. 1959. Mother-young relations and the maturation of pup behaviour in the Alaska Fur Seal. Animal Behaviour 7(3-4): 163-171.

Blair, W. Frank. 1953. Population dynamics of rodents and other small mammals. Advances in Genetics 5: 2-41.

Booth, A. H. 1957. Observations on the natural history of the olive colobus monkey, *Procolobus verus* (van Benedin). Proc. Zool. Soc. London 129(3): 421-430.

Buechner, Helmut K. 1950. Life history, ecology, and range use of the pronghorn antelope in trans-Pecos, Texas. Am. Mid. Nat. 43(2): 257-354.

Causey, O. R., H. W. Laemmert, Jr., and G. S. Hayes. 1948. The home range of Brazilian cebus monkeys in a region of small residual forests. Amer. J. Hyg. 47(3): 304-314.

Cowan, I. McT., and Valerius Geist. 1961. Aggressive behavior in deer on the genus *Odocoileus*. J. Mamm. 42(4): 522-526.

Crowcroft, Peter. 1955. Notes on the behaviour of shrews. Behaviour 8(1): 62-80.

Dalquest, Walter W., and Donald R. Orcutt. 1942. The biology of the least shrew-mole, *Neurotrichus gibbsii minor*. Am. Mid. Nat. 27: 387-401.

Dice, L. R. 1952. Natural communities. Univ. Michigan Press: 547 pp.

Flyger, V. F. 1960. Movements and home range of the gray squirrel, *Sciurus carolinensis*, in two Maryland woodlots. Ecol. 41(2): 365-369.

Godfrey, Gillian K. 1955. A field study of the activity of the mole (*Talpa europaea*). Ecol. 36(4): 678-685.

Hayne, Don W. 1949. Calculation of size of home range. J. Mamm. 30(1): 1-18.

Hickman, V. V., and J. L. Hickman. 1960. Notes on the habits of the Tasmanian dormouse phalangers *Cercaertus nanus* (Dasmarest) and *Eudromicia lepida* (Thomas). Proc. Zool. Soc. London 135(3): 365-374.

Holling, C. S. 1958. Sensory stimuli involved in the location and selection of sawfly cocoons by small mammals. Can. J. Zool. 36: 633-653.

Ingles, Lloyd G. 1960. A quantitative study on the activity of the dusky shrew (*Sorex vagrans obscurus*). Ecol. 41(4): 656-660.

Ingram, W. M. 1942. Snail associates of *Blarina brevicauda talpoides* (Say). J. Mamm. 23(3): 255-258.

Innis, Anne C. 1958. The behaviour of the giraffe, *Giraffa camelopardalis*, in the eastern Transvaal. Proc. Zool. Soc. London 131(2): 245-278.

Jonsgard, Age. 1959. Recent investigations concerning sound production in Cetaceans. Norsk Hvalfangst-Tidende 10: 501-509.

Kenyon, Karl W. 1959. The sea otter. Smithsonian Rep. for 1958: 309-407.

King, John A. 1955. Social behavior, social organization, and population dynamics in a black-tailed prairie dog town in the Black Hills of South Dakota. Cont. Lab. Vert. Biol. 67: 1-123.

Koford, Carl B. 1957. The vicuña and the puna. Ecol. Monog. 27: 153-219.

Layne, James N. 1954. The biology of the red squirrel, *Tamiasciurus hudsonicus loquax* (Bangs), in central New York. Ecol. Monog. 24: 227-267.

Lechleitner, R. R. 1958. Certain aspects of behavior of the black-tailed jack rabbit. Am. Mid. Nat. 60(1): 145-155.

Lord, Rexford D. 1961. A population study of the gray fox. Am. Mid. Nat. 66(1): 87-109.

MacLulich, D. A. 1951. New technique of animal census with examples. J. Mamm. 32: 318-328.

McHugh, Tom. 1958. Social behavior of the American buffalo (*Bison bison bison*). Zoologica 43(1): 1-40.

Miller, Richard S. 1955. Activity rhythms in the wood mouse, *Apodemus sylvaticus* and the bank vole, *Clethrionomys glareolus*. Proc. Zool. Soc. London 25(3-4): 505-519.

Moehres, F. P. 1960. Sonic orientation of bats and other animals. Symp. Zool. Soc. London 3: 57-66.

Moore, Joseph Curtis. 1956. Observations of manatees in aggregations. Am. Mus. Novitates. 1811: 1-24.

Myers, K., and W. E. Poole. 1961. A study of the biology of the wild rabbit, *Oryctolagus cuniculus* (L.), in confined populations, *C.S.I.R.O.* Wildl. Res. 6(1): 1-41.

Norris, Kenneth S., John Prescott, Paul V. Asa-Dorian and Paul Perkins. 1961. An experimental demonstration of echo-location behavior in the porpoise, *Tursiops truncatus* (Montagu). Biol. Bull. 120(2): 163-176.

Pearson, Oliver P. 1959. A traffic survey of *Microtus-Reithrodontomys* runways. J. Mamm. 40(2): 169-180.

Petrie, G. F., and R. E. Todd. 1923. A report on plague investigations in Egypt. Ministry of Interior (Egypt) 5: 1-114.

Scott, John Paul. 1957. Animal behavior. Univ. Chic. Press: xi + 281 pp.

Sharp, Ward M., and Louise H. Sharp. 1956. Nocturnal movements and behavior of wild raccoons at a winter feeding station. J. Mamm. 37(2): 170-177.

Shelton, Maurice. 1960. Influence of the presence of a male goat on the initiation of estrous cycling and ovulation in angora does. J. Anim. Sci. 19(2): 368-375.

Southern, H. N. 1948. Sexual and aggressive behaviour in the wild rabbit. Behaviour 1(3-4): 173-194.

Stenlund, Milton H. 1955. A field study of the timber wolf (*Canis lupus*) on the Superior National Forest, Minnesota. Minn. Dept. Cons. Tech. Bull. 4: 1-55.

Stickel, Lucille F. 1954. A comparison of certain methods of measuring ranges of small mammals. J. Mamm. 35(1): 1-15.

Thompson, Harry V. 1953. The edible dormouse (*Glis glis* L.) in England, 1902-1951. Proc. Zool. Soc. London 122(4): 1017-1024.

Young, Howard, R. L. Strecker, and J. T. Emlen, Jr. 1950. Localization of activity in two indoor populations of house mice, *Mus musculus*. J. Mamm. 31(4): 403-410.

APPENDIX A

Systematic Arrangement for Mammals Cited in Text

Biologists, other than mammologists, may wish to know merely the group to which a mammal belongs and the relation of this group to others rather than the taxonomic details of classification. The following list of orders, suborders, and families is intended to satisfy this need. Most mammals mentioned in the text are included in the list, with the exception of species mentioned only in Chapter 2. The families and higher groups are taken from Simpson (1945). Not all families are included, and the arrangement is simplified to facilitate use. The vernacular names are placed within the appropriate groups and arranged systematically. The technical name is not given, since it can be found from the books listed in Chapter 2 or from the specific reference. Consider an example: In Chapter 7 (p. 177) the important point to illustrate is the effect of irrigation on breeding, not the life history of gophers. However, the reader may want to know what kind of a mammal a gopher is. From the list below he can see that it belongs in a big group of rodents that resemble squirrels. The fact that they are called *Talpoides bottae* is unimportant for this illustration. A person really interested in the technical name and identification can find it in the reference (Miller, 1946) mentioned in Chapter 7.

Unfortunately not all groups have accepted, or acceptable, English names. Therefore the technical name has been anglicized to "ids" for a family and "oids" for a superfamily.

MAMMALS CITED

Order MONOTREMATA—Monotremes
      Family Tachyglossidae—Echidnas
      Family Ornithorhynchidae—Duckbills

Order MARSUPIALIA—Marsupials
    Superfamily Didelphoidea—Opossum
    Superfamily Dasyuroidea—Dasyures
    Superfamily Perameloidea—Perameloids
    Superfamily Caenolestoidea—Caenolestoids
    Superfamily Phalangeroidea—Phalangers

Order INSECTIVORA—Insectivores
    Family Chrysochloridae—Golden Moles
    Family Tenrecidae—Tenrec
    Family Potamogalidae—Ottershrew
    Family Erinaceidae—Hedgehog
    Family Macroscelididae—Elephant Shrew
    Family Soricidae—Shrew (various species), Shrew Mole
    Family Talpidae—Moles, Star-nosed Mole

Order DERMOPTERA—Flying Lemurs

Order CHIROPTERA—Bats
  Suborder MEGACHIROPTERA—Flying Fox
  Suborder MICROCHIROPTERA—Little Brown Bat, Free-tailed Bat, Big
      Brown Bat, Red Bat, Hoary Bat

Order PRIMATES
  Suborder PROSIMII
   Infraorder LEMURIFORMES
    Family Tupaiidae—Tree-Shrews
    Family Lemuridae—Lemurs
    Family Indridae—Indrids
    Family Daubentoniidae—Aye-Aye
   Infraorder LORISIFORMES
    Family Lorisidae—Lorisids
   Infraorder TARSIIFORMES
    Family Tarsiidae—Tarsids
  Suborder ANTHROPOIDEA
    Family Cebidae—Howling Monkeys, Spider Monkeys
    Family Callithricidae—Marmosets
    Family Ceropithecidae—Colobus Monkey, Mandrill, Rhesus
      Macaque
    Family Pongidae—Gibbon, Gorilla
    Family Hominidae—Man

Order EDENTATA—Edentates
      Family Myrmecophagidae—Anteaters
      Family Bradypodidae—Sloths
      Family Dasypodidae—Armadillo

Order PHOLIDOTA—Pangolin

Order LAGOMORPHA—Rabbits and Hares
      Family Ochotonidae—Pikas
      Family Leporidae—Jack Rabbits, Cottontails, European Rabbit, Snowshoe Hare, European Hare, Swamp Rabbit

Order RODENTIA—Rodents
  Suborder SCIUROMORPHA—Sciuromorphs
      Superfamily Aplodontoidea—Mountain Beaver
      Superfamily Sciuroidea—Flying Squirrels, Red Squirrel, Gray Squirrel, Prairie Dog, Ground Squirrel, Woodchuck, Chipmunk
      Superfamily Geomyoidea—Gopher, Kangaroo Rat
      Superfamily Castoroidea—Beaver
  Suborder MYOMORPHA—Myomorphs
      Superfamily Muroidea—Murine rodents
        Family Cricetidae—Muskrat, Lemmings, Red-backed Mouse, White-footed Mouse, Deer Mouse, Brush Mouse, Cotton Mouse, Voles (several kinds), Gerbill, Black Akodon, Water Rat, Meadow Mouse, Field Mouse, Harvest Mouse, Rice Rat, Old-field Mouse, Hamster
        Family Spalacidae—Naked mole-rat
        Family Muridae—Norway Rat, House Mouse, Long-tailed Field Mouse, Roof Rat
      Superfamily Gliroidea—Dormouse
      Superfamily Dipodoidea—Jumping Mouse
  Suborder HYSTRICOMORPHA—Hystricomorphs
      Superfamily Hystricoidea—Porcupine (Old-World)
      Superfamily Erethizontoidea—Porcupine
      Superfamily Cavioidea—Guinea Pig
      Superfamily Chinchilloidea—Viscacha
      Superfamily Octodontoidea—Spiny Rats
      Superfamily Bathyergoidea—Mole-rat

Order CETACEA—Whales
  Suborder ODONTOCETI—Dolphins, Porpoise, Sperm Whales, Bottle-nosed Whale
  Suborder MYSTICETI—Fin Whales, Hump-backed Whale, Rorqual Blue Whales, Bowhead Whale

Order CARNIVORA—Carnivores
  Suborder FISSIPEDIA
        Family Canidae—Wolves, Coyote, Fox (several kinds), Jackal
        Family Ursidae—Bears
        Family Procyonidae—Coatis, Raccoon
        Family Mustelidae—Fisher, Sea Otter, Skunks, Mink, Marten, Ferret,
          Weasels (several species)
        Family Viverridae—Mongoose
        Family Hyaenidae—Hyaena
        Family Felidae—Lynx, Bobcat, Mountain Lion, Cheeta, Lion
  Suborder PINNIPEDIA
        Family Otariidae—Cape Fur Seal, Northern Fur Seal, Sea Lions
        Family Odobenidae—Walrus
        Family Phocidae—Grey Seal, Harp Seal, Common Seal, Elephant
          Seal

Order TUBULIDENTATA—Aardvark

Order PROBOSCIDEA—Elephants

Order HYRACOIDEA—Conies

Order SIRENIA—Manatee

Order PERISSODACTYLA—Odd-toed Ungulates
        Family Equidae—Wild Ass, Zebra
        Family Tapiridae—Tapirs
        Family Rhinocerotidae—Rhinoceros

Order ARTIODACTYLA—Even-toed Ungulates
  Suborder SUIFORMES
        Family Suidae—Wart Hog
        Family Hippopotamidae—Hippopotamus
  Suborder TYLOPODA
        Family Camelidae—Llama, Camel, Vicugna
  Suborder RUMINANTIA
        Family Cervidae—Deer (various species), Elk, Reindeer, Caribou,
          Moose, Roe Deer
        Family Giraffidae—Giraffe
        Family Antilocapridae—Pronghorn
        Family Bovidae—Bison, Bighorn, Goats, Mountain Sheep, Roan
          Antelope, Springbok, Hartebeeste, Musk Ox, Gazelles, Wild-
          beest, Kouprey, Buffalo

APPENDIX B

Dental Formulae

The number of teeth of mammals may be expressed in a formula that facilitates comparisons and memory. Several procedures are used, but the simplest seems to be to express for each side of the jaw the number of upper teeth as numerators and the number of lower teeth as denominators of fractions. The incisors are represented by I, the canines by C, the premolars by P and the molars by M. Thus the formula for a fox is:

$$I\ 3/3;\ C\ 1/1;\ P\ 4/4;\ M\ 2/3;\ \text{or } 42 \text{ teeth}$$

A more technical aspect is the identity of each tooth. Different mammals may have the same number of, say, premolars. However, the particular premolars may be different ones in the sequence in the jaw. Thus the woodchuck has lost premolars 1 and 2 in the upper jaw and 1, 2, and 3 in the lower. This condition is represented by P 0-0-3-4/0-0-0-4.

The lacteal (milk) teeth are represented similarly, but either using a subscript 1 or a lower case letter.

Table of Representative Dental Formulae

	I	C	P	M	Total
Opossum	5/4	1/1	3/3	4/4	50
Coenolestes	4/3-4	1/1	3/3	4/4	46-48
Vombatus	1/1	0/0	1/1	4/4	24
Solenodon	3/3	1/1	3/3	3/3	40
Hedgehog	3/2	1/1	3/2	3/3	36
Short-tailed shrew	3/1	0/0	4/2	3/3	32
Brown bat	2/3	1/1	1/2	3/3	32

Table of Representative Dental Formulae (*contin.*)

	I	C	P	M	Total
Little brown bat	2/3	1/1	3/3	3/3	38
Lemur	2/2	1/1	3/3	3/3	36
Tarsius	2/1	1/1	3/3	3/3	34
Armadillo	0/0	0/0	8/8	?/?	16
Gray squirrel	1/1	0/0	2/1	3/3	22
Norway rat	1/1	0/0	0/0	3/3	16
Guinea pig	1/1	0/0	1/1	3/3	20
Elephant	2/0	0/0	3/3	3/3	30
Raccoon	3/3	1/1	4/4	2/2	40
Cat	3/3	1/1	3/2	1/1	30
Cottontail	2/1	0/0	3/2	3/3	28
Elk	0/3	1/1	3/3	3/3	34
White-tailed deer	0/3	0/1	3/3	3/3	32

GLOSSARY

Specialized terms that might not be familiar to readers are defined according to use in this text. Few anatomical or physiological terms are included, since they should be familiar to the average reader and can be found in other places. Names of groups of mammals can be found in the index. Terms or concepts that require a paragraph or a page for definition can best be found through the index.

Aggregation—An unorganized group of mammals brought together by a temporary aspect of the habitat (e.g., food supply).

Aggressive behavior—Actions, including threats, that result in withdrawal or submission of an opponent.

Angiosperm—A class of plants having the seed in an enclosed ovary.

Arboreal—Having a tendency to live or move in trees.

Auricular-ventricular dissociation—The interruption of the normal orderly or co-ordinate contraction of the auricle and ventricle of the heart.

Bias—A prejudice toward a certain observation or conclusion.

Bicornate—Refers to a uterus with two "horns" formed by the junction at the vagina of the uterus from each side.

Biogeochemical—Chemical materials which circulate through the biosphere, through the environment, and back again.

Biomass—The weight of live tissues; may be expressed as wet or dry weight.

Birth rate—The number of births per individual in some time interval.

Blastocyst—A body which develops from cleavage of the fertilized ovum.

Breeding season—The period of active reproduction. In species having a long pregnancy the mating season precedes the breeding season by several months.

Bronchi—The main branches of the trachea, leading to the lungs.

Browse—Leaves and twigs of bushes and trees.

Cellulose—A carbohydrate $(C_6H_{10}O_5)_x$ which is the chief component of the cell wall of plants.

Climax—The final stage in community succession.

Cloud forest—Tropical forests at high altitudes where persistent fogs cause an extremely humid atmosphere and hence luxuriant growth.

Coelom—A body cavity.

Competition—Use of a resource by one species to the detriment of another species.

Community—The collection of plants and animals living together in a circumscribed area.

Continuum—A state in which the characteristic being studied is organized in a continuous manner, rather than as discrete units.

Crepuscular—Active at dawn or dusk.

Crude rate—A rate based on miscellaneous mammals, i.e., not separated into classes.

Death rate—The number of deaths divided by the average population.

Delayed implantation—Postponement of embedding of blastocyst in uterine epithelium for several days or months; caused by several factors.

Density—The number per unit area.

Density dependence—A process changes percentagewise as density changes.

Diastema—The gap between the incisor and premolar teeth due to the absence of the canines in certain orders of mammals.

Diploid organisms—Animals with maternal and paternal chromosomes in the somatic cells.

Disjunct distribution—Occurrence of a species in areas widely separated geographically.

Dormancy—A period of inactivity, usually lasting weeks or months.

Echolocation—Detection or location by means of echoes from sounds given by the mammal.

Ecotype—A population adapted to local environmental conditions, and differing from the populations surrounding it.

Emigration—Movement out of an area.

Endemic—Confined and indigenous to a certain region.

Endothelium—A cellular membrane that lines the blood vessels, heart, uterus, and lymphatic vessels.

Entoderm—The innermost layer of the newly formed embryo which gives rise to the lining of the digestive tract.

Environment—The collection of external physical and biological factors which act upon a mammal.

Estivation—Inactivity during the summer.

Estuarine ecosystem—Ecological systems which occur in the interphase between the land and ocean.

Equilibrium—Strictly. a balance of forces resulting in a constant number; generally means persistence of a population at some level.

Fatality rate—The number of deaths divided by the number of cases of a disease or accident.

Feedback—A process that regulates itself.

Fibula—The outer, and usually smaller, of the two bones of the hind limb between the knee and ankle.

Finite—Limited in number.

Fluctuation—Irregular changes in numbers.

Food chain—A series of organisms, representing a trophic level of a system, which eat the preceding organism and are eaten by the succeeding organism.

Food web—The complex relationship of all the food chains of a community.

Fossorial—Living in burrows or holes in the ground.

Gametes—A mature germ cell; egg or sperm.

Habitat—The physical and chemical aspects of the environment.

Helix—A spiral.

Heme unit—A constituent of hemoglobin.

Hibernation—Inactivity during the winter.

Homeostasis—Maintenance of a constant state.

Homeothermic—Having a constant body temperature.

Home range—The area normally used by a mammal for his usual activities.

Hybrid—An individual resulting from a union of egg and sperm differing in one or more genes.

Incidence of pregnancy—The number of times pregnancy occurs in a time period.

Infinitesimal—Immeasurably small.

Immigration—Movement into an area.

Implantation—The attachment of the blastocyst to the lining of the uterus, the penetration through its epithelium, and the embedding in the endometrium.

Interstitial cells—Cells which are located between intervals in the primary, functional tissues of an organ.

Intrinsic rate—Inherent rate dependent upon physiological capacities and ecological conditions.

Leukocytes—A type of white blood cells.

Life table—A description of the number of survivors from an original population at specified time intervals.

Lignin—An organic compound of high carbon content, distinct from the carbohydrates, which is associated with cellulose in the cell walls of plants.

Limiting factor—A factor in least supply for growth or other process.

Logistic—A particular equation that describes growth of many populations.

Mechanism—The physical and chemical processes that carry out a function.

Mesentery—A thin membrane that supports an organ in the abdominal cavity.

Migrality—The local wanderings of mammals; usually excludes daily activity within the home range.

Monogamy—Mating with only one individual.

Mortality—The process of removal from a population by deaths.

Movements—The wanderings of mammals; usually excludes daily activity within the home range.

Natality—The process of addition to a population by births.

Oro-pharyngeal region—The region of the mouth and throat.

Oscillation, damped—A cycle whose amplitude decreases with time.

Pathogen—An organism that creates a diseased condition.

Pectoral girdle—The arch of bones which supports the fore limbs.

Pelvic girdle—The arch of bones supporting the hind limbs.

Pentadactyl—Having five phalanges on the foot or hand.

Pepsin—An enzyme of the stomach which, in the presence of hydrochloric acid, splits food protein into simple protein.

Peristalsis—Contraction of the circular muscles of the digestive tract, which act to move food forward.

Plantigrade—Walking on the sole of the foot with the heel touching the ground.

Poikilotherms—Animals not possessing a precise mechanism for regulating their body temperature, with the result that it fluctuates with the environmental temperature.

Polyandry—A female mating with several males.

Polyestrous—Several estrous cycles in succession during one breeding season.

Polygamy—An individual mating with several of the opposite sex.

Polygyny—A male mating with several females.

Porphyrin unit or ring—A flat 16-membered ring of pyrrole nuclei which form the building units for many biologically important pigments.

PPM—Parts per million.

Predation—The process resulting from action of predators.

Predator—A species that kills another.

Prevalence of pregnancy—The number pregnant divided by the number of females examined.

Primitive—Species that are morphologically little changed from their ancestors. Contrast with advanced.

Probability of dying—The number of deaths divided by the initial population.

Rate of increase or decrease—The difference in population between two time intervals divided by the population at the first. (Increase if positive; decrease if negative.)

Relict—A species still present in a small part of the area it formerly inhabited.

Reproductive rate—The number of female births per female in some time interval.

RQ—Respiratory quotient; the quantity of carbon dioxide exhaled, divided by the quantity of oxygen inhaled.

Scapula—The shoulder blade; in mammals the principal bone of the pectoral girdle.

Sigmoid—A curve shaped like an S.

Specialized—Extensive morphological adaptations of some characters. The mammal may otherwise be primitive. Contrast with unspecialized.

Spontaneous ovulation—Release of ovum from follicle without need of external stimulus.

Stable population—Unvarying in percentage (or ratio) of some aspect (usually age).

Stationary population—Constant in numbers (although individuals may enter and leave the population).

Stratified sample—Division of a population into separate parts for sampling.

Stratigraphic column—A local column of rocks, the layers of which were deposited at successively later periods of time.

Succession—A sequence of plants and animals in time on an area.

Territory—A defended area.

Thermogenesis—The production of heat.

Thermolysis—The loss of heat from the body.

Taiga—The boreal or northern coniferous forest which extends below the arctic tundra in North America and Eurasia.

Tibia—The inner, and usually larger, of the two bones of the hind limbs between the knee and ankle.

Top carnivore—The last tropic level on the food chain; animals which consume other carnivores.

Trophic level—A level of nourishment consisting of organisms eating the same kind of food.

Tundra—The low shrub-like or grassy vegetation of the arctic regions.

Ulnar border of the manus—The inner border of the hand.

Urogenital—Combined structures for excretory and reproductive systems.

Vasoconstriction—Constriction of the blood vessels.

Vibrissae—Long, specialized hairs near the mouth.

Visible pregnancy—A condition in which swellings of the embryos in the uterus can be easily seen upon examination.

Viviparous—Born alive.

INDEX

The index indicates a discussion of a topic in bold-face type and incidental mention in light-face type. Mammals may be found under their common name except where the technical name, for some special reason, was used. Mammals listed in the Appendices and terms defined in the Glossary are not included in the Index.